CHEMI

for

biologists

at advanced l   l

Bernard Rockett
Raul Sutton

JOHN MURRAY

Acknowledgements

Val and Catherine without whose continued support this book would not have been possible. Friends and colleagues for support while writing this book.

The authors would also like to acknowledge the following who have given permission for reproduction of figures within this book:

Jane Richardson for Figure 12.3(a), reproduced from A Fersht *Enzyme structure and mechanism.* New York: W.H. Freeman, 1984;

Nature and J.E. Walker for Figure 12.3(b), reproduced from G. Biesecker *et al* (1977) *Nature* **266**, pp. 328–33;

Irving Geis for Figure 12.5, reproduced from A.L. Lehninger, D.L. Nelson and M.M. Cox *Principles of biochemistry, 2nd edn.* New York: Worth, 1993;

J.A. Bassham and Academic Press Inc. for Figure 19.3, reproduced from J. Bonner and J.E. Varner (eds) *Plant biochemistry, 2nd edn.* New York: Academic Press, 1965.

The publishers have made every effort to trace copyright holders, but if they have inadvertently overlooked any they will be pleased to make the necessary arrangements at the earliest opportunity.

Dedication

To Val and Catherine.

First published in 1996
by John Murray (Publishers) Ltd
50 Albemarle Street
London W1X 4BD

Reprinted 1996.

Typeset in Palatino and Futura by Wearset, Boldon, Tyne and Wear.
Printed by Athenaeum Press, Gateshead.

A CIP catalogue record for this book can be obtained from the British Library.

ISBN 0-7195-7146-4

Contents

Introduction

Tertiary-level life science courses such as A-level biology, and 'access to science' courses are becoming increasingly popular. Changes to the secondary science curriculum have meant that many of the students entering tertiary-level biology courses have not had the traditional education of three separate sciences at GCSE level. In addition, many students study biology and human biology in combination with non-science subjects. Such students do not have the traditional scientific background and have not studied the associated scientific principles that underpin tertiary-level biology courses. This can make such courses difficult and will discourage many students from attempting to continue their interest in biology. The chemistry knowledge required is particularly difficult.

The biochemical content of many life science courses is a considerable proportion of the total syllabus. Without the traditional chemistry background, students undertaking such courses struggle with the chemistry. Most chemistry textbooks are written for students undertaking traditional chemistry courses and cover a broad spectrum of chemistry. Biologists need a more focused course of biological chemistry concentrating on the aspects of chemistry that are important to biology courses. One example of the difference is the statement in many chemistry textbooks of reaction conditions. In biology, many chemical reactions take place in the cell. Conditions inside cells are reasonably uniform. Thus, for the purposes of this book, we can assume that reactions take place at pH 7.0 and 37 °C unless otherwise stated. Some books on 'biological chemistry' are published, but they are generally aimed at first-year undergraduates taking degrees in biology or chemistry and the subject matter is too advanced for tertiary-level courses. No book was available that addressed the needs of these tertiary-level students.

We felt that such a textbook should enhance the tertiary student's knowledge of biology without disrupting the flow of a traditional tertiary-level biology course. In consequence, a self-study approach has been taken when preparing this book. We are also aware that students wishing to use this book may already be familiar with the material in parts of the text. Thus we have divided the text into self-contained chapters, which may be bypassed if the student understands the relevant subject matter. More about this is explained in 'How to use this book'. By making the book an open-learning text we hope to ease the burden imposed on many teachers who have to divert attention from the biology syllabus to teach relevant aspects of chemistry.

We have tried not to overlap with the subject matter covered in most biology textbooks. Thus we have focused our attention on the chemistry rather than making this a biochemistry textbook. Where we have overlapped with conventional textbooks, we have concentrated on those areas where, traditionally, students have problems. By and large, we have tried to pitch the material at a level appropriate to tertiary-level courses. The only chapter that deviates from this is Chapter 13 on sugars and carbohydrates, where we feel that a more complete coverage is important.

The book is divided into three parts. Part 1, Introducing Biological Chemistry is intended to cover basic biological chemistry at GCSE level. Parts 2 and 3 are companions to tertiary-level biology courses. We hope that you will find the book useful.

How to use this book

This book has been written for the biology student who seeks some help with the chemical concepts that are useful in biology. These include structure, bonding, reaction rates, acids and bases, and the effect of heat and electricity, together with some basic reactions. This is followed by a survey of biological substances: aldehydes, ketones, alcohols, amines, organic acids, carbohydrates, fats, proteins and nucleotides. The role of light and radioactivity in biology is also outlined. Each chapter is self-contained and uses a biological context. Examples are included within the text. The links between chapters are shown and you should find the sequence of chapters logical. Each chapter assumes that you are familiar with the ideas in the earlier parts. However, some chapters may be easy and others more difficult. It is useful to be as thorough as possible with those that are challenging.

Within each chapter, we suggest that you look over the objectives first. This will help you to decide whether or not you know the subject well. If you are happy that you do, then work through the questions at the start of the chapter. Check your answers, and if they are satisfactory then there is no need to work through the chapter. On the other hand, should the objectives seem unfamiliar or should you have difficulty with the questions, then it is valuable to study the topic.

As you work through the chapter, it is important to make sure that you understand each example as it appears. Then try the question following the example. Sometimes you may need to go back and look over the section again before continuing. At the end, check the summary and then work through the final set of questions, and, if you have not tried them, the questions at the start of the chapter. There are a lot of questions. Don't skip them. Answering the full range of questions will confirm that you have a real understanding of the subject. Be strict with yourself and write an answer down before checking the answer in the book. Don't be satisfied with thinking that you probably know the answer and could write it out if you wanted to. Try not to sneak a quick look at the answer before trying the question! You may well give wrong answers in some cases, almost everyone does: it is part of the learning process. But do go back and look over the appropriate parts of the chapter again. Each chapter has full answers to the questions, with hints and extra points where they may be useful.

Each chapter is quite short, which means that you can learn it thoroughly in a short time. It is better to focus on a single chapter and become really familiar with it than to skip quickly over several chapters.

Remember that this is not a textbook to dip into for extra material or reinforcement, but a specific short course for you as a biology student. It is not long and you can readily work right through it. Finally, let us know what you think of it. We would be glad to have your views on its strengths and weaknesses so that we can improve it. Enjoy your biology!

PART 1

Introducing Biological Chemistry

Atoms, Elements and Formulae

Introduction

Biological molecules may be quite large and to help understand their nature and behaviour, it is useful to look first at more simple substances. This chapter will discuss elements, the properties of atoms and the ways in which molecules can be written in a shorthand form as formulae.

Objectives

After studying this chapter you should be able to:
- appreciate that an element is composed of atoms;
- state which elements are metals or non-metals;
- write the symbols for several common elements;
- recognise the need to use a large number of atoms to compare the masses of atoms with one another;
- explain the meaning of the mole and relative atomic mass;
- calculate number of moles from relative atomic mass;
- appreciate that compounds are formed in chemical reactions;
- explain the meanings of the terms molecule and valency;
- use valencies of elements and groups to determine the formulae of compounds;
- write the formulae of compounds;
- appreciate that some elements have more than one valency and show how this is indicated in the names of compounds.

Questions

If this material seems familiar, try the following questions. If your answers are correct you could go on to Chapter 2.

Q1.1 Give the chemical symbols for the following elements: oxygen, phosphorus, potassium and iron. O_2 P K^+ Fe^{2+}

Q1.2 Calculate the mass of 0.2 mole of sulphur, $A_r = 32$. $12 \cdot m$

Q1.3 Select the structure (i) to (iv) that best represents these molecules:
   (a) methane; (b) carbon dioxide; (c) ammonia.

   (i)   (ii)   (iii)   (iv)

Q1.4 Write the chemical formulae for water, calcium carbonate, hydrogen chloride and sodium sulphate.

1.1 Elements

The huge variety of animals and plants, together with all other materials in the world around us, is formed by combining just 92 naturally occurring simple substances in various ways. These substances are called **elements** and each one is made up of a large number of identical particles called atoms. An element is described as a single substance that cannot be split into simpler things by a chemical process. Thus carbon is an element; it consists entirely of carbon

Table 1.1 Elements essential to living organisms as macronutrients

Element	Symbol	Importance in living organisms	Food source for human beings
Nitrogen	N	Component of proteins, nucleic acids, coenzymes, chlorophyll	Meat, fish, milk
Phosphorus	P	Found in nucleic acids, phospholipids (membranes), ATP, bone	Milk
Sulphur	S	Constituent of proteins, coenzyme A	Meat, fish, milk
Chlorine	Cl	Anion–cation balance across membranes, nerve impulses, stomach acid	Table salt, salted meats
Potassium	K	Maintaining electrical balance across membranes, nerve impulses, cofactor in photosynthesis	Green vegetables, meat
Sodium	Na	Similar functions to potassium, but often at lower concentrations	Table salt, salted meats
Calcium	Ca	Constituent of plant cell walls, bones, shells, teeth, blood clotting	Hard water, milk

atoms. No chemical change can make carbon into anything simpler. Carbon can join with other elements to make different substances, such as the chemical compound methane.

Although there are 92 naturally occurring elements, only a few are of direct interest to biologists and need be discussed here. Elements that are significant in the living world as macronutrients and trace elements are given in Tables 1.1 and 1.2.

Elements show two types of behaviour, they may be **metals** like sodium, potassium and calcium, or **non-metals** like carbon, hydrogen and oxygen. Metals are usually solids with a shiny appearance. They are dense and have a high melting point. Non-metals are usually solids or gases. The solids appear dull and have a low density and melting point.

For convenience, each element may be written in a shorthand form called a symbol. The symbol for carbon is C and for oxygen O. If the symbols for two elements could be confused, a second letter is added. For example, hydrogen is H while helium is He. Symbols are sometimes derived from the Latin name of the element, thus sodium is Na, from natrium, and potassium is K, from kalium. It is important to write each symbol in its usual form, thus sodium cannot be written as NA or na. Some symbols are given in Table 1.3 (page 5).

1.2 Atoms

An element, such as carbon, consists of carbon **atoms**. These are the smallest particles of carbon. They are so small that 12 g of carbon contain 6.02×10^{23} atoms. A small particle like a carbon atom cannot be weighed. The masses of atoms in different elements are compared by weighing a large number of them, 6.02×10^{23} atoms. This number of atoms is called a **mole**. Thus one mole of carbon atoms has a mass of 12 g, and one mole of hydrogen atoms a mass of 1 g. The mass of one mole of atoms of an element compared to the mass of one mole of hydro-

Table 1.2 Trace elements important in plants and animals

Element	Symbol	Importance in living organisms	Food source for human beings
Iodine	I	Constituent of thyroxine (thyroid hormone)	Drinking water, iodised table salt, seafood
Fluorine	F	In tooth enamel, bone	Drinking water, milk
Boron	B	Plants only. Promotes healthy cell division in growing points	—
Iron	Fe	In haemoglobin and myoglobin as oxygen carriers, in cytochromes, cofactor with catalase	Red meat, liver, spinach
Copper	Cu	In haemocyanin as oxygen carrier for some invertebrates, electron carrier in cytochrome oxidase	Traces in many foods
Manganese	Mn	Bone growth	Traces in many foods
Cobalt	Co	Component of vitamin B_{12} for development of red blood cells	Red meat, liver
Zinc	Zn	Constituent of carbonic anhydrase for carbon dioxide transport in blood	Traces in many foods
Molybdenum	Mo	In enzymes used for nitrogen fixation and amino acid formation in plants	Trace in many foods

gen atoms is called the **relative atomic mass** (A_r). The concept of the mole and the relative atomic mass can be used to determine the masses of elements that combine together in chemical reactions. Moles and relative atomic masses are readily converted from one into the other.

Example 1.1
How many moles are there in 57.5 g of sodium? The A_r for sodium can be found in Table 1.3.

A_r for sodium $= 23$
Thus 1 mole of sodium $= 23\,g$

Number of moles in 57.5 g $= \dfrac{57.5\,g}{23\,g} = 2.5$ moles

Example 1.2
What is the mass of 0.4 moles of potassium? (See Q1.2, page 2).

A_r for potassium $= 39$
Thus 1 mole of potassium $= 39\,g$
Mass of 0.4 mole $= 39 \times 0.4$
$= 15.6\,g$

Example 1.3
What mass of oxygen has the same number of moles as 3 g of carbon?

A_r for carbon $= 12$

Number of moles in 3 g of carbon $= \dfrac{3}{12} = 0.25$ mole

A_r for oxygen $= 16$
Mass of 0.25 mole of oxygen atoms $= 16 \times 0.25 = 4$ g

1.3 Compounds and formulae

When the element carbon burns in air, energy is released as heat and light. A new substance, the gas carbon dioxide, is formed. Carbon has combined with the element oxygen in a chemical reaction to give the **compound** carbon dioxide. A chemical compound is a single substance whose properties differ from those of the elements it contains. The elements in a compound always occur in the same simple proportions; thus carbon dioxide contains carbon and oxygen atoms in the ratio 1 : 2. Carbon dioxide is made up of a large number of tiny particles called **molecules**. Each molecule contains two oxygen atoms and one carbon atom. In the same way, a water molecule contains two hydrogen atoms and one oxygen atom and a methane molecule has one carbon atom and four hydrogen atoms.

The symbols used to represent elements can be combined to represent compounds. Carbon dioxide, with a C : O ratio of 1 : 2, is shown as CO_2. The number '2' is placed after the symbol for oxygen and below the line to show that there are two oxygen atoms. The number '1', which would appear after the carbon in this case, is omitted. This way of representing a molecule is called a **formula**. A water molecule has the formula H_2O; this time the '2' indicates two hydrogen atoms. The formula for a methane molecule is CH_4. The formulae of compounds can be worked out from the combining power of each of the elements present. This combining power is termed the **valency** of the element. The valencies of several elements are listed in Table 1.3. Valencies are always small whole numbers. The method used for determining formulae is shown in the following examples.

Table 1.3 Elements, symbols, valencies and relative atomic masses

Element	Symbol	Valency	Relative atomic mass (A_r)
Calcium	Ca	2	40
Carbon	C	4	12
Chlorine	Cl	1	35.5
Hydrogen	H	1	1
Iron	Fe	2 or 3	56
Magnesium	Mg	2	24
Nitrogen	N	3	14
Oxygen	O	2	16
Phosphorus	P	3 or 5	31
Potassium	K	1	39
Sodium	Na	1	23
Sulphur	S	2 or 4	32

Example 1.4

What is the formula for water (hydrogen oxide)? The valencies of hydrogen and oxygen are given in Table 1.3.

	Hydrogen	Oxygen
Write symbols for the elements	H	O
Write valencies	1	2
Balance valencies	$1 \times 2 = 2$	$2 \times 1 = 2$

Thus the water molecule contains 2 hydrogen atoms and 1 oxygen atom, formula H_2O.

Molecules may be pictured by drawing each atom in the molecule as a circle. The molecules for water, carbon dioxide and methane are shown below (see Q1.3, page 2).

water   carbon dioxide   methane

◯ = hydrogen atom

● = carbon atom

⊗ = oxygen atom

The idea of valency may be understood more easily by imagining that each atom has a number of spring links equal to its valency. When a compound is formed, the atoms link up so that no links are left over. The formula of water using spring links as valencies would be:

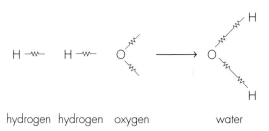

hydrogen   hydrogen   oxygen   water

Example 1.5

Give the formula of the compound formed between carbon and oxygen. Carbon has valency 4. Oxygen has a valency of 2.

	Carbon	Oxygen
Symbols	C	O
Valencies	4	2
Balance valencies	$4 \times 1 = 4$	$2 \times 2 = 4$

Carbon oxide (called carbon dioxide) contains one carbon atom and two oxygen atoms, formula CO_2. If we look at how the atoms in carbon dioxide are linked, it is clear that we do not need two carbon atoms and four oxygens.

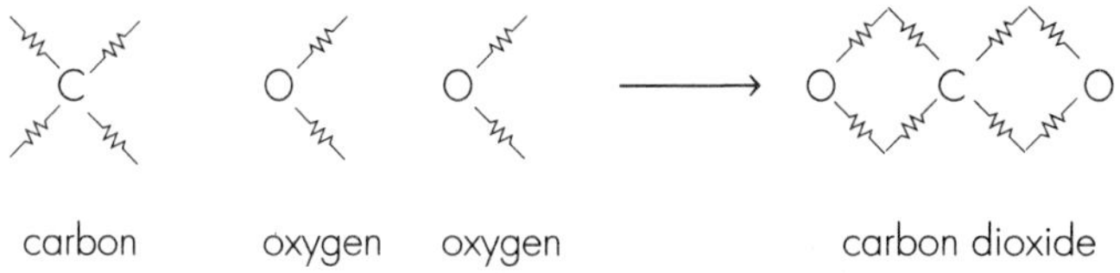

carbon   oxygen   oxygen   carbon dioxide

Example 1.6

Determine the formulae of the compounds formed between phosphorus and chlorine. Phosphorus can have valency 3 or 5, so consider each in turn. Chlorine has valency 1.

For phosphorus valency 3:

	Phosphorus	Chlorine
Symbols	P	Cl
Valencies	3	1
Balance valencies	$3 \times 1 = 3$	$1 \times 3 = 3$

Phosphorus(III) chloride contains one phosphorus atom and three chlorine atoms. Writing the Roman 'III' in a bracket after the phosphorus makes it clear that we have phosphorus valency 3. The formula using spring links as valencies is:

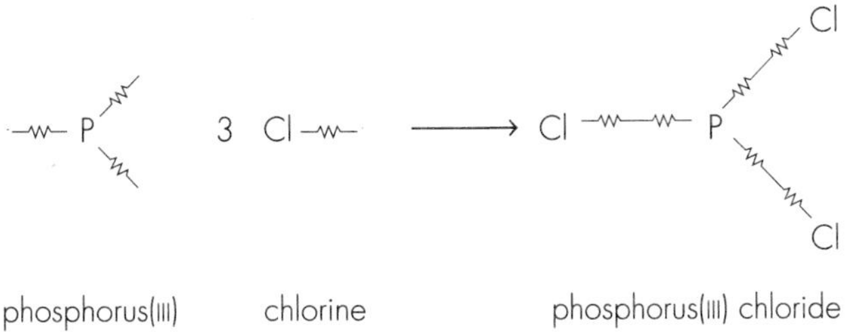

phosphorus(III)   chlorine   phosphorus(III) chloride

For phosphorus valency 5:

	Phosphorus	Chlorine
Symbols	P	Cl
Valencies	5	1
Balance valencies	$5 \times 1 = 5$	$1 \times 5 = 5$

Phosphorus(V) chloride has one phosphorus atom and five chlorine atoms. The formula using spring links as valencies is:

phosphorus(V)   chlorine   phosphorus(V) chloride

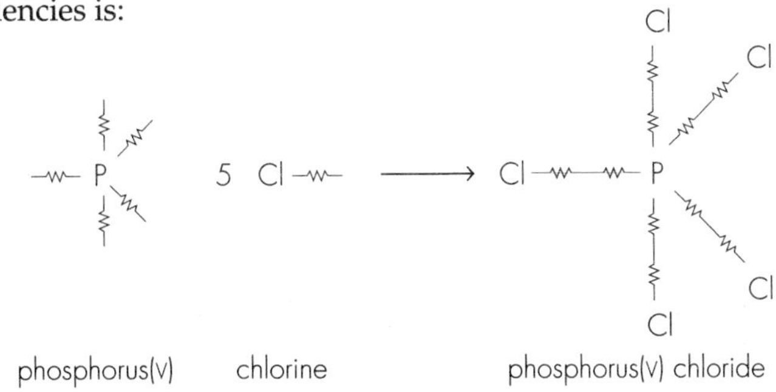

When writing formulae it is useful to give valencies to some groups of elements since these groups often stay together in chemical reactions. These groups are shown in Table 1.4. The formulae of compounds containing these groups are found in the same way as for simple compounds.

Table 1.4 Formulae and valencies for some groups of elements

Group	Formula	Valency
Ammonium	NH_4	1
Carbonate	CO_3	2
Hydrogencarbonate	HCO_3	1
Hydroxide	OH	1
Sulphate	SO_4	2
Phosphate	PO_4	3

Example 1.7
Determine the formula of magnesium hydroxide.

	Magnesium	Hydroxide
Symbols	Mg	OH
Valencies	2	1
Balance valencies	$2 \times 1 = 2$	$1 \times 2 = 2$

Magnesium hydroxide contains one magnesium atom and two hydroxide groups, formula $Mg(OH)_2$. The hydroxide group is placed in brackets because there is more than one of them; the '2' outside the bracket refers to each of the atoms inside the bracket. In other words, the formula means MgOHOH.

Example 1.8
Calculate the formula of the compound ammonium sulphate.

	Ammonium	Sulphate
Symbols	NH_4	SO_4
Valencies	1	2
Balance valencies	$1 \times 2 = 2$	$2 \times 1 = 2$

Ammonium sulphate contains two ammonium groups and one sulphate group, formula $(NH_4)_2SO_4$ (see Q.1.4, page 2).

The '2' outside the bracket means that there are two lots of the atoms inside it; this shows that the formula refers to NHHHHNHHHHSOOOO. It is easy to see that formulae really are shorthand forms for molecules!

Now that we have considered the way in which valencies lead to the formulae of compounds, we can use a simple method to obtain the same result. In this method, the valency of each element or group is written after the other group and below the line to give the formula.

Example 1.9
What is the formula of sodium oxide?

	Sodium	Oxygen
Symbol and valency	Na 1	O 2
Change over numbers and put below the line	Na_2	O_1

The formula is Na_2O (the '1' is not usually written in formulae).

Example 1.10
Determine the formula of calcium phosphate.

	Calcium	Phosphate
Symbol and valency	Ca 2	PO_4 3
Change over numbers and put below the line	Ca_3	$(PO_4)_2$

The formula of the compound is $Ca_3(PO_4)_2$.

Example 1.11
What is the formula of the compound formed between carbon and oxygen?

	Carbon	Oxygen
Symbol and valency	C 4	O 2
Change over numbers and put below the line	C_2	O_4
If possible change numbers to the lowest ratio	C	O_2

The formula of the compound is CO_2

Summary

All substances are formed by chemical combination of elements, which are simple substances made up of atoms. Elements may be metals or non-metals. Each one is given a symbol consisting of one or two letters. The masses of elements are compared by using the relative atomic mass and the mole. A chemical compound contains elements combined together in simple, fixed proportions. Compounds are represented by formulae based on the symbols of the elements. Formulae are found by using the valencies of elements or groups.

Self-assessment questions

Try these questions.

Q1.5 Write symbols for the elements calcium, chlorine and magnesium.

Q1.6 What are the names of the elements represented by the symbols C, N, Na, S?

Q1.7 Which has the larger mass, 0.8 mole of sodium or 0.6 mole of potassium? Sodium $A_r = 23$, potassium $A_r = 39$.

Q1.8 How many moles of carbon are there in 3.6 g of the element? Carbon $A_r = 12$.

Q1.9 Give the chemical formulae for the following compounds: calcium oxide, iron(III) chloride, phosphorus(V) oxide, calcium hydroxide and sodium carbonate.

Atomic Structure and Bonding

Introduction

A single plant or animal cell contains elements such as carbon, hydrogen and oxygen. These elements may be joined together as molecules or as ions. Both ions and molecules play an essential role in the activities of the cell. To understand how molecules and ions are formed and how they react, it is useful to look at the structure of the atom. The atomic structure determines the ways in which atoms may join together to give molecules and ions.

Objectives

After studying this chapter you should be able to:

- describe the particles that make up an atom;
- appreciate that electrons in atoms are arranged in shells;
- write electron structures for biologically important elements;
- draw atomic structure diagrams for biologically important elements;
- understand that covalent bonds involve the sharing of pairs of electrons between atoms;
- appreciate that each atom in a covalent molecule has a full shell of outer electrons;
- draw electron structure diagrams to show covalent bonding;
- appreciate that ionic bonding requires the transfer of electrons from the outer shell of a metal atom to the outer shell of a non-metal atom;
- understand that cations and anions with full electron shells are formed by ionic bonding;
- recognise that the ions formed in ionic bonding are held together by attraction between opposite charges;
- draw electron structure diagrams to show ionic bonding.

Questions

If the objectives are familiar, try the following questions. If your answers are correct, you could go on to Chapter 3.

Q2.1 Write the electron structures for nitrogen, atomic number 7, and sodium, atomic number 11.

Q2.2 Draw atomic structure diagrams for carbon, which has 6 protons and 6 neutrons, and for magnesium, which has 12 protons and 12 neutrons.

Q2.3 Draw electron shell diagrams to show covalent bonding in the hydrogen molecule H_2 and the methane molecule CH_4.

Q2.4 Give the electron structures of the sodium cation Na^+ and the chloride anion Cl^- in sodium chloride. Atomic numbers: sodium, 11; chlorine, 17.

Q2.5 Draw outer electron shell diagrams to illustrate ionic bonding in magnesium oxide. Atomic numbers: magnesium, 12; oxygen, 8.

2.1 Atomic structure

Chapter 1 discussed atoms, the smallest individual particles of an element. Each atom is made up of three smaller types of particles. The arrangement and number of these particles determine the way in which an atom will react and which element it is. The three particles are called **protons, neutrons** and **electrons**. Protons and neutrons are found in the small central part of the atom called the nucleus. Each proton carries a positive electrical charge. Neutrons, which occur with protons, have no charge. Tiny, light electrons, each with a negative electrical charge, move around the nucleus. An atom of carbon has six protons, six neutrons and six electrons, so it is electrically neutral with the six positive charges on the protons balancing out the six negative charges on the electrons. This is because the charge on an electron and a proton are the same size but have opposite signs.

An atom of any element always has the same number of protons and electrons. The atomic structure diagram for the carbon atom is shown in Figure 2.1: the six electrons in the carbon

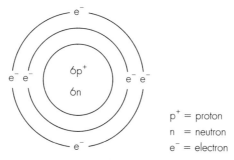

p^+ = proton
n = neutron
e^- = electron

Figure 2.1 Atomic structure diagram for carbon

atom are arranged in two layers, called **shells**. All atoms have electron shells. The innermost shell can have one or two electrons. The second and third shells can also have up to eight electrons. The **electron structure** of the element is obtained when the number of electrons in each shell is written down, starting with the innermost shell.

The atomic structure of the carbon atom shows that the inner shell has two electrons and the next shell has four electrons, so the electron structure is 2.4.

The atomic and electron structures of some biologically important elements are given in Table 2.1.

Example 2.1
Phosphorus, an important element in cell membranes, has 15 protons in each atom. How many electrons are present in the atom? What is the electron structure?

Table 2.1 Atomic structure of biologically important elements

Element	Number of protons	Number of neutrons	Number of electrons	Electron structure
Hydrogen	1	0	1	1
Carbon	6	6	6	2.4
Nitrogen	7	7	7	2.5
Oxygen	8	8	8	2.6
Sodium	11	12	11	2.8.1
Magnesium	12	12	12	2.8.2

Each atom has the same number of protons and electrons, thus phosphorus has 15 electrons in the atom.

The inner shell has two electrons, the second shell has eight, therefore the remaining five electrons are in the third shell. This gives an electron structure of 2.8.5.

Example 2.2
Use the information in Table 2.1 to draw the atomic structure diagrams for hydrogen and oxygen.

From Table 2.1, hydrogen has one proton, no neutrons and one electron, this gives the structure in Figure 2.2.

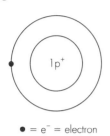

<u>Figure 2.2</u> Atomic structure diagram for hydrogen

● = e⁻ = electron

Oxygen has eight protons, eight neutrons and eight electrons. The first two electrons are in the inner shell, the remaining six are in the second shell. This gives the structure shown in Figure 2.3.

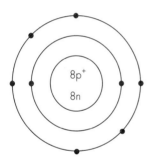

<u>Figure 2.3</u> Atomic structure diagram for oxygen

2.2 Covalent bonding

The atoms in a biological molecule such as glucose are held together by a type of attraction called **covalent bonding**. This occurs because an atom with a full outer shell of electrons is very stable.

A full outer shell for hydrogen contains two electrons while a full shell for most other common elements contains eight electrons. These elements include carbon, nitrogen, oxygen, phosphorus, sulphur and chlorine. Thus these non-metal elements need to gain electrons to achieve a full shell. One way of doing this is to share electrons between atoms.

Each atom involved obtains a share in the number of electrons needed to fill its outer shell. Hydrogen needs just two electrons to do this, while carbon, oxygen and nitrogen need eight electrons.

The hydrogen molecule is a good example of covalent bonding. Each hydrogen atom has one electron in the first shell with an electron structure H 1 (Table 2.1, page 11). Two of these hydrogen atoms join together so that the shells overlap and the electrons are shared, Figure 2.4.

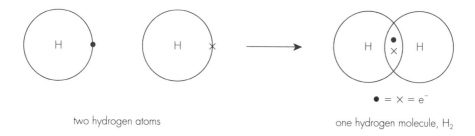

two hydrogen atoms   one hydrogen molecule, H_2

Figure 2.4 Covalent bonding in the hydrogen molecule

In this way, each atom has a share in two electrons and each has a full shell. The atoms are held close together and form a hydrogen molecule. The two shared electrons are known as a covalent bond. This is often drawn as a line between the symbols for the element, showing the hydrogen molecule as H—H.

The important biological molecule methane has one carbon and four hydrogen atoms linked together by covalent bonds. Although the carbon atom has the electron structure C 2.4 (Table 2.1) with two shells of electrons, only the outer shell is used in forming bonds, so only this shell is drawn in diagrams. The carbon atom needs a share in four more electrons to gain a full shell. Each hydrogen atom requires only one more electron for a full shell. The carbon and hydrogen atoms join together with the outer shells overlapping (Figure 2.5).

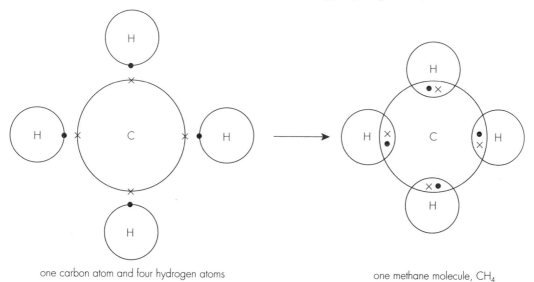

one carbon atom and four hydrogen atoms   one methane molecule, CH_4

Figure 2.5 Covalent bonding in the methane molecule

If you count the electrons, you will see that the carbon atom has a total of eight in its outer shell and each hydrogen atom has two. The methane molecule has four covalent bonds. The shorthand form of the methane molecule can be written as:

$$H-\overset{\displaystyle H}{\underset{\displaystyle H}{C}}-H$$

The bonding in other molecules of interest to the biologist can be shown in the same way.

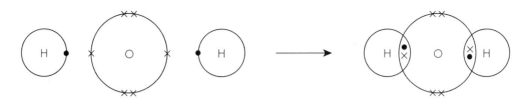

one oxygen atom and two hydrogen atoms

one water molecule, H_2O

Figure 2.6 Covalent bonding in the water molecule

Example 2.3

Draw diagrams to show the covalent bonds in water, H_2O.
Electron structures of atoms: H 1, O 2.6 (see Table 2.1, page 11).
Each oxygen atom requires a share in two extra electrons to give a full shell of eight. Each hydrogen atom requires a share in one further electron to give a full shell of two (Figure 2.6).

Example 2.4

Draw diagrams to show covalent bonding in the ammonia molecule, NH_3.
Electron structures of atoms: H 1, N 2.5 (see Table 2.1, page 11).
Each hydrogen atom needs a share in one more electron for a full shell of two. Each nitrogen atom needs three electrons for a full shell of eight electrons (Figure 2.7).

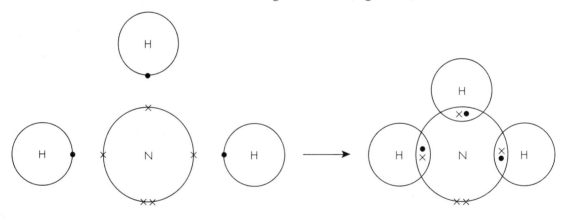

one nitrogen atom and three hydrogen atoms

one ammonia molecule, NH_3

Figure 2.7 Covalent bonding in the ammonia molecule

Question

Q2.6 Phosphine, PH_3, and hydrogen sulphide, H_2S, are covalent molecules. Draw structures to represent the bonding in each one. Phosphorus has five electrons and sulphur six electrons in the outer shell.

The methane, water and ammonia molecules were formed by the sharing of pairs of electrons to give single covalent bonds. Molecules can also be formed by sharing two pairs (four electrons) to give a double covalent bond. The oxygen molecule, O_2, is an example. Oxygen is central in the processes of respiration and photosynthesis. The oxygen atom has the electron structure O 2.6. It needs a share in two extra electrons to give a full shell of eight. Each oxygen atom obtains this number by sharing two of its electrons with a second oxygen atom (Figure 2.8).

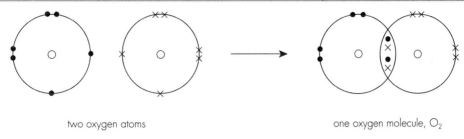

two oxygen atoms   one oxygen molecule, O_2

Figure 2.8 Double covalent bonding in the oxygen molecule

If you count the electrons around each oxygen atom, you will see that it has a full shell. A double covalent bond can be drawn in a simplified form as two lines joining the atoms, $O{=}O$.

Example 2.5
Draw diagrams to show the covalent bonds in the respiration product carbon dioxide, CO_2. Electron structures of atoms: C 2.4, O 2.6 (see Table 2.1, page 11).
Each carbon atom needs to share a further four electrons for a full shell of eight. Oxygen needs two further electrons for a full shell. Double covalent bonds are formed between one carbon and two oxygen atoms (Figure 2.9). This can be written simply as $O{=}C{=}O$.

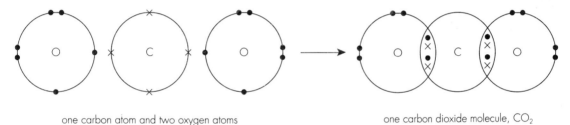

one carbon atom and two oxygen atoms   one carbon dioxide molecule, CO_2

Figure 2.9 Double covalent bonding in the carbon dioxide molecule

The electron structures of atoms in Table 2.1 allow us to determine the number of electrons each atom needs to lose, gain or share for a full outer shell. We can compare these values with the valencies of elements given in Table 1.3 (page 5) and see that they are the same. Thus electron structures and covalent bonding can provide an explanation of the use of valencies.

2.3 Ionic bonding
Each atom involved in forming a covalent bond gains a full shell of electrons. A full shell can be formed in a different way, by the transfer of an electron from one atom to another without sharing (overlap) of electron shells. Atoms with only one or two electrons in the outer shell, usually metals, transfer these electrons to atoms with an outer shell that is nearly full, usually non-metals. The result is that one atom has an empty outer shell and the second atom has a full outer shell. Since an electron has a negative charge, its transfer leads to a change in the electrical charge of the atom. The atom losing an electron is left with one more proton than the number of electrons (the numbers were equal to start with). The proton has a positive charge and so the resulting atom has a positive charge; it is now called a **cation**. The atom gaining the electron gains its charge as well and becomes negatively charged; it is an **anion**. The terms cation and anion are discussed in Section 5.3.

Sodium chloride, NaCl, is a compound that is formed by electron transfer. The electron structures of the atoms are:

Na 2.8.1   Cl 2.8.7

After transfer of one electron from sodium to chlorine the electron structures become:

$$Na^+ 2.8 \qquad Cl^- 2.8.8$$

The '+' sign, to show the positive charge on sodium, is always written after the symbol for sodium and above the line. The '−' sign for chloride is shown in the same way. It is important to remember that only electrons are transferred, not protons or neutrons. The sodium atom, Na, and the sodium cation, Na^+, each have 11 protons. The cation has one less electron, leaving it with a positive charge. The chlorine atom, Cl, and the chloride anion, Cl^-, each have 17 protons. The anion has one more electron and so has a negative charge. The electron shell diagrams in Figure 2.10 show the formation of sodium chloride by transfer of an electron from the outer shell of sodium to the outer shell of chlorine.

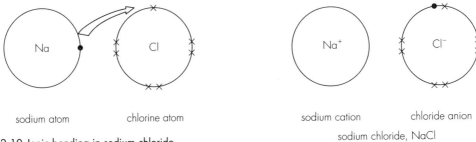

sodium atom   chlorine atom   sodium cation   chloride anion

sodium chloride, NaCl

Figure 2.10 Ionic bonding in sodium chloride

The shells do not overlap, but the negative charge of the anion attracts the positive charge of the cation and the two ions are held close together. The numbers of protons and electrons and the electrical charges for sodium chloride are shown in Table 2.2. The positive charge on the cation balances the negative charge on the anion, making the compound electrically neutral.

Table 2.2 Protons, electrons and charges involved in the formation of sodium chloride

	Sodium atom Na	Chlorine atom Cl	Sodium cation Na^+	Chloride anion Cl^-
Number of electrons	11	17	10	18
Number of protons	11	17	11	17
Overall charge	0	0	1^+	1^-

Example 2.6

Use electron structures and diagrams to show the ionic bonding in potassium chloride, KCl. The electron structures of the atoms are:

$$K\ 2.8.8.1 \qquad Cl\ 2.8.7$$

One electron is transferred from potassium to chlorine to give the electron structures:

$$K^+\ 2.8.8 \qquad Cl^-\ 2.8.8$$

The electron shell diagrams in Figure 2.11 show the formation of a cation and an anion.

Question

Q2.7 Draw diagrams to show the formation of an ionic bond between lithium, Li, and fluorine, F. The lithium atom has one electron in the outer shell, the fluorine atom has seven.

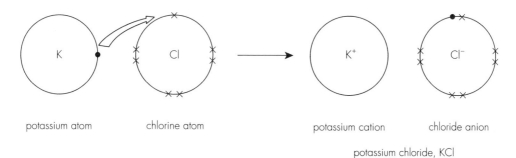

potassium atom   chlorine atom   potassium cation   chloride anion

potassium chloride, KCl

Figure 2.11 Ionic bonding in potassium chloride

An ionic compound may also be formed by transfer of more than one electron, and the numbers of cations and anions produced need not be the same. Calcium chloride, $CaCl_2$, is obtained when calcium transfers two electrons, one to each of two chlorine atoms. The atoms have the following electron structures:

$$Ca\ 2.8.8.2 \qquad Cl\ 2.8.7$$

Two electrons are transferred from one calcium atom to two chlorine atoms to form ions:

$$Ca^{2+}\ 2.8.8 \qquad 2 \times Cl^-\ 2.8.8$$

The calcium cation has two positive charges because it has two more protons than electrons (see Table 2.3). The electron shell diagrams for the formation of calcium chloride show how the electrons move (Figure 2.12).

Table 2.3 Protons, electrons and charges involved in the formation of calcium chloride

	Calcium atom Ca	Chlorine atom $2 \times Cl$	Calcium cation Ca^{2+}	Chloride anion $2 \times Cl^-$
Number of electrons	20	2×17	18	2×18
Number of protons	20	2×17	20	2×17
Overall charge	0	0	2^+	$2 \times 1^- = 2^-$

The two positive charges on the calcium cation balance the two negative charges on the two chloride anions, giving a neutral compound.

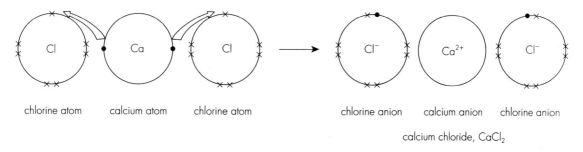

chlorine atom   calcium atom   chlorine atom   chlorine anion   calcium anion   chlorine anion

calcium chloride, $CaCl_2$

Figure 2.12 Ionic bonding in calcium chloride

Example 2.7

Explain the formation of the ionic compound magnesium oxide, MgO, by using electron structures and diagrams.

The electron structures of the atoms are:

$$Mg \; 2.8.2 \qquad O \; 2.6$$

Two electrons are transferred from the magnesium atom to the oxygen atom to give ions with the electron structures:

$$Mg^{2+} \; 2.8 \qquad O^{2-} \; 2.8$$

Electron shell diagrams show how an anion and a cation are formed and the ionic bonding in magnesium oxide (Figure 2.13).

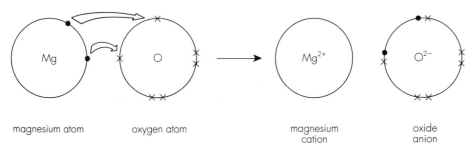

magnesium atom   oxygen atom   magnesium   oxide
                                                     cation   anion

                                                 magnesium oxide, MgO

Figure 2.13 Ionic bonding in magnesium oxide

It is important to remember that the shorthand representation of ionic bonding does not use lines to join the ions together.

Summary

Each atom of an element is made up of positively charged protons, neutral neutrons and negatively charged electrons. An atom can be represented by an atomic structure diagram showing electrons arranged in shells. Molecules may be formed by sharing pairs of electrons between atoms – covalent bonding. Atoms receive full shells of electrons by covalent bonding. Metals combine with non-metals by the transfer of electrons from one to the other to form positively charged cations and negatively charged anions. These ions are attracted to one another – ionic bonding.

Self-assessment questions

Try these questions to test your understanding of this chapter.

Q2.8 Complete the following table for the electron structures of carbon, oxygen and chlorine.

Element	Number of protons	Number of electrons	Electron structure
Carbon	6	—	——
Oxygen	—	8	——
Chlorine	—	—	2.8.7

Q2.9 Draw atomic structure diagrams for oxygen (eight protons and eight neutrons) and sodium (11 protons and 12 neutrons).

Q2.10 (a) Write the electron structures for hydrogen and fluorine.
Atomic numbers: hydrogen 1; fluorine 9.

(b) Draw a diagram showing outer shell electrons only to illustrate covalent bonding in the hydrogen fluoride molecule, HF.

Q2.11 (a) Give the electron structures of the carbon and oxygen atoms.
Atomic numbers: carbon 6; oxygen 8.

(b) Use the electron structures to help you complete the outer electron shell diagram for carbon dioxide, Figure 2.14, by adding the required number of electrons to the shells.

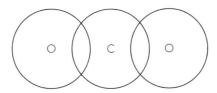

Figure 2.14 Outer electron shells in carbon dioxide

Q2.12 Complete this table, which refers to the formation of the ionic compound magnesium chloride, $MgCl_2$.

	Magnesium atom Mg	Chlorine atom 2 × Cl	Magnesium cation Mg^{2+}	Chloride anion 2 × Cl^-
Number of protons	12	_____	___	_____
Number of electrons	___	_____	___	2 × 18
Electron structure	___	2 × (2.8.7)	___	_____
Overall charge	0	_____	2+	_____

Q2.13 Complete the diagram, Figure 2.15, to show the formation of the ionic compound sodium oxide, Na_2O.

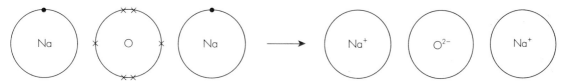

Figure 2.15 Ionic bonds in sodium oxide

Moving Particles and Speed of Reaction

Introduction

The living world is in constant movement and change. Plants grow, seed and die, while animals move, eat, interact and reproduce. The small particles of matter – molecules and ions – exist in a similar state of continuous activity. This chapter will explore the movement of particles, how they react with one another, and the factors that control these processes.

Objectives

After completing this chapter you should be able to:
- describe the three states of matter;
- use particle theory to explain the properties of these states;
- interpret the processes of diffusion, dissolving and evaporation in terms of particle theory;
- appreciate that different biological and chemical reactions proceed at different rates;
- explain the effect of a catalyst or changes in concentration, temperature, particle size, light and pH on rates of reaction;
- understand how rates of reaction can be measured;
- appreciate that reactions may be reversible;
- explain the concept of dynamic equilibrium and appreciate its importance in biology.

Questions

Try the following questions. Your answers will help you decide if you need to study this chapter or if you can go on to the next.

Q3.1 Describe the differences between the three states of matter – solid, liquid and gas – in terms of particle theory.

Q3.2 Explain the meaning of the terms diffusion and evaporation.

Q3.3 List four factors that can alter the rate of a biological or chemical reaction.

Q3.4 'Sugars undergo fermentation, in the presence of yeast enzymes as catalysts, to produce ethanol and carbon dioxide.'
(a) Define the term catalyst as used in this sentence.
(b) What is an enzyme?

Q3.5 How do changes in the pH value of a solution affect the activity of an enzyme?

Q3.6 Consider the following reactions:
(a) the burning of methane in air to form carbon dioxide and water;
(b) the reaction between carbon dioxide and water to give carbonic acid;
(c) the dissociation of ethanoic acid in water to form hydrogen ions and ethanoate ions;
(d) the reaction between sodium and chlorine to produce sodium chloride.
  (i) Select the reaction(s) that are reversible.
  (ii) Explain how one of the reversible reactions you chose involves a dynamic equilibrium.

3.1 Solids, liquids and gases in motion

The molecules or ions in a **solid** are held close together. The attraction between the particles is strong, allowing only limited movement. This movement takes the form of vibrations about the fixed position of the particle. When a solid is heated, the vibrations of the particles increase. When the temperature reaches the melting point of the solid, the particles break away from each other and move freely. The solid has **melted** to form a **liquid**. The particles are still strongly attracted to each other but can move easily. Thus a liquid has no fixed shape and flows from one container to another. Liquids and solids cannot be compressed to a smaller volume under normal conditions.

When a liquid is heated, its particles move faster. Eventually the particles are moving so fast that the forces of attraction between them are broken and they escape from the pool of liquid to become a **gas**.

In a gas, the particles move very quickly and are much further apart. There is almost no attraction between the particles. A gas occupies a much larger volume than a solid or a liquid. Thus when $18\,cm^3$ of liquid water at room temperature and pressure is converted into a gas, water vapour, under the same conditions it occupies a volume of $24\,000\,cm^3$. The particles in a gas collide frequently with one another and with the walls of the container, exerting a pressure on the walls. A gas can be compressed to a small volume.

Questions

Q3.7 List three differences between a solid and a gas.

Q3.8 Explain the properties of a liquid by using particle theory.

3.2 Diffusion, dissolving and evaporation

When a few drops of perfume are brought into a room, it can soon be smelt all around the room. The particles of perfume have mixed with the particles of air and gradually spread evenly through the room. This process of gas particles mixing is called **diffusion**. It depends on the rapid, random movement and collision between particles of different substances, causing them to mix more and more. Diffusion takes place in liquids as well as gases. It is important in photosynthesis, respiration, transport in cells and in the absorption of a solution of digested food from the gut cavity into the bloodstream.

A lump of sugar placed in a glass of water slowly **dissolves** until after a time it has disappeared completely. This happens because the moving water particles collide with the sugar crystals causing sugar molecules to break away and mix with the water molecules. Random movement of the water molecules carries the sugar molecules away – they diffuse into the water. Many substances can dissolve in water, which is the main transport medium in animals and plants.

A puddle of rain water in the road soon disappears in the sun. The liquid has turned to vapour and the vapour has diffused away – this is **evaporation**. When water, or another liquid, evaporates, the remaining liquid becomes cooler. This is because only the fastest moving water molecules escape from the liquid, leaving behind the slower moving molecules. These slower moving molecules have less energy, in other words they are cooler. When your clothes get wet in the rain you soon get cold. Mammals use evaporation to cool down. They produce droplets of water on the skin as perspiration, which evaporates and cools the body.

Questions

Q3.9 How may particle theory be used to describe salt dissolving in water?

Q3.10 Complete the following passage using words from the list below. 'The mixing of one gas with another when the two are brought together is called _____. It takes place by the gas _____ colliding _____ and _____ with one another.'

Word list: cooling, diffusion, evaporation, particles, randomly, rapidly, speed, vibrating.

3.3 Rate of reaction

When moving particles in a solution or in a gas collide with one another they usually rebound. However, in some cases, the particles join together and undergo a **chemical reaction**. Water and carbon dioxide molecules collide and react together in the blood to give carbonic acid. This chemical reaction occurs very rapidly. Other reactions occur much more slowly. For example, the chemical change that occurs when green tomatoes ripen takes days or weeks. There is a great range of speeds for chemical reactions. Each reaction requires a certain time which can be measured.

When reactions are studied, it is found that several factors cause the speed of reaction, termed the **reaction rate**, to change. These are:

- the concentrations of substances;
- the temperature of the reaction mixture;
- the presence of a catalyst;
- the presence of light;
- the acidity or pH value of the reaction mixture;
- the particle size of a solid substance.

Concentration

An increase in the concentration of a reacting substance, called a **reactant**, increases the rate of reaction. The fermentation of sugars and starch by yeast goes faster when there is a higher concentration of sugar. This can be explained in terms of the particles present. A reaction takes place only when a sugar molecule collides with an enzyme molecule in a yeast cell. When more sugar molecules are present, then there is a greater chance of collision. This increases the rate of reaction. Increasing the volume of the reaction mixture does not alter the rate of reaction if the concentration stays the same.

Temperature

Raising the temperature of the reaction mixture will increase the rate of reaction. In the home, the fermentation of sugar to make wine is usually carried out in the airing cupboard, which is a little warmer than the rest of the house. This speeds up the process. At a higher temperature, the particles are moving faster. They will collide more often, leading to more reactions.

Catalyst

A **catalyst** is a substance that speeds up a reaction, but is unchanged at the end of the process and may be used again. Enzymes are catalysts of the greatest significance in biological reactions. Each enzyme is tailored to a specific reaction. In that reaction, it will increase the rate, often by a factor of a million, but it does not affect the rate of other reactions. Cell processes rely on a range of specific enzymes to bring about reactions under the mild conditions found in the organism. The fermentation of sugar does not take place in the absence of yeast, which contains enzymes that catalyse the reaction. An enzyme functions by using a special site on the molecule to bring together the reactants. After the reaction, the products diffuse away from the enzyme, leaving it unchanged.

Light

Sunlight contains energy, which can be used to bring about or speed up a number of reactions. The best known of these is the process of photosynthesis. The leaves of green plants use carbon dioxide and water, in the presence of the pigment chlorophyll as a catalyst, to give sugars and oxygen. The considerable amount of energy required is provided by sunlight, which is absorbed by the leaves.

Acidity or pH value

The concentration of an acid in water is usually measured by the **pH scale**. A value of 1 corresponds to a high concentration of acid. Higher values of 4 to 6 indicate lower concentrations of acid, while pH 7 is neutral. When the pH value is greater than 7, the solution is alkaline; pH 14 shows that a solution is strongly alkaline (see Section 4.2, page 29).

Reactions in living cells usually take place around a neutral pH value. Many enzyme catalysts are most effective in promoting reactions around this value. As the pH value becomes more acidic or more alkaline, enzymes become less effective as catalysts until, at values outside the normal range, they are almost ineffective. Within living cells and in body fluids, mechanisms operate to ensure that the pH value is held as close as possible to the most effective pH for enzymes.

Particle size

The products of a reaction are formed when collisions occur between reactant particles. Decreasing the size of the particles (that is, increasing their surface area) will increase the rate of reaction, owing to the increased amount of surface with which they can collide.

Questions

Q3.11 Will the following changes increase or decrease the rate of photosynthesis in the leaves of a green plant:
(a) an increase in the air temperature;
(b) the loss of chlorophyll from the leaves;
(c) an increase in the intensity of sunlight;
(d) a decrease in the percentage of carbon dioxide in the air.

Q3.12 Suggest how the rate of breakdown of the sugar maltose by the intracellular enzyme maltase will be changed when the pH value of the solution changes slowly from:
(a) pH 7 to pH 12;
(b) pH 1 to pH 7;
(c) pH 3 to pH 9.

3.4 Measuring the rate of reaction

It is often useful to know how fast a reaction takes place. The speed can be measured by using a suitable experiment. It can be done by following the disappearance of one of the starting materials or the formation of one of the products of the reaction. In the fermentation of sugar by yeast, we can follow the reaction by measuring the carbon dioxide produced since the process takes place as follows:

$$\text{glucose} \xrightarrow[\text{by enzymes}]{\text{fermentation}} \text{ethanol} + \text{carbon dioxide}$$

This reaction is often carried out in a bottle closed with a bubble trap to prevent air getting into the mixture (Figure 3.1). Carbon dioxide bubbles out through the trap as it is produced. The number of bubbles produced in a short time, say 15 minutes, could be counted at the start of the reaction and the count repeated at intervals until no more bubbles are produced. When the number of bubbles in 15 minutes is plotted on a graph against the time, a curve is obtained (Figure 3.2). From this it can be seen that the reaction starts off rapidly but soon slows down and eventually stops. Most reactions give a curve like this one. It can be explained in terms of the particles involved. At the start of the reaction there are many glucose molecules. These

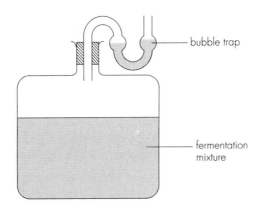

<u>Figure 3.1</u> Fermentation of sugar by yeast

collide often with the yeast enzymes and react, using up the glucose. As the glucose is consumed, there are fewer and fewer glucose molecules to collide with the yeast, so the reaction slows down. Eventually there are almost no glucose molecules left and the reaction stops.

Question

Q3.13 Cellular respiration involves the oxidation of glucose by oxygen to gluconic acid, which is catalysed by glucose oxidase. It is represented by the overall equation:

$$\text{glucose} + \text{oxygen} \xrightarrow{\text{glucose oxidase}} \text{gluconic acid}$$

Suggest a method for measuring the rate of the reaction.

3.5 Reversible reactions

Many reactions continue until all the starting materials have been used up and converted into products. Thus a piece of wood burns until all the cellulose and other components have combined with oxygen to give carbon dioxide and water. Some reactions, however, do not go to completion. They continue for a time, then slow down and stop before all the starting materials

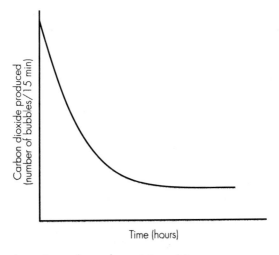

<u>Figure 3.2</u> Rate of carbon dioxide production from a fermentation mixture

have been changed into the final products. At the end of the reaction, a mixture of the initial components and the products is left. The proportions of the initial materials used up before the process stops depends on the conditions used and on the concentrations of the reactants. Thus the reaction may be less than half complete under one set of conditions, but 90 per cent complete under other conditions. Such a process is called a **reversible reaction**. An example is the combination of carbon dioxide with water to form carbonic acid, which can be expressed as follows:

$$\text{carbon dioxide} + \text{water} \rightleftharpoons \text{carbonic acid}$$
$$CO_2 + H_2O \rightleftharpoons H_2CO_3$$

When the temperature is increased, less carbonic acid is present in the mixture. When a mineral such as chalk is added, more carbonic acid is formed. The symbol $\rightleftharpoons$ means that the reaction can go from left to right to form carbonic acid or it may take place in the opposite direction to give carbon dioxide and water. This is termed an equilibrium process, which is referred to in biology as a **dynamic equilibrium**.

The idea of dynamic or mobile equilibrium can be appreciated if we imagine that we can observe a busy disco. People dance in the centre of the floor, others sit or stand around the sides. Some are buying drinks at the bar, while a few may be in the cloakroom. Perhaps we may count 100 people dancing. When we return in 30 minutes and look again, there may be the same number of dancers so that the situation appears to be the same. But most of the individuals will be different. Those people around the sides or at the bar half an hour ago may now be dancing, while those who were active earlier may be resting or drinking at this time. The disco is in dynamic equilibrium with a balance between the number joining and the number leaving the crowd on the floor.

The carbon dioxide–water reaction is like this when it has finished and is at equilibrium. The concentrations remain the same, but carbon dioxide and water molecules are combining at the same rate as carbonic acid molecules are breaking down to give carbon dioxide and water. This reaction is important in ensuring that blood does not become too acidic. Many processes in living cells such as respiration, protein synthesis and energy storage are in dynamic equilibrium, with enzyme catalysts determining in which direction the reversible reaction shifts at any particular time.

Question

Q3.14 Within the liver, an enzyme mediates the conversion of glucose-6-phosphate into fructose-6-phosphate in the process:

$$\text{glucose-6-phosphate} \overset{enzyme}{\rightleftharpoons} \text{fructose-6-phosphate}$$

Use this reaction to explain the terms 'reversible reaction' and 'dynamic equilibrium'.

Summary

All materials exist in one of three phases – solid, liquid or gas. These phases can be described in terms of particle theory, which also explains the processes of diffusion, dissolving and evaporation. Biological and chemical reactions take a certain amount of time, which is measured as the rate of reaction. The reaction rate is altered by changes in concentration, temperature, a catalyst, particle size, light and pH. Some important biological reactions are reversible; they do not go to completion but remain in a state of dynamic equilibrium.

Self-assessment questions

Try these questions.

Q3.15 Complete the following passage with appropriate words from the list below.

The particles in a solid have only limited movement; this takes the form of _____ about a _____ _____ When a solid is heated the structure breaks down to give a ____ in which the particles can ____ _____. The particles in a gas are moving _____; they are well separated and have little _____ between them. A gas occupies a much larger _____ than a solid or liquid.

Word list: attraction, fixed, freely, liquid, move, point, quickly, vibrations, volume.

Q3.16 Name the process involved in each of the following observations and explain it in terms of particle theory.

(a)   The male moth in certain species is attracted to the female over a considerable distance by the traces of pheromone that she produces.

(b)   Perspiration on the surface of the skin disappears in a few minutes.

(c)   A house fly, which can only ingest liquids, takes in a crystal of sugar after secreting saliva on it.

Q3.17 List four factors that can alter the rate of a reaction.

Q3.18 The decomposition of hydrogen peroxide to water and oxygen proceeds much faster in the presence of the enzyme catalase.

(a)   What is the name of the effect brought about by catalase?

(b)   Explain the effect in terms of particle theory.

Q3.19 An increase in the concentration of urea, which is converted into ammonia and carbon dioxide by the enzyme urease, increases the rate of conversion. Use particle theory to interpret this effect.

Q3.20 Use the reaction:

$$\text{glucose} + \text{fructose} \rightleftharpoons \text{sucrose}$$

to explain the meaning of the terms 'reversible reaction' and 'dynamic equilibrium'.

Acids and Bases

Introduction

Within plants or animals a range of acids and bases are present. They carry out a number of diverse functions but have important properties in common. In this chapter we will recognise and discuss these features. An understanding of the general principles of acidity regulation by cells is an important part of biology.

Objectives

After working through this chapter you should be able to:
- describe the typical properties of acids;
- give examples of common acids;
- understand the formation of hydrogen ions in water by acids;
- explain the use of indicators to detect acids and bases;
- correlate the use of the pH scale with the colour of universal indicator;
- understand the difference between strong and weak acids and alkalis;
- describe the typical properties of bases and alkalis;
- understand the process of neutralisation of an acid by a base;
- give examples of common alkalis.

Questions

Try the following questions. Your answers will help you to decide if you need to study this chapter.

Q4.1 Select from the following list three properties that are typical of an acid:
(a) soluble in water;	(e) turns universal indicator red;
(b) turns universal indicator blue;	(f) gives hydroxide ions in water;
(c) has a sour taste;	(g) has a pH value greater than 7.
(d) reacts with a base;	

Q4.2 Consider the following chemical formulae:
(a) H_2CO_3;	(d) HCl;
(b) CH_3COOH;	(e) H_2O_2;
(c) $Ca(OH)_2$;	(f) HNO_3

Pick from this list: (i) two strong acids; (ii) two weak acids.

Q4.3 On the pH scale of 0 to 14 give the approximate pH value for a solution of:
(a) a weak acid;	(c) a weak base;
(b) a strong base;	(d) a strong acid.

Q4.4 Write the names and formulae of two ions that always react together when an acid is neutralised by a base. What is the product?

4.1 Acids

Many of us enjoy the sharp, tingling taste of fruit juice, cola drinks and lemonade, and we sprinkle vinegar on our fish and chips. On the other hand, milk is spoiled when it goes sour and butter is ruined when it becomes rancid. These foods and flavours all have one thing in common – they contain **acids** that occur naturally in animals and plants. Fruit juices, cola and lemonade contain the common plant product citric acid; vinegar, originally made from sour wine, is based on ethanoic acid. The activity of microorganisms is responsible for the production of lactic acid in milk causing it to taste sour, and for the revolting smell of butanoic acid in rancid butter.

The tissues lining our own stomachs secrete a strong acid, hydrochloric acid, which kills harmful bacteria in the food we have eaten as well as beginning the process of digestion. Sometimes the stomach produces too much acid; this causes 'heart-burn' or 'acid indigestion', which is relieved by taking an antacid remedy. This product reacts with the acid to remove, or neutralise, it. Some common acids are given in Table 4.1.

Table 4.1 Names and formulae of acids

Acid name	Formula	Strong or weak	Where it is found	Name of anion
Hydrochloric acid	HCl	Strong	In the stomach	Chloride
Nitric acid	HNO_3	Strong	Traces in rain water	Nitrate
Phosphoric acid	H_3PO_4	Strong	Plant and animal cells	Phosphate
Citric acid	$C_6H_8O_7$	Weak	Lemon juice	Citrate
Ethanoic acid	CH_3COOH	Weak	Vinegar	Ethanoate
Lactic acid	$CH_3CHCOOH$ 丨 OH	Weak	Sour milk	Lactate
Carbonic acid	H_2CO_3	Weak	Rain water, lemonade	Carbonate and bicarbonate

Acids share a number of properties in common; these enable us to recognise a substance as an acid.

Sour taste
The sharp taste of an acid dissolved in water is familiar from lemon juice or vinegar. **Do not taste acids in the laboratory: many strong acids are poisonous and corrosive.**

Indicators
Some substances, called **indicators**, change colour when mixed with acids. For example, litmus and universal indicator become red. This is a useful way to test for an acid.

Corrosive nature
Acids attack and dissolve flesh, clothes and other materials such as metals and minerals.

Reaction with bases
Basic substances combine with acids, removing the properties of the acid and leaving it neutral. This reaction is therefore known as neutralisation. The products of the reaction are a salt and water.

These properties of acids will be discussed in more detail but first it is useful to decide why acids show these features. When any acid dissolves in water it forms **hydrogen ions**. These ions give the characteristic reactions we have seen. In Section 2.1 (page 12), the hydrogen atom was shown to consist of a proton and an electron. Loss of this electron leaves the proton with a positive charge; this is the hydrogen ion.

$$\text{hydrogen atom in an acid} \xrightarrow{\text{water}} \text{hydrogen ion} + \text{electron}$$

$$\text{H} \xrightarrow{\text{H}_2\text{O}} \text{H}^+ + e^-$$

The ion is surrounded by water molecules and is often written $H^+(aq)$, H^+(hydrated) or H_3O^+. The electron is not free, but is now part of an anion. So we can write the **ionisation** (dissociation) of an acid such as hydrochloric acid as follows.

$$\text{hydrogen chloride} \xrightarrow{\text{water}} \text{hydrogen ion} + \text{chloride ion}$$

$$\text{HCl} \xrightarrow{\text{H}_2\text{O}} \text{H}^+(aq) + \text{Cl}^-(aq)$$

The chloride ion formed carries the electron transferred from hydrogen.

Questions

Q4.5 Suggest one way of testing for an acid. What do you observe?

Q4.6 Both phosphoric acid and sulphuric acid are corrosive and each of them is neutralised by the base sodium hydroxide. What common feature causes them to show these properties?

4.2 Indicators and pH

A simple indicator shows one colour when placed in an acid solution and a different colour when the mixture is not acid. **Universal indicator** is a mixture of several different indicators. It changes colour at different levels of acidity so that the difference between a strong acid and a weak acid can be seen. A strong acid gives a red colour while a weak acid gives yellow or orange. Neutral solutions are green. Scientists find it useful to give numbers to different strengths of acids and bases. The value is called the **pH** number, meaning 'power of hydrogen', of the solution. Strong acids have a low pH number of 0 to 2, the pH of weaker acids is 3 to 6, a neutral solution has pH 7, and bases give alkaline solutions with pH 8 to 14. The colour of universal indicator is linked to pH numbers (Figure 4.1).

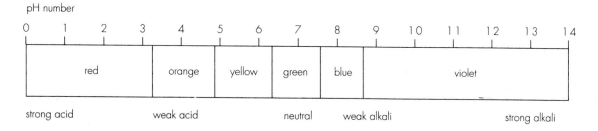

Figure 4.1 The pH number and colour of universal indicator

A solution is tested by adding one or two drops of universal indicator or by dipping in a piece of universal indicator paper. The colour is then compared with a standard colour chart. The pH values of common acids and solutions of biological interest are given in Figure 4.2 (page 30).

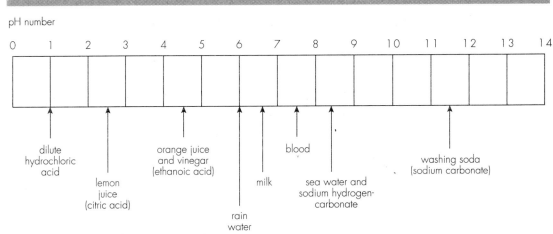

pH number

Figure 4.2 pH numbers of some common substances

Question

Q4.7 When universal indicator paper is dipped into a solution of each of the following compounds, what colour will you observe in each case?

(a) lactic acid;

(b) sodium hydroxide;

(c) phosphoric acid;

(d) citric acid;

(e) rain water.

4.3   Bases and neutralisation

A **base** is the opposite of an acid. An acid and a base combine together to remove or neutralise the properties of the acid. For this reason, a base is described as a substance that will neutralise an acid to form a salt and water only. Many bases are insoluble in water. Those that are soluble are given the additional name of **alkalis**. The excretory product ammonia dissolved in water is a weak alkali. Sodium hydroxide is a strong alkali used for industrial cleaning. Alkalis have a number of properties in common that we can use to recognise them.

Neutralise acids

See the discussion above.

Indicators

Alkalis have a pH number greater than 7. Sodium hydroxide solution has pH 14, while ammonia solution has pH about 11. They turn universal indicator a purple colour.

Corrosive nature

Strong alkalis attack the skin and burn holes in clothing.

Alkalis show these properties because they produce a hydroxide ion when dissolved in water (see Section 2.3, page 15). This ion is formed when the metal part of an alkali transfers an electron to the hydroxide group. In sodium hydroxide, the sodium provides an electron and is left as a cation with a positive charge (Section 2.3, page 15); the hydroxide takes up this electron to become an anion with a negative charge.

$$\text{hydroxide group in an alkali} \xrightarrow{\text{water}} \text{hydroxide ion}$$

$$\text{sodium hydroxide} \xrightarrow{\text{water}} \text{sodium ion} + \text{hydroxide ion}$$

$$\text{NaOH} \xrightarrow{H_2O} Na^+ + OH^-$$

When an acid reacts with an alkali, the hydrogen ion of the acid combines with the hydroxide ion of the alkali to give neutral water.

hydrogen ion from acid + hydroxide ion from alkali ⟶ water
$$H^+ \quad + \quad OH^- \quad \longrightarrow \quad H_2O$$

This is the process that underlies the **neutralisation** of an acid by an alkali, for example the neutralisation of hydrochloric acid (HCl) by sodium hydroxide (NaOH):

hydrochloric acid + sodium hydroxide ⟶ sodium chloride + water
$$HCl \quad + \quad NaOH \quad \longrightarrow \quad NaCl \quad + \quad H_2O$$

We can see that the reaction produces a neutral compound, the **salt** sodium chloride, and water. A salt is a substance containing a metal part, such as sodium, and a non-metal part, such as chloride, and is formed by neutralisation. The general equation for the process can be written:

$$acid \; + \; base \longrightarrow salt \; + \; water$$

Questions

Q4.8 Explain the difference between a base and an alkali.

Q4.9 Write the word and formula equations for the neutralisation of hydrochloric acid, HCl, with ammonia solution, NH_4OH.

Summary

Acids produce the hydrogen ion, H^+, in water. They have a sour taste, are corrosive and have a low pH value. They are neutralised by bases to give salts and water. Strong acids turn universal indicator red, while weak acids give an orange or yellow colour. Bases may be insoluble or soluble. Bases turn universal indicator purple/blue. Soluble bases are called alkalis. Alkalis give the hydroxide ion, OH^-, when dissolved in water. They are corrosive and have a high pH value.

Self-assessment questions

Try the following questions.

Q4.10 Give three examples of acids that are found in plants or plant products.

Q4.11 Write a symbol equation to show how the hydrogen ion is formed when an acid dissolves in water.

Q4.12 List four properties that are typical of acids.

Q4.13 Suggest approximate pH values for the following substances:
(a) dilute hydrochloric acid;
(b) blood;
(c) rain water;
(d) citric acid;
(e) dilute sodium hydroxide;
(f) milk.

Q4.14 (a) Explain the difference between a base and an alkali.
(b) Which two ions are involved in the neutralisation of an acid with an alkali?
(c) Write word and formula equations to show how these ions combine in neutralisation.

Q4.15 Write a word equation to describe the neutralisation of phosphoric acid with calcium hydroxide (see Table 4.1, page 28, and Section 2.3, page 15).

The Effect of Heat and Electricity

Introduction

The temperature over the surface of the Earth shows wide variations, from the perpetual frosts of the polar regions to the heat of the deserts and the boiling water of thermal springs. In these places, life has adapted to the environment but few species can survive here. Growth usually focuses on a short favourable period of the year. In temperate and tropical regions with moderate temperatures, the range and variety of species is much greater. Animals are usually active throughout the year and plants enjoy a long season of growth. Thus we can see that the amount of heat supplied to organisms by the background is important. Biological processes and simple substances are affected by heat.

A number of substances, in particular acids, bases and salts, may exist as ions. They carry a positive or negative charge and so will be affected by an electric current. Ions are present in all parts of an organism, indicating that electricity plays a role in controlling life processes.

Objectives

After studying this chapter you should be able to:
- list the changes in a substance that can be caused by the action of heat;
- interpret the effect of heat in causing a chemical change or a change in reaction rate;
- understand the concept of exergonic and endergonic reactions;
- interpret energy-level diagrams in terms of exergonic and endergonic stages;
- use bond energies to calculate heat changes in biological reactions;
- appreciate the significance of the sign used for the heat of reaction;
- describe an experiment that detects electrical conductivity in an aqueous solution;
- explain electrical conductivity in terms of the movement of ions and electrons;
- understand the terms cathode, anode, electrolyte and electrolysis;
- give examples of good, weak and non-conductors;
- explain how acids, bases and salts conduct electricity;
- interpret the poor conductivity of weak electrolytes in terms of their slight tendency to form ions;
- explain why some substances are non-conductors.

Questions

Try the introductory questions. Your answers will help you to decide if you need to work through this chapter.

Q5.1 Describe the changes that may occur when a solid substance is heated.

Q5.2 What change in the rate of fermentation of sugars by yeast would you expect when the temperature of the mixture was increased from 20 °C to 30 °C?

Q5.3 Calculate the heat of reaction when hydrogen combines with ethene, $CH_2{=}CH_2$, to form ethane, $CH_3{-}CH_3$. (Bond energies in $kJ\,mol^{-1}$: H—H 436; C—H 412; C—C 348; C=C 612).

Q5.4 Outline an experiment you would carry out to decide whether or not a solution is a conductor of electricity.

Q5.5 Suggest which of these substances can conduct electricity when dissolved in water:

(a) sodium chloride;

(b) ethanol;

(c) sulphuric acid;

(d) ammonium hydroxide.

Q5.6 Explain why a solution of sodium ethanoate in water is a good conductor of electricity, while a solution of ethanoic acid is a poor conductor.

5.1   The effect of heat

Higher animals have elaborate internal mechanisms to maintain body temperature close to a specific value. This is because the life processes in an organism function best under these conditions. Even a small variation in temperature can lead to lower activity and even death. Lower animals and plants have little internal control over temperature. They show wide variations in growth and movement with changes in the temperature of the environment. They merely survive during periods when it is too cold or hot for normal activity.

A knowledge of the effect of heat on simple substances helps us understand its effect on organisms. Heating a material can bring about one or more of the following changes:

(i)   a change of state;

(ii)   a change in reaction rate;

(iii) a chemical change.

Change of state

When a solid is heated, its temperature is raised until it melts to a liquid at a fixed temperature called the melting point. The liquid becomes hotter and eventually boils at a given temperature, the boiling point, to form a gas. Water is found in all three states at temperatures commonly encountered in the environment. Water is a universal medium for body fluids.

Change in reaction rate

Rates of reaction increase sharply with an increase in temperature. Usually the rate will double when the temperature rises by 10 °C. This corresponds to a four-fold increase when the temperature increases by 20 °C. Thus it is clear that metabolic activity in a plant or animal can increase sharply with a small rise in temperature. Living things with a stable high temperature can maintain a high level of activity throughout life.

Chemical change

As well as speeding up a reaction, heating a stable substance might cause it to reach a temperature where a chemical change will take place. When sugar is heated, the white crystalline solid melts to a liquid and then goes brown as chemical breakdown of the molecule occurs. This process is widely used in the food industry and is called caramelisation. If a protein such as albumen, egg white, is heated in water, the colourless solution forms a white solid as the giant protein molecules in albumen are degraded. This change is called denaturation.

Question

Q5.7 Describe the changes that you would expect to observe on heating:

(a) a solution of albumen in water;

(b) solid magnesium chloride.

5.2   Measuring the heat of reaction

When a chemical change takes place, heat either is given out to the surroundings or is taken in from the surroundings. Cellular respiration involves the oxidation of carbohydrates:

$$\text{sugars} + \text{oxygen} \longrightarrow \text{carbon dioxide} + \text{water}$$

It gives out heat energy, which is used by the organism for its life processes. The burning of petrol in vehicles or of natural gas in central-heating boilers are processes that also give out heat. We use the heat to power our cars or keep our houses warm. Chemical reactions in which heat is evolved are called **exergonic** (or exothermic) reactions.

Processes that require energy to be supplied from the surroundings include photosynthesis, in which sugars are formed from carbon dioxide and water:

$$carbon\ dioxide\ +\ water\ \longrightarrow\ sugars\ +\ oxygen$$

The energy required for green plants to carry out this change is supplied by sunlight. Changes of this type are termed **endergonic** (or endothermic) reactions.

The amount of heat given out or taken in can be determined accurately from the energies of individual bonds formed between atoms. Energy values for some bonds are given in Table 5.1. For the hydrogen molecule, H_2, the bond energy is given as 436 kilojoules per mole ($kJ\ mol^{-1}$). This means that the energy required to break the bonds in one mole (see Section 1.2, page 3) of hydrogen, H_2, is exactly 436 kJ.

Breaking bonds is always an endergonic process:

$$\begin{array}{ccc} hydrogen\ molecule & \longrightarrow & two\ hydrogen\ atoms \qquad endergonic \\ H—H & \longrightarrow & H\ +\ H \end{array}$$

When hydrogen atoms combine in pairs to give one mole of hydrogen molecules, 436 kJ of heat are given out.

Forming bonds is an exergonic process:

$$\begin{array}{ccc} two\ hydrogen\ atoms & \longrightarrow & hydrogen\ molecule \qquad exergonic \\ H\ +\ H & \longrightarrow & H—H \end{array}$$

These changes can be shown on an **energy diagram** (Figure 5.1).

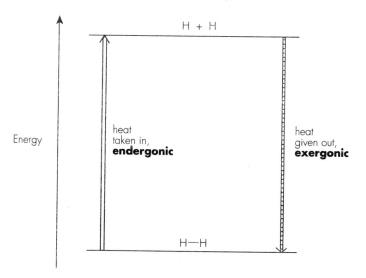

Figure 5.1 Energy-level diagram for exergonic and endergonic changes in the formation and breakdown of the covalent bond in the hydrogen molecule

When a chemical change takes place to give products that are different from the starting materials, then different bond energies are involved and an overall energy change takes place. This change is called the **heat of reaction**.

Table 5.1 Energies for some biologically important bonds

Bond name	Bond symbol	Bond energy/kJ mol^{-1}
hydrogen–hydrogen	H—H	436
carbon–hydrogen	C—H	412
carbon–carbon (single)	C—C	348
carbon–carbon (double)	C=C	612
oxygen–oxygen	O=O	496
hydrogen–oxygen	H—O	463
carbon–oxygen	C=O	743

Example 5.1

Calculate the heat of reaction when hydrogen burns in air. What is the heat change for the formation of one mole of water?

Write the equation for the reaction:

$$\text{hydrogen} + \text{oxygen} \longrightarrow \text{water}$$

Show the bonds joining the atoms in the formula equation, then write the bond energies from Table 5.1 under the formulae involved:

$$2\,H\text{—}H + O=O \longrightarrow 2\,H\text{—}O\text{—}H$$
$$2 \times 436 \qquad 496\,kJ \qquad 4 \times 463$$
$$= 872\,kJ \qquad\qquad\qquad = 1852\,kJ$$

Add the bond energies for the reactants (left-hand side) and for the products (right-hand side):

Reactants: 872 + 496 = 1368 kJ   Products: 1852 kJ

The bond energies of the products are greater than the bond energies for the reactants. Thus the heat taken in to break the bonds in hydrogen and oxygen is 1368 kJ, while the heat given out in forming the bonds in water is 1852 kJ. The heat of reaction is

$$1852 - 1368 = 484\,kJ.$$

This is the heat of reaction for two moles of water. For one mole the heat of reaction is

$$484 \div 2 = -242\,kJ\,mol^{-1}.$$

Since heat is given out, the reaction is exergonic and the value calculated has a negative sign. The energy-level diagram in Figure 5.2 shows that water, the product, is at a lower energy level than the reactants, hydrogen and oxygen, from which it is formed. The fall in energy on the production of water is indicated by the negative sign for the heat of reaction.

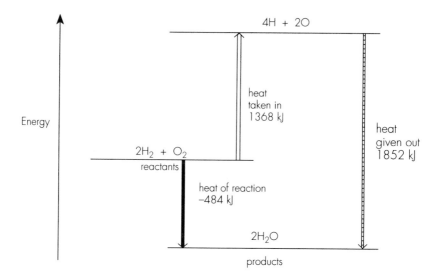

Figure 5.2 Energy changes on the conversion of hydrogen and oxygen into water

Example 5.2

Ethene burns in air to form carbon dioxide and water. Determine the heat of reaction for one mole of ethene.

ethene   +   oxygen $\longrightarrow$ carbon dioxide +   water

$$
\begin{array}{cccc}
\text{H} \quad\quad \text{H} & & & \\
\diagdown \quad \diagup & & & \\
\text{C}{=}\text{C} \quad + \quad 3\text{O}{=}\text{O} & \longrightarrow & 2\text{O}{=}\text{C}{=}\text{O} & + \quad 2\text{H}{-}\text{O}{-}\text{H} \\
\diagup \quad \diagdown & & & \\
\text{H} \quad\quad \text{H} & & &
\end{array}
$$

$(4 \times 412) + 612$ 3×496 4×743 4×463
   $= 2260\,\text{kJ}$ $= 1488\,\text{kJ}$ $= 2972\,\text{kJ}$ $= 1852\,\text{kJ}$

Reactants: $2260 + 1488 = 3748\,\text{kJ}$ Products: $2972 + 1852 = 4824\,\text{kJ}$

Heat of reaction is

$$4824 - 3748 = 1076\,\text{kJ}$$

Only one mole of ethene is involved in the equation and the bond energies of the products are greater than the bond energies for the reactants. Thus the reaction is exergonic, and the value calculated has a negative sign. The heat of reaction is $-1076\,\text{kJ mol}^{-1}$.

Question

Q5.8 Natural gas, methane, is burnt in air to give carbon dioxide and water. Calculate the heat of reaction for one mole of methane, CH_4.

5.3 Ions and electricity

The formation of ions by electron transfer was considered in Section 2.3 (page 15). Because they are charged, ions are affected by an electric current. A nerve impulse, which is electrical in nature, moves along an axon by migration of sodium ions across the membrane surrounding

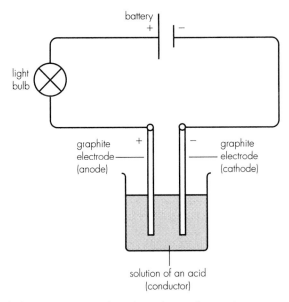

Figure 5.3 A circuit in which a current passes through a solution of an acid

the axon. Ions occur in acids, bases and salts, and are able to move when the ionic substance is dissolved in water. Ions in solid materials are fixed in one position and they are not affected by a current.

When a battery is connected to a solution of an acid by means of two copper wires linked to graphite rods dipping into the acid (Figure 5.3), the ions in the solution carry the current from one rod to the other. A solution that carries an electric current is a **conductor**; the graphite rods dipping into it are **electrodes**. The electrode joined to the positive terminal of the battery is called the **anode**, the positive electrode. The electrode linked to the negative terminal is the **cathode**. Positively charged ions in the solution, cations, are attracted to the negative cathode. Negative ions, anions, move to the positive anode. A light bulb is included in the circuit so that it is obvious when a current is flowing.

Within the solution, each anion carries a negative charge to the anode. On reaching it, the anion gives up its negative charge to the anode in the form of an electron. The electron passes through the electrode, the wires and the battery to the cathode where it is available to combine with a cation at the cathode (Figure 5.4). When ions give up or gain electrons at electrodes, they lose the charges they carried and become atoms.

Example 5.3

How does a solution of hydrochloric acid conduct an electric current?

Hydrochloric acid, HCl, forms hydrogen ions, H^+, and chloride ions, Cl^-, in water. The positive hydrogen ions, cations, move to the cathode (negative) and at the cathode each ion gains an electron:

$$H^+ + e^- \text{(from cathode)} \longrightarrow H$$
$$\text{cation} \qquad\qquad\qquad\qquad \longrightarrow \text{atom}$$

The negative chloride ions, anions, move to the anode (positive) and each gives up an electron to the anode:

$$Cl^- \longrightarrow Cl + e^- \text{(to anode)}$$
$$\text{anion} \longrightarrow \text{atom}$$

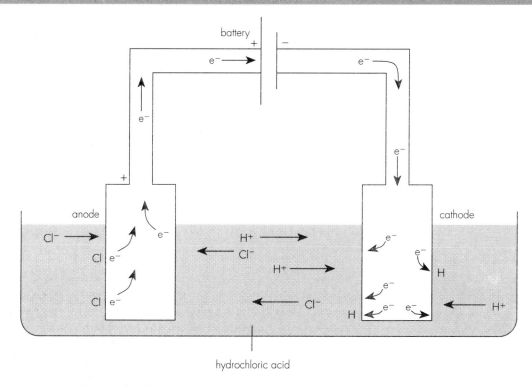

hydrochloric acid

<u>Figure 5.4</u> Hydrochloric acid, HCl, is the conductor: Cl^- ions give up electrons at the anode; H^+ ions gain electrons at the cathode

The chlorine atoms combine in pairs to give chlorine gas, Cl_2. Hydrogen atoms similarly combine to give hydrogen gas, H_2.

The conversion of ions into atoms and then molecules by an electric current, as in the above example, is termed **electrolysis**. A solution that contains ions, conducts electricity and that undergoes electrolysis is called an **electrolyte**. Other acids conduct electricity in the same way, thus sulphuric acid and phosphoric acid are electrolytes and undergo electrolysis.

Question

Q5.9 How does a solution of sulphuric acid in water conduct electricity? (Consider only the movement of ions, not reactions at the electrodes.)

Salts (see Section 2.3, page 15) are made up of a metal part and a non-metal part. In most cases, these parts are ions and so a solution of a salt contains ions that are free and mobile. The ion formed from the metal part is a cation; the ion obtained from the non-metal part is an anion. Passing an electric current through the solution allows it to conduct electricity by the migration of charged ions to the electrodes.

Example 5.4
How does a solution of sodium chloride conduct electricity?

Sodium chloride, NaCl, dissolves in water to form free sodium cations, Na^+, and free chloride anions, Cl^-. Under the influence of the electric current, the sodium ions move to the negative electrode, the cathode. Chloride ions are attracted to the anode, which is positive.

While solutions of salts are important as conductors, they also behave as electrolytes since they undergo electrolysis. This means that the ions undergo chemical change at the electrodes. A few bases, called alkalis, are soluble in water. They contain ions that become free to move when the alkali is in solution. The cations are usually metal ions, while the anions are hydroxide ions, OH^-.

Example 5.5
How does a solution of potassium hydroxide conduct electricity?
Potassium cations, K^+, and hydroxide ions, OH^-, are present in the solution. The positively charged potassium ions move towards the negative cathode. The anode attracts the negative hydroxide ions.

Question

Q5.10 How does a solution of sodium hydroxide in water conduct electricity? (Consider only the movement of ions, not reactions at the electrodes.)

Many substances, such as the acids, bases and salts already discussed, are good conductors of electricity. Others are less efficient conductors because few ions are present in solution. Although the substance may be soluble in water, only a small proportion of the molecules present form ions. Ethanoic acid, CH_3COOH, gives solutions that behave in this way. If ethanoic acid is tested using the circuit shown in Figure 5.3, the bulb glows only faintly, if at all. The solution contains mainly molecules of the acid, CH_3COOH, with only a few hydrogen cations, H^+, and ethanoate anions, CH_3COO^-. The current is carried only by the ions; the molecules are non-conductors. The formation of ions in this way is a reversible reaction (see Section 3.5, page 24):

$$\text{ethanoic acid} \underset{\text{water}}{\rightleftharpoons} \text{hydrogen ions} + \text{ethanoate ions}$$
$$CH_3COOH \rightleftharpoons H^+(aq) + CH_3COO^-(aq)$$

Ethanoic acid is known as a **weak electrolyte**. In the same way, bases may be weak electrolytes if they provide only a small proportion of ions in solution.

Example 5.6
Explain why ammonia solution is a weak electrolyte.
Ammonia solution is a weak electrolyte because only a small number of ammonia molecules form ions. Ammonia reacts with water to form ammonium cations, NH_4^+, and hydroxide anions, OH^-, in a reversible reaction:

$$\text{ammonia} + \text{water} \rightleftharpoons \text{ammonium ions} + \text{hydroxide ions}$$
$$NH_3 + H_2O \rightleftharpoons NH_4^+ + OH^-$$

Question

Q5.11 A solution of lactic acid, $CH_3CHCOOH$, is a poor conductor.
$$\overset{\displaystyle |}{\underset{\displaystyle OH}{}}$$
Use word and formula equations for reversible reactions to demonstrate this fact.

Sometimes a substance in solution will not conduct electricity, even to a small extent. Organic compounds often behave like this, the molecules remaining unchanged in water; no ions are formed. The solution is termed a non-conductor. Table 5.2, overleaf, lists some acids, bases and salts together with the ions they produce in water.

Table 5.2 Solutions of acids, bases and salts as conductors of electricity

Substance	Behaviour in water	Electrical conductivity
Hydrogen chloride (HCl)	$HCl \rightarrow H^+ + Cl^-$	Good
Sulphuric acid (H_2SO_4)	$H_2SO_4 \rightarrow H^+ + HSO_4^-$	Good
Phosphoric acid (H_3PO_4)	$H_3PO_4 \rightarrow H^+ + H_2PO_4^-$	Good
Carbonic acid (H_2CO_3)	$H_2CO_3 \rightleftharpoons H^+ + HCO_3^-$	Poor
Ethanoic acid (CH_3COOH)	$CH_3COOH \rightleftharpoons H^+ + CH_3COO^-$	Poor
Ammonia (NH_3)	$NH_3 + H_2O \rightleftharpoons NH_4^+ + OH^-$	Poor
Sodium ethanoate (CH_3COONa)	$CH_3COO^-Na^+ \rightarrow Na^+ + CH_3COO^-$	Good
Sodium chloride (NaCl)	$Na^+Cl^- \rightarrow Na^+ + Cl^-$	Good
Ammonium nitrate (NH_4NO_3)	$NH_4^+NO_3^- \rightarrow NH_4^+ + NO_3^-$	Good
Sodium hydrogencarbonate ($NaHCO_3$)	$Na^+HCO_3^- \rightarrow Na^+ + HCO_3^-$	Good
Glucose ($C_6H_{12}O_6$)	No ions formed	None
Ethanol (CH_3CH_2OH)	No ions formed	None
Sucrose ($C_{12}H_{22}O_{11}$)	No ions formed	None

Summary

Heat may cause a substance to change state, a reaction rate to increase, or a substance to decompose. During a reaction, heat may be given out (exergonic) or taken in (endergonic). The heat change may be calculated from bond energy values. Acids, bases and salts when dissolved in water give ions that are free to move. An electric current causes ions in a solution to migrate. Positively charged cations move to the negative electrode, the cathode. Negatively charged anions go to the positive electrode, the anode. Good conductors of electricity are strong electrolytes, which are completely converted into ions in water. Poor conductors are weak electrolytes and are partly converted into ions in water. Non-conductors do not form ions in water.

Self-assessment questions

Try these questions on heat and electricity.

Q5.12 List the changes that will be observed when
(a) sodium chloride;
(b) glucose are heated until no further change takes place.

Q5.13 Explain why a solution of magnesium chloride is a good conductor of electricity while solid magnesium chloride is a non-conductor of electricity when both contain the ions Mg^{2+} and Cl^-.

Q5.14 Describe the way in which a solution of hydrochloric acid conducts electricity.

Q5.15 'Phosphoric acid solution is an electrolyte and undergoes electrolysis.' Carefully explain the meaning of the terms 'electrolyte' and 'electrolysis' in this statement.

Q5.16 Why is a solution of ammonia in water a weak electrolyte?

Q5.17 Give an example of the movement of ions in a biological process.

Oxidation and Reduction

Introduction

Animals convert the storage material glycogen into carbon dioxide and water by reaction with oxygen. The process takes place in a series of steps. Plants use starch in the same way. In each case it is an oxidation process that releases energy for use by the organism. The opposite of oxidation is reduction, which takes place when water combines with carbon dioxide to give sugars in green plants. This is photosynthesis.

Objectives

When you have completed this chapter you should be able to:
- understand that oxidation is the gain of oxygen or the loss of hydrogen;
- appreciate that reduction is the gain of hydrogen or the loss of oxygen;
- explain that an oxidant (oxidising agent) causes oxidation and a reductant (reducing agent) brings about reduction;
- give examples of oxidation and reduction processes involving oxygen and hydrogen;
- describe the use of the term 'redox';
- understand that oxidation is the loss of electrons from a substance and reduction is the gain of electrons;
- discuss examples of redox reactions in terms of electron transfer.

Questions

Work through the following questions to decide whether or not you need to study this chapter.

Q6.1 Mark each of the reactants in the following processes with one of the letters O, R or N to show if it is being oxidised, reduced or neither in the process.
   (a)   sucrose + oxygen $\longrightarrow$ carbon dioxide + water
   (b)   sodium + chlorine $\longrightarrow$ sodium chloride
   (c)   hydrochloric acid + sodium hydroxide $\longrightarrow$ sodium chloride + water
   (d)   ethanol + oxygen $\longrightarrow$ carbon dioxide + water
   (e)   carbon dioxide + water $\longrightarrow$ carbonic acid

Q6.2 Explain the term oxidation in terms of the gain or loss of electrons.

Q6.3 (a)   What is a reductant (reducing agent)?
   (b)   Which of the following substances are reductants (reducing agents)?
   (i)   ammonia;   (iv) hydrogen sulphide;
   (ii) ethanoic acid;   (v)   sodium hydroxide;
   (iii) magnesium;   (vi) calcium chloride.

Q6.4 The reaction of calcium metal with chlorine gas to form calcium chloride is a redox reaction.
   (a)   What do you understand by the term 'redox'?
   (b)   Write the word and formula equations for the reaction.
   (c)   Use electron transfer in the formula equation to demonstrate that this is a redox process.

Q6.5 The carbon cycle includes the following stages:
  (a) conversion of carbon dioxide and water into sugars in photosynthesis;
  (b) consumption of plant proteins by animals and their subsequent assimilation;
  (c) breakdown of sugars to carbon dioxide and water in cell respiration;
  (d) conversion of sugars into glycogen in the animal body.
  Identify in each stage the change taking place in the carbon compounds as a reduction or an oxidation or neither of these two.

6.1 Oxygen and hydrogen

Oxidation may be seen as the addition of oxygen to a substance or as the removal of hydrogen. Natural gas, methane, burns in air to form carbon dioxide and water:

$$\text{methane} + \text{oxygen} \longrightarrow \text{carbon dioxide} + \text{water}$$
$$CH_4 + 2O_2 \longrightarrow CO_2 + 2H_2O$$

Respiration causes sugars to combine with oxygen to give the same products:

$$\text{glucose} + \text{oxygen} \longrightarrow \text{carbon dioxide} + \text{water}$$
$$C_6H_{12}O_6 + 6O_2 \longrightarrow 6CO_2 + 6H_2O$$

In each case, oxygen has been added to the carbon compound. We say that it has been **oxidised**. A substance that causes a compound like methane or glucose to be oxidised is called an **oxidant** (oxidising agent). Oxygen is an oxidant.

The reverse of oxidation is **reduction**; this corresponds to the addition of hydrogen or to the removal of oxygen. In the process of photosynthesis, water acts as a source of hydrogen which then reduces carbon dioxide to sugars. The overall reaction can be written as an equation:

$$\text{carbon dioxide} + \text{water} \longrightarrow \text{sugars} + \text{oxygen}$$
$$6CO_2 + 6H_2O \longrightarrow C_6H_{12}O_6 + 6O_2$$

Hydrogen has been added to the carbon dioxide while half the oxygen has been removed.

Green and purple sulphur bacteria live in the mud of pools rich in hydrogen sulphide. They use this instead of water to provide the hydrogen needed for the reduction of carbon dioxide:

$$\text{carbon dioxide} + \text{hydrogen sulphide} \longrightarrow \text{sugars} + \text{sulphur} + \text{water}$$
$$6CO_2 + 12H_2S \longrightarrow C_6H_{12}O_6 + 12S + 6H_2O$$

This is clearly a similar reduction process, with carbon dioxide undergoing reduction to sugars. From these equations, we can see that water and hydrogen sulphide can be called **reductants** (reducing agents) since they have brought about the reduction.

Although we have looked at oxidation and reduction as separate reactions, they do in fact take place together. This is because if one substance is oxidised (i.e. oxygen is added), another substance must be reduced (i.e. oxygen is taken away). In the combustion (burning) of methane, the addition of oxygen to the carbon, which is oxidation, occurs at the same time as the addition of hydrogen to some of the oxygen, which is reduction.

$$CH_4 + 2O_2 \xrightarrow{\quad\text{oxidation}\quad} CO_2 + 2H_2O$$
$$\text{reduction}$$

Thus methane is a reductant while oxygen is an oxidant. A reaction in which oxidation and reduction take place together is known as a **redox** reaction.

REDuction OXidation

REDOX

All of the processes considered so far are redox reactions.

Example 6.1

Ammonia and oxygen are converted into nitrogen and water by denitrifying bacteria in soil and water. Show that this is a redox reaction.

Write the word and symbol equations for the reaction:

$$\text{ammonia} + \text{oxygen} \longrightarrow \text{nitrogen} + \text{water}$$
$$4NH_3 + 3O_2 \longrightarrow 2N_2 + 6H_2O$$

Ammonia loses hydrogen and so it is oxidised; oxygen gains hydrogen and is reduced. Ammonia is the reducing agent; oxygen is the oxidising agent:

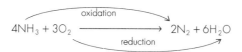

$$4NH_3 + 3O_2 \longrightarrow 2N_2 + 6H_2O$$

Question

Q6.6 Methanol (CH_3OH) burns in oxygen to give carbon dioxide and water. Use word and symbol equations to explain that this is a redox process.

6.2 Oxidation and electrons

Oxidation and reduction have been seen as the gain or loss of oxygen and hydrogen. Redox processes can be looked at in another way as the gain or loss of electrons. This is useful when a redox reaction does not actually involve oxygen or hydrogen, a situation that is quite common in biology. In Section 2.3, page 15, the formation of the ionic compound magnesium oxide from magnesium and oxygen was explained. We saw that electrons were transferred from the metal to oxygen to form magnesium cations and oxide ions:

$$\text{magnesium} + \text{oxygen} \longrightarrow \text{magnesium oxide}$$
$$2Mg + O_2 \longrightarrow 2(Mg^{2+}O^{2-})$$

From the reactions discussed in Section 6.1, we know that the addition of oxygen is oxidation. So magnesium, which has lost electrons, is oxidised. In the same way, oxygen has gained electrons and is reduced.

In general terms it can be seen that:
- (i)   a substance that is oxidised loses electrons,
- (ii)   a substance that is reduced gains electrons.

So an oxidant is a substance that takes up electrons provided by a reductant.

Example 6.2

Potassium chloride is an ionic compound formed by the combination of potassium and chlorine (see Section 2.3, page 15). Use electron transfer to show that this is a redox process. Write the word and formula equations for the reaction.

$$\text{potassium} + \text{chlorine} \longrightarrow \text{potassium chloride}$$
$$2K + Cl_2 \longrightarrow 2(K^+Cl^-)$$

Potassium loses electrons to chlorine and forms potassium cations, while chlorine gains electrons to give chloride anions (Section 2.3, page 15).

$$2K + Cl_2 \longrightarrow 2K^+Cl^-$$

Potassium loses electrons and is a reductant. Chlorine gains electrons and is an oxidant. This can be illustrated as two separate reactions:

$$K \longrightarrow K^+ + e^- \qquad \text{oxidation}$$
$$Cl + e^- \longrightarrow Cl^- \qquad \text{reduction}$$

Questions

Q6.7 Calcium oxide, CaO, is ionic. It is formed from calcium, Ca, and oxygen, O_2. Explain the reaction as redox by using the idea of electron transfer.

Q6.8 Sodium, Na, and chlorine, Cl_2, combine together in a redox process to give the ionic salt sodium chloride, NaCl. Use the gain and loss of electrons to confirm this as a redox reaction.

We shall see in Part 2 that electron transfer is closely involved in the detailed steps that make up the cyclic photosynthesis and respiratory processes in the cell.

Summary

Oxidation is the gain of oxygen or the loss of hydrogen by a substance. Reduction is the gain of hydrogen or the loss of oxygen by a substance. An oxidant is a substance that provides oxygen or takes up hydrogen and a reductant provides hydrogen or can gain oxygen. In terms of electron transfer, oxidation is the loss of electrons by a substance. Reduction is the gain of electrons. Oxidation and reduction always take place together; such a process is called a redox reaction.

Self-assessment questions

Try these questions on oxidation and reduction.

Q6.9 In each of the following reactions:
  (a) hydrogen + oxygen $\longrightarrow$ water
  (b) calcium + chlorine $\longrightarrow$ calcium chloride
  state which substance is oxidised and which reduced.

Q6.10 Select a suitable example to explain the meaning of the term 'redox'.

Q6.11 Consider the following substances:
  (a) sodium;   (d) hydrogen;
  (b) methane;   (e) glucose;
  (c) chlorine;   (f) calcium.
  Identify each one as a reductant, an oxidant or neither of these two.

Q6.12 Use the formation of magnesium chloride from magnesium and chlorine to describe oxidation and reduction by means of electron transfer.

Q6.13 In the nitrogen cycle:
  (a) atmospheric nitrogen is converted into proteins by bacteria in soil and root nodules of leguminous plants;
  (b) nitrates are taken up by plants and metabolised to form proteins;
  (c) animals eat plant proteins and excrete urea, which is changed to nitrogen gas by denitrifying bacteria;
  (d) proteins in the tissues of dead animals give nitrates in the presence of decomposing bacteria.
  Classify each of these processes as oxidation, reduction or neither. Give reasons for your choice.

The Biological Chemistry of Hydrogen, Nitrogen and Phosphorus

Introduction

A number of simple substances are closely involved in the reactions of the natural world. Some of these, such as water, methane and nitrogen, occur in vast quantities. Others, such as phosphates, are relatively scarce. All are important in the metabolism of organisms. It is useful to appreciate the nature of these materials and some of the chemical reactions in which they take part.

Objectives

After working through this chapter you should be able to:
- recall the use of hydrogen as a reducing agent;
- write the names and formulae of important hydrogen compounds;
- appreciate the biological significance of hydrogen compounds;
- understand the formation of the hydrogen ion in water;
- recognise the properties of the isotope deuterium;
- appreciate the importance of water in the environment and the biosphere;
- recall the main components of the water cycle;
- understand the importance of nitrogen compounds in plants and animals;
- write the names and formulae of nitrogen compounds and ions;
- understand the processes of nitrification by which nitrogen gas is converted into nitrogen compounds;
- appreciate the ways in which nitrogen compounds are broken down into nitrogen gas by denitrification;
- describe the ways in which people intervene in the processes of nitrification and denitrification;
- recall the main stages of the nitrogen cycle;
- write the names and formulae of phosphorus compounds and ions;
- understand the importance of phosphorus compounds in energy-transfer processes used by plants and animals.

Questions

If the concepts are familiar, try the following questions. If your answers are correct, proceed to the next chapter.

Q7.1 Write chemical formulae for methane, water, hydrogen chloride and hydrogen sulphide. Give an example of the biological importance of each of these compounds.

Q7.2 How does hydrogen form the hydrogen ion? List two properties of the hydrogen ion.

Q7.3 How does hydrogen differ from deuterium? Why is deuterium useful to the biologist?

Q7.4 Water is of great significance in the environment. Give three ways in which it is involved in the living world.

Q7.5 Explain the processes that enable nitrogen gas to be converted into plant or animal proteins.

Q7.6 Give chemical formulae for the nitrate, nitrite and ammonium ions. Write the names and chemical formulae of compounds containing these ions.

Q7.7 How does the harvesting of crops from arable land affect the fertility of the soil? What steps can be taken to redress this problem?

Q7.8 Animal and plant proteins released by excretion or death are converted into simple nitrogen compounds or ions. Name three of these substances.

Q7.9 Write the chemical formulae for phosphoric acid and the phosphate group. Give the name of an energy-transfer phosphate used in respiration.

7.1 Hydrogen and water

In the natural world, the element hydrogen is found combined with oxygen as water and with carbon as methane or other organic compounds. Hydrogen always has a valency of 1 as is shown in the compounds it forms with many metal and non-metal elements. Some important hydrogen compounds are listed in Table 7.1, together with their significance in biology.

Table 7.1 Hydrogen compounds and their significance in biology

Name	Formula	Biological significance
Methane	CH_4	Natural gas, product of anaerobic decay
Ammonia	NH_3	Excretion product, formed by anaerobic decay, used in fertilisers
Water	H_2O	Solvent for nutrients and waste, transport medium in organisms
Hydrogen chloride	HCl	Stomach acid when dissolved in water
Hydrogen sulphide	H_2S	Energy source for sulphur bacteria

Hydrogen is a reducing agent. It combines with (reduces) carbon dioxide in photosynthesis. Oils, such as olive oil and palm oil, contain carbon–carbon double bonds, $C{=}C$. These are called 'unsaturated' bonds. They can take up hydrogen and be reduced to 'saturated' carbon–carbon single bonds, $C{-}C$. This reduction converts the liquid oil into a solid fat, which is used in margarine. Hydrogen often acts as a reducing agent by removing oxygen to form water, which has strong oxygen–hydrogen bonds. One of the stages in photosynthesis uses hydrogen in this way, producing water and carbohydrates from carbon dioxide in a complex sequence of reactions.

When a hydrogen atom loses an electron it forms a hydrogen cation. This dissociation process takes place in water:

$$\text{hydrogen atom} \longrightarrow \text{hydrogen ion} + \text{electron}$$
$$H \longrightarrow H^+(aq) + e^-$$

The hydrogen ion is acidic and so hydrogen is an important element in acids (see Section 4.1, page 28). Hydrogen atoms do not occur uncombined, but in acids are linked to oxygen, chlorine or sulphur. The hydrogen ion released is bound to water molecules, while the electron is part of an anion. This can be seen in the dissociation of nitric acid:

$$\text{nitric acid} \longrightarrow \text{hydrogen ion} + \text{nitrate ion}$$
$$HNO_3 \longrightarrow H^+(aq) + NO_3^-(aq)$$

Question

Q7.10 Write word and symbol equations for the dissociation (ionisation) of phosphoric acid, H_3PO_4.

Ordinary hydrogen contains a small proportion of 'heavy hydrogen'. This is a second form, or **isotope**, of the element in which the atom contains a neutron as well as a proton (see Section 2.1, page 11). This isotope is called deuterium. Hydrogen and deuterium are compared in Table 7.2. Deuterium is important to the biologist because it is used to replace hydrogen when a metabolic pathway or other process is to be studied. The changes involving the deuterium can be traced without it being confused with hydrogen. The deuterium isotope is called a tracer. Deuterium can be used as a tracer because although hydrogen and deuterium have the same chemical properties, they have different masses. The deuterium is traced by its higher mass.

Table 7.2 Hydrogen and deuterium

Name	Symbol	Number of protons	Number of neutrons	Number of electrons	Relative mass
Hydrogen	H	1	0	1	1
Deuterium	D	1	1	1	2

Water is the most common compound on Earth. It is the main component in nearly all living things. Within the body, water dissolves ions and molecules so that they can be transported. It maintains the structure of large molecules, provides a medium for the excretion of urea and helps regulate body temperature through perspiration. Water is used in vast quantities for crop irrigation and provides an environment for aquatic plants and animals. We use it for drinking, washing, waste disposal and heating.

The water cycle

The movement of water within the environment and to and from living organisms forms a closed cycle called the water cycle. This is powered by the Sun's energy, which causes evaporation from lakes and oceans. Water vapour condenses to droplets in clouds, which are moved by the wind. Clouds produce rain, which collects into streams, lakes and rivers that make their way to the sea. Some of this water is diverted into plants, especially trees, and into animals. Plants lose water vapour by transpiration and respiration, while animals respire and excrete. The cycle is shown in Figure 7.1.

Question

Q7.11 Explain how each of the following is involved in the water cycle in terms of the gain and loss of water:
(a) a beech tree; (b) a pigeon; (c) the ocean.

7.2 Nitrogen, ammonia and nitrates

The element nitrogen makes up 78 per cent of the atmosphere. Nitrogen is a common substance but it does not easily take part in chemical reactions. It is a colourless gas, with no smell or taste, and is slightly soluble in water. Nitrogen gas has little biological interest, but when it is linked with carbon in amino acids, proteins or nucleotides, nitrogen is of great importance. Few plants and animals can take up nitrogen gas: it has to be combined as ammonia or nitrate. This is difficult in the biosphere because of the strong bonds joining together the atoms in nitrogen gas and the large amount of energy needed to break the bonds. Thus the growth of organisms may be restricted by a lack of nitrogen compounds. Nitrogen has valencies of 3 and 5.

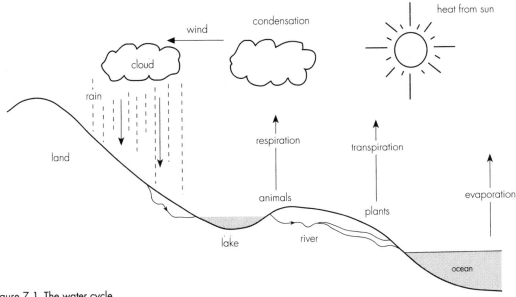

Figure 7.1 The water cycle

It usually exerts these valencies by sharing electrons with oxygen, hydrogen and carbon. Some important nitrogen compounds are given in Table 7.3 and Chapter 11 (page 91) together with their significance in the biological world.

In discussing the chemistry and biochemistry of nitrogen, we often mention ions. It is important to remember that ions do not occur alone but always have a counter ion present. Thus the nitrate anion, NO_3^-, will have a cation such as sodium, Na^+, or magnesium, Mg^{2+}, linked with it. In such cases nitrate will occur as sodium nitrate, $Na^+NO_3^-$, or magnesium nitrate, $Mg^{2+}2NO_3^-$. These are usually written as $NaNO_3$ and $Mg(NO_3)_2$.

Table 7.3 Nitrogen compounds and their significance in biology

Name	Formula	Biological significance
Nitrogen	N_2	Inert, unreactive gas, converted into proteins by nitrogen-fixing organisms
Ammonia	NH_3	Formed by plant or animal decay and by denitrifying bacteria
Nitrate ion	NO_3^-	Assimilated by plants. Formed by nitrifying bacteria and by thunderstorms. Used in fertilisers
Nitrite ion	NO_2^-	Intermediate in the synthesis of nitrates by nitrifying organisms
Ammonium ion	NH_4^+	Obtained when ammonia combines with an acid or with water. Used in fertilisers
Urea	NH_2CONH_2	Major excretion product of animals. Fertiliser
Ammonium nitrate	NH_4NO_3	Fertiliser
Ammonium sulphate	$(NH_4)_2SO_4$	Fertiliser
Sodium nitrate	$NaNO_3$	Fertiliser

Questions

Q7.12 Suggest a name and formula for a salt that could contain each of the following ions:

(a) nitrate;   (b) ammonium;   (c) nitrite.

Q7.13 Vast quantities of nitrogen are present in the atmosphere, but plants may have their growth limited by a shortage of the element. Why is this?

Plants obtain nitrogen from the air indirectly by the involvement of nitrogen-fixing bacteria and blue–green algae/cyanobacteria. The bacteria may be free living or found in the root nodules of plants such as beans and clover. They convert nitrogen gas into ammonia and then into amino acids and proteins. This can be shown as a reaction scheme:

$$\text{nitrogen} \xrightarrow{\text{reduction}} \text{ammonia} \xrightarrow{\text{assimilation}} \text{amino acids}$$
$$N_2 \longrightarrow NH_3 \longrightarrow H_2NCH_2COOH$$

In food chains, animals ultimately obtain their nitrogen from plants. Excretion, together with the death and decay of organisms, releases nitrogen compounds, which are transformed into ammonia. In turn ammonia is oxidised by nitrifying bacteria to nitrite ions and eventually nitrate ions. In this form, nitrogen is available to plants. The changes are as follows:

$$\text{protein} \longrightarrow \text{ammonia} \xrightarrow{\text{oxidation}} \text{nitrite ion} \xrightarrow{\text{oxidation}} \text{nitrate ion}$$
$$(-NH-CH_2-CO-) \longrightarrow NH_3 \longrightarrow NO_2^- \longrightarrow NO_3^-$$

Questions

Q7.14 How do animals obtain nitrogen compounds?

Q7.15 Give the name of an important compound of nitrogen that is excreted by animals.

Nitrates may be produced in a completely different way, by direct oxidation of atmospheric nitrogen by lightning in thunderstorms. Oxides of nitrogen are the initial products. These form nitric acid in the air, which forms nitrate salts in the soil. The reactions are:

$$\text{nitrogen} \xrightarrow{\text{oxidation}} \text{nitrogen(IV) oxide} \xrightarrow{\text{water}} \text{nitric acid}$$
$$N_2 \longrightarrow NO_2 \longrightarrow HNO_3$$

Nitrates formed by this process, or from ammonia, may undergo further changes. Denitrifying bacteria can reduce nitrates to nitrogen, nitrites or ammonia with the release of oxygen. These bacteria live in environments low in oxygen, and they use denitrification to provide oxygen for their life processes. The reaction scheme is:

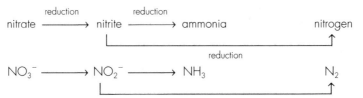

Nitrates released by the decay of marine organisms may sink and be incorporated into deep-sea sediments. They are lost to the cycle of reactions for long periods of time. This loss is countered by the release of sediments from the ocean depths in those places where strong rising currents carry them to the surface. Such areas of the sea are unusually rich in plant and animal life.

Questions

Q7.16 Explain the natural process that converts nitrogen gas into nitrates without involving plants.

Q7.17 What is meant by the term denitrification? Explain how nitrate ions undergo this change.

People take part in these processes by harvesting crops from arable fields. This removes nitrogen compounds as well as leaving the soil impoverished. Crop yields become lower in successive years. The nitrogen can be replaced by treating the land with manure, compost or, more usually, artificial fertilisers. Fertilisers are compounds that contain nitrogen in the form of the ammonium or nitrate ions. Some typical nitrogen fertilisers are given in Table 7.3.

It is often difficult to determine how much fertiliser should be added to an arable field. If an excess is used, or if it is applied at the wrong season, then the surplus may be washed out by rain. The run-off will eventually reach a natural watercourse, causing the water to be enriched with nitrate or phosphate. In turn this causes dense growth of aquatic plants, especially algae. The water becomes heavily shaded, inhibiting the development of higher plants and animals. The seasonal death and decay of the algae can cause the water to become anaerobic. Higher organisms are again adversely affected. These changes are called eutrophication. Many rivers and streams are subjected to this problem in countries that practise intensive agriculture. Domestic and industrial wastes such as sewage and effluent from paper manufacturing and slaughterhouses can cause eutrophication. Thus this pollution is often linked with high population density and industrialisation. The circulation of nitrogen compounds in the environment is shown in Figure 7.2.

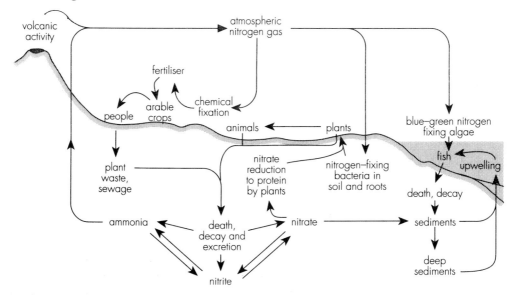

Figure 7.2 The nitrogen cycle

Question

Q7.18 How does ammonia arise in the nitrogen cycle? What is it converted into in the cycle?

The important chemical changes in the cycle can be separated and shown in a simplified form (Figure 7.3). This enables the biochemical features to be seen more clearly.

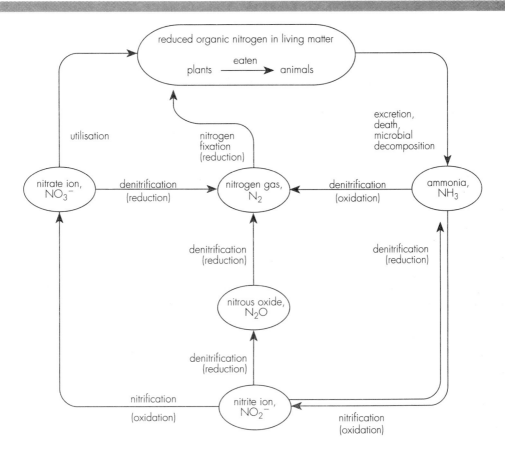

Figure 7.3 Major reactions in the nitrogen cycle

Question

Q7.19 Describe the reactions in the nitrogen cycle that involve oxidation.

7.3 Phosphorus and phosphates

Phosphorus is a reactive element found in the environment as insoluble calcium phosphate. This material is scarce and so phosphorus is uncommon. Plants and animals require phosphorus for many vital functions. Cell membranes contain phosphorus as phospholipids. The breakdown of sugars in respiration involves phosphorylation with phosphates. Photosynthesis requires the intervention of complex phosphates at several points. Phosphorus is a vital component of the nucleic acids found in the nucleus of the cell (see Chapter 15, page 140).

The scarcity of phosphorus compounds in the natural world means that the growth of organisms may often be limited by its availability. Phosphorus is referred to as the biosphere limiting element. Some important compounds and ions are given in Table 7.4, overleaf.

Plants obtain phosphorus by taking up soluble phosphates from the soil. Often the proportion of soluble phosphates is small, with most being found as insoluble calcium phosphate or tightly bound in clay minerals. Phosphorus-containing fertilisers are given in Table 7.4. They are often applied to arable land in a mixture with nitrogen fertilisers.

Table 7.4 Names, formulae and significance of phosphorus compounds

Name	Formula	Biological significance
Phosphine	PH_3	Formed by plant or animal decay in the absence of air
Phosphoric acid	H_3PO_4	Strong acid from which energy-transfer phosphates (ADP and ATP) are derived
Dihydrogenphosphate ion	$H_2PO_4^-$	Formed from phosphoric acid, present in super-phosphate fertilisers
Calcium phosphate	$Ca_3(PO_4)_2$	Important constituent of bone
Phosphate group	$-PO_3H_2$	Transferred between ATP and sugars in the release of energy during respiration

Summary

Hydrogen behaves as a reducing agent in biology and chemistry. It combines with oxygen, nitrogen and carbon to form important compounds. Acids form hydrogen ions in water. Deuterium exists as an isotope of hydrogen. Water as liquid, vapour or solid moves between the physical and living worlds in a series of linked changes called the water cycle. Water is an essential component of living organisms.

Nitrogen gas in the atmosphere forms nitrogen compounds by various nitrification processes. Plants take up these compounds and incorporate them into proteins and nucleotides. The death and decay of organisms, together with excretion, release nitrates and ammonia back into the environment. These may be recycled back to plants and animals or denitrified to nitrogen gas. These reactions form a part of the nitrogen cycle. People take part in this cycle through their activities in agriculture. Oxidation and reduction reactions are important in the cycle.

The oxygen compounds of phosphorus are taken up by plants. They are essential components of membranes and energy-transfer materials. Fertilisers contain nitrogen and phosphorus as vital ingredients.

Self-assessment questions

Try these questions on hydrogen, nitrogen and phosphorus.

Q7.20 Give an example of the use of hydrogen as a reducing agent. Include a word equation in your answer.

Q7.21 List five major stages in the water cycle.

Q7.22 Explain the dissociation (ionisation) of ethanoic acid, CH_3COOH, using a symbol equation.

Q7.23 What is meant by the term nitrification? Give the steps by which nitrates are produced by this process.

Q7.24 Describe three reduction stages that occur in denitrification.

Q7.25 What benefit do denitrifying bacteria obtain by carrying out this process?

Q7.26 Write the names and formulae of three synthetic nitrogen-containing fertilisers.

Q7.27 Explain the formation and reactions of the nitrite ion in the nitrogen cycle.

Q7.28 Why do plants and animals require nitrogen compounds?

Q7.29 Explain clearly why people devote resources on a large scale to the conversion of nitrogen gas into nitrogen compounds.

Q7.30 Why is phosphorus an essential element for animals and plants?

Q7.31 In what form is phosphorus used as an energy-transfer medium in cell respiration?

Q7.32 Write the name and formula of an insoluble phosphorus compound used in the mammalian skeleton.

Carbon Compounds and the Shapes of Biological Molecules

Introduction

It is useful to discuss carbon compounds in two groups. Simple compounds are based on carbon dioxide and carbonates. Organic compounds are more complex and usually have several carbon atoms joined together. Living organisms are based on organic substances, many of which have large, complex molecules. The two areas of carbon chemistry are linked together in the carbon cycle.

Within the biological world, the concept of shape is important. Protein molecules form many different shapes, which are linked to their function. For example, enzymes rely for their remarkable catalytic power and specificity to particular reactions on the detailed shape of the enzyme molecule. Sugars and other carbohydrates are based on small rings of atoms with particular shapes. Lipid membranes are highly ordered bilayers. In each case, the types of elements and the way they are linked together determine the shapes of the molecules.

Objectives

After completing this chapter you should be able to:

- recall the forms in which carbon occurs in the natural world;
- write the names and formulae of important compounds and ions of carbon;
- appreciate the significance of simple carbon compounds in the biosphere;
- explain the formation of carbonic acid, the bicarbonate ion and the carbonate ion from carbon dioxide and water;
- understand the principal stages of the carbon cycle;
- explain the significance of catenation in carbon compounds;
- write typical formulae and structures for alkanes and describe their properties;
- understand the concept of isomerism;
- write typical formulae and structures for alkenes and describe their properties;
- recall the names, formulae and reactions of alcohols;
- calculate the number of electron pairs around the central atom in a molecule or ion;
- assign these electron pairs as bond pairs and unshared pairs;
- determine the shape of a molecule or ion using bond pair and unshared pair electrons;
- appreciate the differences in repulsion between unshared pair and bond pair electrons;
- determine the shape of molecules with more than one centre about which atoms or groups are distributed;
- describe the relationship between organic compounds and living organisms;
- understand the role of alkyl groups in the structure of organic molecules.

Questions

If this material looks familiar to you, try the questions given below. Your answers will help you to decide if you need to study the chapter.

Q8.1 List three forms in which carbon occurs on a large scale in the Earth.

Q8.2 Write the formulae for carbon dioxide, the bicarbonate ion and calcium carbonate. How are these substances involved in the living world?

Q8.3 In what form is calcium taken up by plants and animals? How is this substance formed?

Q8.4 List four major stages in the carbon cycle.

Q8.5 What is an organic compound?

Q8.6 Write molecular and structural formulae for the alkane, propane.

Q8.7 What is meant by the term isomerism?

Q8.8 Write word and symbol equations to show how the alkene ethene reacts with water.

Q8.9 What is the functional group in each member of the alcohol series of compounds?

Q8.10 Carbon has the electron structure 2.4. It forms the compound methane, CH_4. Predict the shape of the methane molecule by considering repulsion between pairs of electrons around the carbon atom.

Q8.11 Water exists as the molecule H_2O. What is the shape of this molecule? (The oxygen atom has the electron structure 2.6).

Q8.12 When an acid is dissolved in water the hydroxonium ion, H_3O^+, is formed. Determine the shape of the ion by working out the arrangement of electron pairs around the central oxygen atom.

Q8.13 The amine methylamine, CH_3-NH_2, contains a carbon atom linked to nitrogen. Each of them is surrounded by hydrogen atoms. What is the arrangement of groups around the carbon and the nitrogen? Draw the overall shape of the molecule, showing clearly the three-dimensional relationship between the atoms.

8.1 Simple carbon compounds

Many carbon compounds that occur in the living world, such as carbohydrates, lipids and proteins, have relatively large molecules. A few others have only small molecules or ions but are nevertheless important. This chapter will review these simple substances. The more complex ones will be discussed in Chapters 12 to 14.

Carbon compounds and ions

Carbon often occurs as the remains of long-dead plants and animals. These remains are known as coal, peat, oil or natural gas depending on how they have been subjected to heat and pressure in the Earth. We extract these materials for fuels. When they are burnt, carbon dioxide is released into the atmosphere, where it is available for use by plants in photosynthesis. The minerals marble, limestone and chalk are quite different. They contain mainly calcium carbonate. This substance was formed from the shells of tiny marine organisms that lived and died in vast numbers. The shells sank to the bottom of shallow seas, accumulating in layers. Eventually these formed the deposits we find today. Important carbon compounds and ions are given in Table 8.1, page 56.

Carbon has a valency of 4. It is a less reactive element than hydrogen or oxygen and forms covalent compounds by sharing electrons. The element is often bonded to oxygen as in carbon dioxide, carbonates (containing the ion CO_3^{2-}), and bicarbonates (containing the ion HCO_3^-). These ions are formed from carbonic acid which is obtained when carbon dioxide from the air dissolves in rain water. The reaction is reversible (see Section 3.5, page 24):

$$\text{carbon dioxide} + \text{water} \rightleftharpoons \text{carbonic acid}$$
$$CO_2 + H_2O \rightleftharpoons H_2CO_3$$

Carbonic acid shows acidic properties because it forms hydrogen ions in water by two reversible reactions:

$$\text{carbonic acid} \rightleftharpoons \text{hydrogen ion} + \text{bicarbonate ion}$$
$$H_2CO_3 \rightleftharpoons H^+(aq) + HCO_3^-$$

Table 8.1 Some important carbon compounds and ions

Name	Formula	Biological significance
Carbon dioxide	CO_2	A small proportion of the air; used in photosynthesis; a respiration product
Carbonic acid	H_2CO_3	Formed in solution from carbon dioxide and water
Carbonate ion	CO_3^{2-}	Found in carbonate minerals
Bicarbonate ion	HCO_3^{-}	Formed in red blood cells during transport of carbon dioxide
Calcium bicarbonate	$Ca(HCO_3)_2$	Soluble form of calcium carbonate taken up by plants and animals
Sodium bicarbonate	$NaHCO_3$	Acts as an acidity regulator (buffer) in blood plasma

The second reaction takes place to only a slight extent:

$$\text{bicarbonate ion} \rightleftharpoons \text{hydrogen ion} + \text{carbonate ion}$$
$$HCO_3^{-} \rightleftharpoons H^{+}(aq) + CO_3^{2-}$$

We can regard these two equilibria as being linked together as a continuous sequence. The first stage is relatively favourable but the second is much less important:

$$H_2CO_3 \rightleftharpoons H^{+}(aq) + HCO_3^{-} \rightleftharpoons 2H^{+}(aq) + CO_3^{2-}$$

Within an animal's body, carbon dioxide is formed by respiration in the tissues. It diffuses into red blood cells. The enzyme carbonic anhydrase catalyses the rapid formation of carbonic acid, and this in turn leads to the formation of the bicarbonate ion. Carbon dioxide is carried in this form by the bloodstream to the lungs.

Calcium carbonate is an insoluble mineral that acts as a source of calcium for plants and animals. The solid must be dissolved in water before it can be used by living things. This is brought about by a chemical reaction. Rain water contains a weak acid, carbonic acid, which attacks calcium carbonate, converting it into a soluble bicarbonate:

$$\text{calcium carbonate} + \text{carbonic acid} \rightleftharpoons \text{calcium bicarbonate}$$
$$CaCO_3 + H_2CO_3 \rightleftharpoons Ca(HCO_3)_2$$

This process occurs when rain water trickles through chalk or limestone rocks, causing high levels of calcium in many streams and rivers. Water containing calcium bicarbonate is called 'hard water'.

Harvesting crops from the land gradually removes calcium from the soil. This leads to a fall in the pH value of the soil and a calcium deficiency in the soil. This causes a drop in crop yields and so farmers restore the balance by 'liming' the soil at intervals. Slaked lime is calcium hydroxide, which is made in large quantities by heating chalk or limestone to give calcium oxide. The oxide is treated with water to form calcium hydroxide.

Questions

Q8.14 Dolomite is a mineral containing magnesium carbonate, $MgCO_3$. When rain water trickles over dolomite, a small amount dissolves. Use word and symbol equations to explain this reaction. Is the product of the reaction likely to be taken up by plants? Explain why.

Q8.15 What reaction demonstrates the acidic nature of carbonic acid?

Carbon has a most unusual property. The atoms can join to other carbon atoms and may form chains or rings of carbons atoms in a huge variety of compounds. Carbon has this property because the carbon–carbon bond is strong relative to the bonds carbon forms with oxygen, hydrogen or nitrogen. The ability of carbon atoms to join together in this way is termed **catenation**. This feature underlies the formation of the large molecules that are the basis of life.

The reactions involving carbon compounds in the environment form part of a cycle that allows the exchange of carbon between organisms and the natural world. Carbon dioxide in the atmosphere is taken up by green plants in photosynthesis. The carbon may be returned to the air through death and decay or alternatively stored in the Earth as coal or oil, the so-called fossil fuels. Within the marine environment, carbon dioxide is fixed as bicarbonate and carbonate in the skeletons of very small organisms such as zooplankton. The action of rain water on rocks containing calcium carbonate mobilises the carbon again. The cycle is outlined in Figure 8.1. The quantities of carbon dioxide and other compounds in the cycle are large, allowing a natural balance to be maintained.

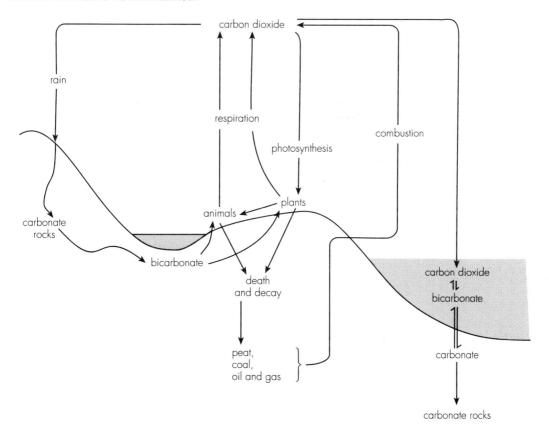

Figure 8.1 The carbon cycle

The proportion of carbon dioxide in the atmosphere has been maintained at about 0.04 per cent over a long period of time. Although it is difficult to disturb such a cycle, human activities on the Earth in recent years suggest that it may be possible. Forests have been felled on a extensive scale, thereby reducing the removal of carbon dioxide from the atmosphere by photosynthesis. At the same time, the burning of fossil fuels has increased sharply, with the release of extra carbon dioxide into the air. This may have profound consequences since carbon dioxide in the atmosphere acts as a thermal blanket around the Earth. It functions by limiting loss of heat from the surface of the Earth by radiation. Thus the surface temperature may be increased when the level of carbon dioxide is raised.

Question

Q8.16 Explain how marine zooplankton play a part in the carbon cycle.

Organic compounds
Organic compounds contain carbon together with a few other elements such as hydrogen and oxygen. For many years it was thought that they could be made only in living cells. We know now that this is not the case, but the link between organic compounds and organisms is still very strong. Plants and animals are made up largely of these substances. Even the simplest creature contains a huge number of organic compounds, often with highly complex molecules. These large molecules exist because carbon atoms can form strong bonds with one another and so join together in chains or other structures.

8.2 Hydrocarbons

Alkanes
Carbon has a valency of four. In organic compounds, it joins with four other atoms using covalent bonds. The simplest molecule that can be formed is when one carbon links with four hydrogens to give methane, CH_4 (see Section 2.2, page 12). Molecules are written as structural formulae to show the individual carbon–hydrogen bonds (see Section 2.2, page 12). Methane contains only carbon and hydrogen: it is called a **hydrocarbon**. Other hydrocarbons have larger molecules with two or more carbon atoms. The first four compounds, which are colourless gases, are compared in Table 8.2. The formula of each one can be written as a molecular formula,

Table 8.2 Names and formulae of alkane hydrocarbons

Name	Molecular formula	Shorthand structural formula	Full structural formula
Methane	CH_4	CH_4	$H-\overset{\displaystyle H}{\underset{\displaystyle H}{C}}-H$
Ethane	C_2H_6	CH_3CH_3	$H-\overset{\displaystyle H}{\underset{\displaystyle H}{C}}-\overset{\displaystyle H}{\underset{\displaystyle H}{C}}-H$
Propane	C_3H_8	$CH_3CH_2CH_3$	$H-\overset{\displaystyle H}{\underset{\displaystyle H}{C}}-\overset{\displaystyle H}{\underset{\displaystyle H}{C}}-\overset{\displaystyle H}{\underset{\displaystyle H}{C}}-H$
Butane	C_4H_{10}	$CH_3CH_2CH_2CH_3$	$H-\overset{\displaystyle H}{\underset{\displaystyle H}{C}}-\overset{\displaystyle H}{\underset{\displaystyle H}{C}}-\overset{\displaystyle H}{\underset{\displaystyle H}{C}}-\overset{\displaystyle H}{\underset{\displaystyle H}{C}}-H$

which gives the numbers of carbon and hydrogen atoms. The structural formula gives more information, showing how the atoms are joined together. As more knowledge of organic compounds is gained, the full structural formula can be bypassed and the shorthand form written.

When the formulae are compared, it can be seen that each compound differs from the next by CH_2 or

$$-\underset{\underset{H}{|}}{\overset{\overset{H}{|}}{C}}-$$

. The hydrocarbons form a series, called the **alkanes**. If n is used for the number of carbon atoms in the molecule, the formula for each compound is C_nH_{2n+2}. This is the **general formula** for the alkane series.

Although the series contains a large number of compounds, they all have similar chemical reactions. We can recognise members of the series because the name of each one ends in '-ane'. Such a group of compounds is called a **homologous series**. Homologous series are common in organic chemistry and biochemistry. The alkanes are rather unreactive and the most important property they show is to produce heat when they are burned. Methane, the main component of natural gas, burns completely to give carbon dioxide and water.

The full structural formula for an alkane with several carbon atoms in the molecule can be written in more than one way. Thus the alkane C_4H_{10} may be drawn as for butane in Table 8.2, or it may be given a branched-chain structure:

$$\text{methylpropane} \quad C_4H_{10} \quad CH_3\underset{\underset{CH_3}{|}}{CH}CH_3 \qquad H-\underset{\underset{H}{|}}{\overset{\overset{\displaystyle H-\underset{\underset{}{|}}{\overset{\overset{H}{|}}{C}}-H}{|}}{C}}-\underset{\underset{H}{|}}{\overset{\overset{H}{|}}{C}}-\underset{\underset{H}{|}}{\overset{\overset{H}{|}}{C}}-H$$

The two structures have the carbon atoms joined together in different ways. Butane and methylpropane have the same **molecular formula**, but different **structural formulae**. The two are distinct chemical compounds with different properties, such as melting point and boiling point. They are called **isomers**. Larger molecules may have more than two isomers. Every alkane with four or more carbon atoms shows isomerism, so this feature is common to all organic compounds.

Questions

Q8.17 Pentane is an alkane with the molecular formula C_5H_{12}.
   (a) Write the full structural formula for pentane.
   (b) What is the name and molecular formula of the compound that is one carbon smaller than pentane and next to it in the alkane series?

Q8.18 Which of the following molecular formulae represent alkanes?
   (a) CH_3;
   (c) C_3H_6;
   (b) C_2H_6;
   (d) C_4H_{10}.
   Explain your answer.

Alkenes

We have seen that alkanes contain carbon atoms joined to each other by single bonds. A second homologous series of hydrocarbons has a carbon–carbon double bond in each compound. These compounds are called **alkenes**. The first two members of the series are given in Table 8.3.

Table 8.3 Names and formulae of alkene hydrocarbons

Name	Molecular formula	Shorthand structural formula	Full structural formula
Ethene	C_2H_4	$CH_2{=}CH_2$	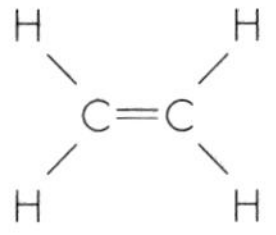
Propene	C_3H_6	$CH_2{=}CHCH_3$	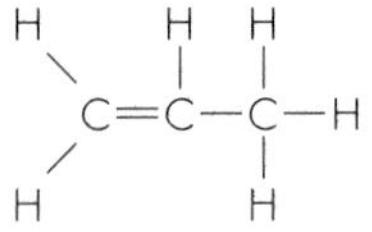

The name of each alkene ends in 'ene'. Alkenes are more reactive than alkanes, because of the double bond. Each alkene undergoes an addition reaction with hydrogen at the double bond to form an alkane. This can be shown for the first member of the series, ethene, which gives ethane:

ethene + hydrogen ⟶ ethane

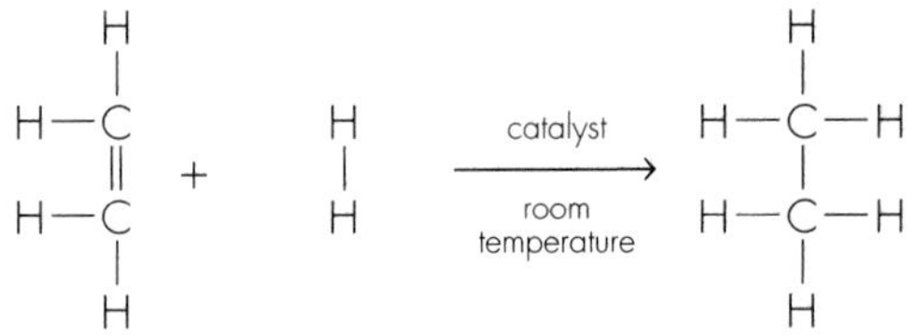

Compounds like ethene that undergo addition reactions are termed '**unsaturated**'. Those compounds that do not take part in these reactions, such as ethane, are called '**saturated**' (see Section 7.1, page 46). Ethene undergoes addition with hydrogen and many other substances. Addition of water gives ethanol:

ethene + water ⟶ ethanol

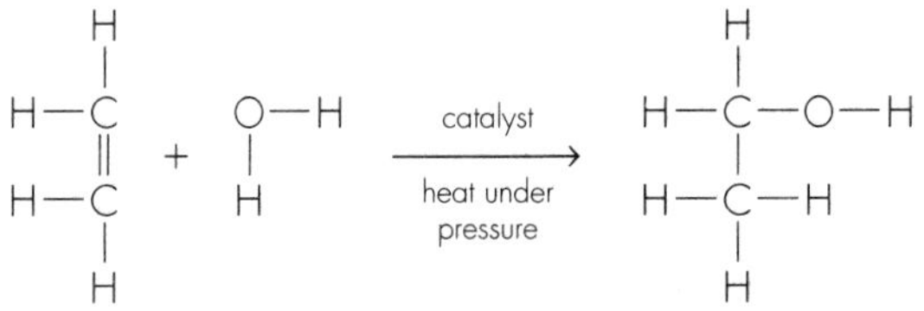

Ethene, like ethane and methane, is a colourless gas. It has no smell and burns in air to form carbon dioxide and water. Tomato plants produce ethene to signal the ripening of green tomatoes.

The group of atoms that undergo chemical reactions within an organic molecule is called the **functional group**. In alkenes the functional group is $-C{=}C-$.

Questions

Q8.19 Give the general formula for the alkene series. What is the name and full structural formula of the simplest member of the alkene series?

Q8.20 Use word and symbol equations to show how propene reacts with hydrogen.

Table 8.4 Names and formulae of alcohols

Name	Molecular formula	Shorthand structural formula	Full structural formula
Methanol	CH_4O	CH_3OH	
Ethanol	C_2H_6O	CH_3CH_2OH	
Propanol	C_3H_8O	$CH_3CH_2CH_2OH$	

8.3 Alcohols

We are all familiar with ethanol, a member of the homologous series of compounds called alcohols. Many people enjoy drinking limited quantities of ethanol mixed with water and flavourings in the form of beer, wine or spirits. It helps them to relax so drinking is often a part of the social activities when people get together in the pub or at home.

Ethanol, like all alcohols, contains the —C—O—H group. The —OH group bound to carbon is called the hydroxyl group. The first three members of the alcohol series are shown in Table 8.4. It can be seen that the name of each one ends in '-ol'. The molecular formula of a simple alcohol shows the presence of one oxygen in the molecule. But only the shorthand and full structural formulae make it clear that the —OH functional group is a part of the molecule. This is because the oxygen could be bound in a different way other than in the hydroxyl group. Each member of the alcohol series differs from the next by the group —CH_2—. The general formula for the series is $C_nH_{2n+1}OH$. All the alcohols have similar chemical and physical properties, which are largely determined by the —OH group.

Alcohols occur widely in the biological world. The storage carbohydrates, starch and glycogen, contain many —OH groups and are poly-alcohols or polyols. Simple sugars, such as glucose and fructose, are alcohols and each has several —OH groups. Glycerol, an important constituent of fats, has three —OH groups and is therefore a triol. Several components of the Krebs or tricarboxylic acid cycle, by which energy is produced in cells, contain —OH groups. Alcohols undergo a number of chemical reactions that are important in metabolic processes.

Oxidation of alcohols

When an open bottle of wine is left to stand for some days, it gradually becomes sour. The alcohol changes to vinegar, an acid. This oxidation process is brought about by microorganisms that use the energy released for their own metabolism. Ethanol in the wine has been oxidised by oxygen from the air to ethanoic acid. The reaction can be written:

ethanol   + oxygen ⟶ ethanoic acid   + water

The oxidation of alcohols can give other products, in particular **aldehydes** and **ketones** (see Chapter 9, page 70). Alcohols burn in air with a blue flame to form carbon dioxide and water. Heat is produced.

ethanol + oxygen $\longrightarrow$ carbon dioxide + water

$$H-\underset{\underset{H}{|}}{\overset{\overset{H}{|}}{C}}-\underset{\underset{H}{|}}{\overset{\overset{H}{|}}{C}}-O-H \ + \ 3O_2 \ \overset{heat}{\longrightarrow} \ 2CO_2 \ + \ 3H_2O$$

We see this happen when brandy burns on the Christmas pudding.

Dehydration of alcohols
An alkene, such as ethene, can combine with water to form an alcohol, such as ethanol. Alcohols can undergo the reverse of this reaction, that is the loss of water to form alkenes. Ethanol is **dehydrated** to ethene:

ethanol $\longrightarrow$ ethene + water

$$H-\underset{\underset{H}{|}}{\overset{\overset{H}{|}}{C}}-O-H \quad \overset{catalyst}{\underset{heat}{\longrightarrow}} \quad H-\overset{\overset{H}{|}}{\underset{\underset{H}{|}}{\overset{C}{\|}}}_{C} \ + \ \overset{O-H}{\underset{H}{|}}$$

The alkyl group
In the alkane, alkene and alcohol series, the functional group is linked to one or more carbon atoms, each of which is surrounded by hydrogen atoms. Methanol, CH_3-OH, and methane, CH_3-H, each have a methyl, CH_3, group bound to the functional group. Ethanol, CH_3CH_2-OH, and ethane, CH_3CH_2-H carry an ethyl group, CH_3CH_2, joined to the active group. These two groups, methyl and ethyl, can be represented by the general formula C_nH_{2n+1}, where n is a whole number. Groups with this formula are called **alkyl** groups and given the symbol R.

Thus, when the formula ROH is used, it refers to any alcohol with an alkyl group bound to a hydroxyl group, such as CH_3-OH, CH_3CH_2-OH and $CH_3CH_2CH_2-OH$. In the same way, the formula $RCH=CH_2$ means any alkene with an alkyl group joined to an alkene group, such as $H-CH=CH_2$, $CH_3-CH=CH_2$ and $CH_3CH_2-CH=CH_2$; these are ethene, propene and butene, respectively. It is convenient to use the alkyl symbol R in formulae depicting any one of several members of an homologous series, and it is often written in equations. Sometimes two different alkyl groups may be present in a molecule; this can be indicated by using the symbols R^1 and R^2 or R' and R''. In some cases R may be $-H$.

8.4 Electron pairs and the shapes of molecules
Simple biological molecules, such as methane, and ions, such as the ammonium ion, have a fixed shape. This is determined by the numbers of atoms and electrons around the central atom.

Example 8.1
What is the shape of the methane molecule?
    Write the formula and count the number of atoms around the central carbon atom:

    CH_4, there are four hydrogens around the carbon.

Count the number of electrons around the carbon in the outer shell and divide them into pairs:

C has the electron structure 2.4. There are four electrons around carbon.

H has the electron structure 1. There are four hydrogen atoms around the carbon atom and each has one electron.

These four hydrogen electrons are added to the four carbon electrons: $4 + 4 = 8$ electrons in total around carbon.

Divide the total number of electrons into pairs: $\dfrac{8}{2} = 4$ pairs of electrons.

Assign each pair to a carbon–hydrogen bond and check if any pairs are left over:

CH_4 has four C—H bonds, so each bond has one pair of electrons and no pairs are left over.

Arrange the electron pairs as far apart as possible. We do this because the electron pairs repel each other. When the four pairs are placed as far apart as possible, a **tetrahedral shape** is formed, with an $H\diagup^{C}\diagdown H$ bond angle of almost 109°. The shape of the methane molecule is shown below. The symbol H►C means the hydrogen is in front of the page while H----C shows that hydrogen is behind the page.

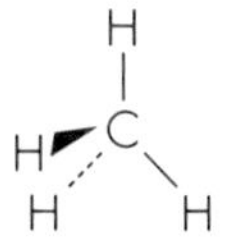

conventional representation
of the tetrahedral shape

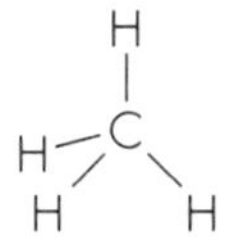

simplified form

Example 8.2
Determine the shape of the ammonia molecule. This can be worked out by the same steps used for methane.

NH_3, there are three hydrogen atoms around the nitrogen atom.

N has the electron structure 2.5. There are five electrons around nitrogen.

H has the electron structure 1. There are three hydrogen atoms around nitrogen, each with one electron:

$5 + 3 = 8$ electrons in total around nitrogen.

Divide the total number into pairs:

$\dfrac{8}{2} = 4$ pairs of electrons.

NH_3 has three N—H bonds, so each bond has one pair of electrons and one pair is left over.

Arrange the electron pairs: four pairs give a tetrahedral shape, but the pair left over, called an **unshared pair** or lone pair, helps to decide the shape. This is because the unshared pair protrudes from the central nitrogen but occupies more space than a **shared pair**. The unshared pair repels the normal electron pair more than normal pairs repel one another. Thus the $H\diagup^{N}\diagdown H$ bond angle is less than 109° and is found to be 106°. The structure below shows that the hydrogens are arranged around the base of a pyramid with the nitrogen at the apex. The molecular shape is described as **pyramidal** and can be represented in three ways:

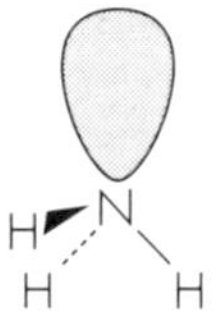

conventional
representation
showing N–H
bonds and
unshared pair
electrons

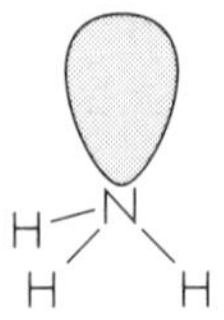

simplified form

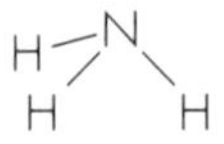

molecule
showing only
the four atoms
and the N–H
bonds

Question

Q8.21 Determine the shape of the phosphine molecule, PH_3. Remember, molecules may have an unshared pair of electrons.

Example 8.3

Calculate the shape of the water molecule.

H_2O, there are two hydrogens around the oxygen.

O has the electron structure 2.6. There are six electrons around oxygen.

H has the electron structure 1. There are two hydrogen atoms around oxygen each with one electron: $6 + 2 = 8$ electrons in total around oxygen.

Divide the total number of electrons into pairs:

$$\frac{8}{2} = 4 \text{ pairs of electrons.}$$

H_2O has two O—H bonds.

Each bond has one pair of electrons, and two pairs are left over.

Arrange the electron pairs: four pairs give a tetrahedral shape, the two pairs left over, unshared pairs, repel one another strongly and cause the $H \diagup O \diagdown H$ angle to be reduced to 104°. Water is called a **bent** molecule and its shape can be drawn in three ways:

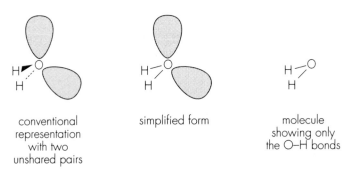

conventional
representation
with two
unshared pairs

simplified form

molecule
showing only
the O–H bonds

The shapes of cations and anions can be predicted in the same way as neutral molecules.

Example 8.4

Evaluate the shape of the ammonium ion.

NH_4^+, there are four hydrogens around the nitrogen.

N has the electron structure 2.5. There are five electrons around a neutral nitrogen.

But the positive charge means that one electron has been lost to leave four around a positive, N^+, nitrogen.

H has the electron structure 1. There are four hydrogens around the nitrogen each with one electron: $4 + 4 = 8$ electrons in total around nitrogen.

Divide the total number of electrons into pairs:

$\dfrac{8}{2} = 4$ pairs of electrons.

Arrange the electron pairs: four pairs give a tetrahedral shape:

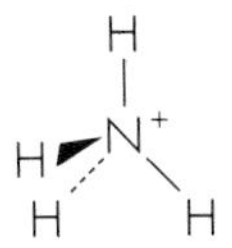

three-dimensional structure 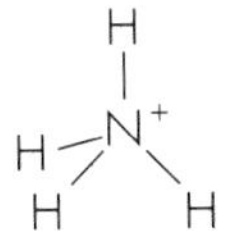   simplified form

When ammonia is compared with methane, it is clear that the two molecules have the same shape. This is because each has four pairs of electrons and four atoms around the central atom.

More complex biological molecules may be discussed in the same way. Often the central atom has groups around it as well as atoms. The ethane molecule, C_2H_6, can be described like a methane molecule in which one hydrogen has been replaced by CH_3, so the molecule is tetrahedral. However, it must be remembered that the second carbon atom has a tetrahedral arrangement of groups around it as well as the first carbon:

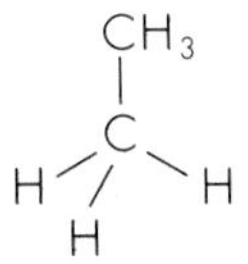

simplified structure based on the tetrahedral shape of methane

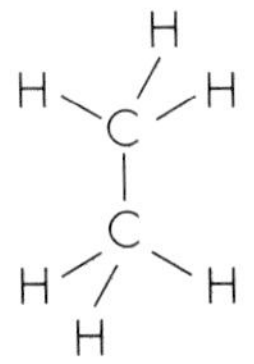

full representation showing both carbon atoms at the centre of tetrahedra

The shape of the methanol molecule, CH_3OH, can be viewed as a combination of methane and water. One hydrogen on methane has been changed to the —OH group, while one hydrogen on water has been replaced by CH_3:

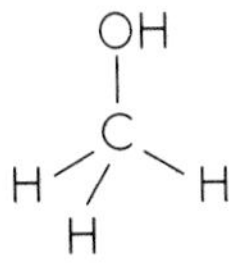

shape based on tetrahedral methane

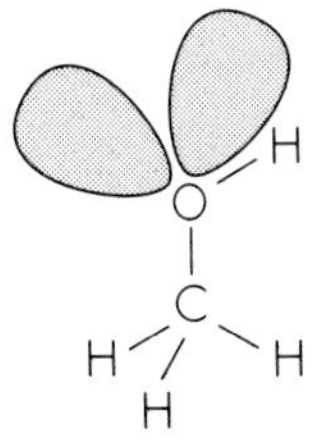

full structure with unshared electron pairs

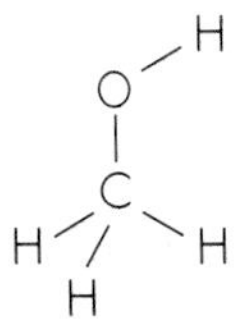

molecule with only electron pair bonds

Summary

Carbon occurs on the Earth as carbon dioxide, carbonate minerals and fossil fuels like oil. Plants take up carbon as carbon dioxide gas and as carbonate in solution, while animals obtain it directly or indirectly from plants. The exchange of carbon compounds between the mineral world and the biosphere is described by the carbon cycle. Carbon atoms link together in chains, forming organic compounds including alkanes, alkenes and alcohols. These compounds undergo reactions such as addition, oxidation and reduction. Organic compounds with the same molecular formula may have different structures; this is isomerism. Biological molecules have a definite shape. This is determined by the number of groups around the central atom and the number of electron pairs linked to the same atom. Methane is tetrahedral, ammonia is pyramidal and water is a bent molecule. The structures of molecules with more than one central atom are described in the same way.

Self-assessment questions

Test yourself with these questions on carbon compounds, organic chemistry and the shapes of molecules.

Q8.22 What is the origin of
    (a) limestone;   (b) crude oil, in the Earth's crust?

Q8.23 Write word and symbol equations to show how:
    (a) carbonic acid and   (b) bicarbonate ion and carbonate ion
    are formed from carbon dioxide and water.

Q8.24 Use the carbon cycle to explain how carbon is immobilised and stored for long periods of time:
    (a) in the terrestrial environment;   (b) in the marine environment.

Q8.25 What is the general formula of the alkane series of hydrocarbons?

Q8.26 Methane is burned as a fuel to provide heat. What products are obtained? Write word and symbol equations for this reaction.

Q8.27 Butene, C_4H_8, is an alkene. Draw the structural formulae of three isomers of butene. (Hint, you can move the double bond.)

Q8.28 Alkenes undergo addition reactions. Give a symbol equation to show the addition of water to ethene.

Q8.29 Look at the shorthand structural formulae
    (a) CH_3OH;   (b) CH_3CH_2OH;   (c) $CH_3CH_2CH_2OH$.
    (i) Write the name of the series to which these compounds belong.
    (ii) Give the names of the three compounds (a) to (c).
    (iii) The compound (c) may be oxidised to an organic acid. Write the full structural formula of this product.
    (iv) The compound (b) undergoes elimination of water. Give a symbol equation for the reaction that takes place.

Q8.30 Consider the structural formulae given below.

(i)   How many different isomers are shown?
(ii) Write the letters that correspond to the different isomers.
(iii) Is the same isomer shown in two (or more) structures?
(iv) Write the letters that correspond to the same compound (if any). If there are none write none.

Q8.31 The element silicon, Si, has the electron structure 2.8.4. Predict the shape of the silane molecule SiH_4.

Q8.32 The methylammonium cation, $CH_3-NH_3^+$, may be regarded as a combination of methane and the ammonium ion. Deduce the shape of the methylammonium cation.

Q8.33 Draw the shape of the ethanol molecule, CH_3-CH_2-OH, including any unshared electron pairs that are present.

Q8.34 The anaerobic decay product phosphine, PH_3, reacts with acids to give the phosphonium ion, PH_4^+. Predict the shapes of these two. Phosphorus has the electron structure 2.8.5.

PART 2

The Molecules of Life

Alcohols, Aldehydes, Ketones and Related Compounds

Introduction

This and successive chapters will look at biologically important combinations of carbon, hydrogen and oxygen. In this chapter you will learn about three types of compounds that involve covalent bonds between oxygen and carbon. Before you start, you should be familiar with the principles of valency, atomic structure and bonding (see Chapters 1 and 2) as well as background information on the chemistry of carbon (Chapter 8).

Objectives

After studying this chapter you will be able to:

- recall the formulae, reactions and simple names for the following groups of compounds: alcohols, aldehydes, ketones, aldols, hemiketals and hemiacetals;
- name simple compounds that contain more than one of these groups;
- be aware of some representative examples of these compounds which are of biological importance;
- understand that reactions carried out by most living organisms involve some of the compounds covered in this chapter.

Questions

Try to answer the following questions. If you answer them correctly, then you may decide to move to the next chapter.

Q9.1 From these structural formulae:

(i)
$$CH_3\overset{\overset{\displaystyle OH}{|}}{\underset{\underset{\displaystyle OCH_3}{|}}{C}}CH_3$$

(ii)
$$H-\overset{\overset{\displaystyle H}{|}}{\underset{\underset{\displaystyle H}{|}}{C}}-\overset{\overset{\displaystyle O}{|}}{\underset{\underset{\displaystyle H}{|}}{C}}-\overset{\overset{\displaystyle H}{|}}{\underset{\underset{\displaystyle H}{|}}{C}}-H$$

(iii)
$$H-\overset{\overset{\displaystyle H}{|}}{\underset{\underset{\displaystyle H}{|}}{C}}-\overset{\overset{\displaystyle H}{|}}{\underset{\underset{\displaystyle H}{|}}{C}}-\overset{\overset{\displaystyle H}{|}}{\underset{\underset{\displaystyle H}{|}}{C}}-\overset{\overset{\displaystyle H}{|}}{\underset{\underset{\displaystyle H}{|}}{C}}-\overset{\displaystyle O}{\underset{\displaystyle H}{C}}$$

(iv)
$$H-\overset{\overset{\displaystyle H}{|}}{\underset{\underset{\displaystyle H}{|}}{C}}-\overset{\overset{\displaystyle H}{|}}{\underset{\underset{\displaystyle H}{|}}{C}}-\overset{\overset{\displaystyle H}{|}}{\underset{\underset{\displaystyle H}{|}}{C}}-\overset{\overset{\displaystyle O}{||}}{C}-\overset{\overset{\displaystyle H}{|}}{\underset{\underset{\displaystyle H}{|}}{C}}-H$$

(v)
$$H-\overset{\overset{\displaystyle H}{|}}{\underset{\underset{\underset{\displaystyle H}{|}}{\displaystyle O}}{C}}-\overset{\overset{\displaystyle H}{|}}{\underset{\underset{\underset{\displaystyle H}{|}}{\displaystyle O}}{C}}-\overset{\displaystyle O}{\underset{\displaystyle H}{C}}$$

(vi)
$$CH_3\overset{\overset{\displaystyle OH}{|}}{\underset{\underset{\displaystyle OCH_3}{|}}{C}}H$$

choose an example of each of the following groups:

(a) aldehyde;
(b) ketone;
(c) alcohol;
(d) aldol;
(e) hemiketal;
(f) hemiacetal.

Q9.2 Name compounds (ii), (iii), (iv) and (v) shown in Q9.1.

Q9.3 Use general formulae to explain the difference between a hemiketal and a hemiacetal.

Q9.4 Give one example of a biologically important
(a) alcohol; (b) aldehyde; (c) ketone.

Q9.5 Write out the reaction of the cleavage of D-fructose-1,6-diphosphate which aldolase helps to carry out, using only the names of the compounds involved.

9.1 Alcohols

The compounds formed by combining carbon, hydrogen and oxygen are many and various. Hydrogen has a valency of 1, carbon 4, and oxygen 2. In a small compound that contains just these atoms, they can combine in a limited number of ways. Alcohols are compounds with the general formulae ROH, and RH is the alkane to which the alcohol is related. An example, methanol, is shown below:

$$H-\overset{\displaystyle \overset{H}{|}}{\underset{\displaystyle \underset{H}{|}}{C}}-O-H$$

methanol	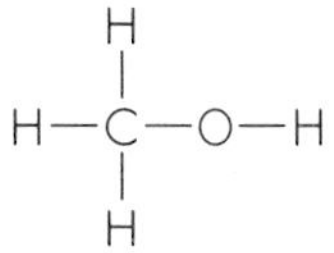	CH_3OH
name	*structural formula*	*condensed formula*

The alkane related to methanol is methane (CH_4) and the alcohol is named by removing the -e from the end of the related alkane and adding the suffix -ol (methane minus -e gives 'methan', add -ol to give the name methanol). Comparison of the structures of methanol and methane (see Table 8.2, page 58) shows their relationship. In methanol, one of the bonding methane hydrogen atoms is removed and replaced by the —OH (hydroxyl) group to form the alcohol. Another example, C_2H_6O (ethanol), is shown below. The name ethanol is derived from ethane (CH_3CH_3):

$$H-\overset{\displaystyle \overset{H}{|}}{\underset{\displaystyle \underset{H}{|}}{C}}-\overset{\displaystyle \overset{H}{|}}{\underset{\displaystyle \underset{H}{|}}{C}}-O-H$$

ethanol	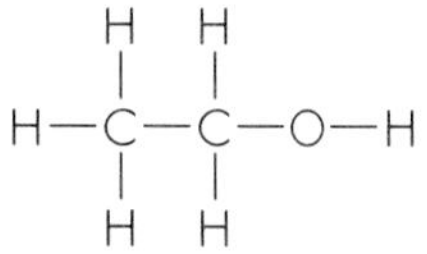	CH_3CH_2OH
name	*structural formula*	*condensed formula*

In larger compounds, the —OH is also referred to as a hydroxyl group and the compound is sometimes named with a hydroxy- prefix (hydroxyproline is an important constituent of tendons and ligaments). Larger compounds with hydroxyl groups attached to carbon skeletons are still considered alcohols, as the hydroxyl group retains many of the characteristics of simple alcohols.

With more than two carbons in the alcohol, a further possibility is introduced. The hydroxyl group can be attached to the end carbon (as the molecule is symmetrical it does not matter which end) or to a middle carbon as shown below:

$$H-\overset{\displaystyle \overset{H}{|}}{\underset{\displaystyle \underset{H}{|}}{\overset{3}{C}}}-\overset{\displaystyle \overset{H}{|}}{\underset{\displaystyle \underset{H}{|}}{\overset{2}{C}}}-\overset{\displaystyle \overset{H}{|}}{\underset{\displaystyle \underset{H}{|}}{\overset{1}{C}}}-O-H$$

propan-1-ol	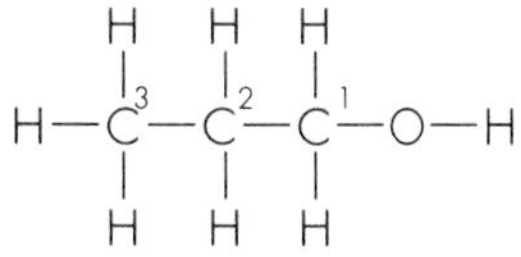	$CH_3CH_2CH_2OH$
name	*structural formula*	*condensed formula*

	H	

<table>
<tr><td></td><td>H</td><td></td></tr>
<tr><td></td><td>|</td><td></td></tr>
<tr><td>H</td><td>O</td><td>H</td></tr>
</table>

propan-2-ol $H-\overset{\overset{H}{|}}{\underset{\underset{H}{|}}{C}}-\overset{\overset{O-H}{|}}{\underset{\underset{H}{|}}{C}}-\overset{\overset{H}{|}}{\underset{\underset{H}{|}}{C}}-H$ $\overset{OH}{|}$
                                              CH_3CHCH_3

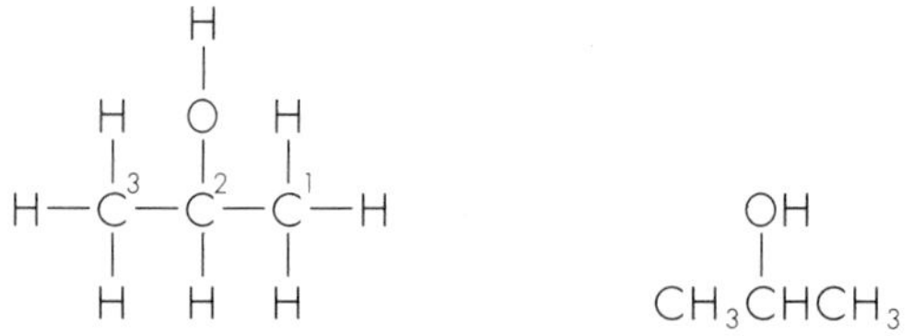

name   *structural formula*   *condensed formula*

Propan-2-ol is compound (ii) from Q9.1. The numbers 1 and 2 included in the names of these compounds refers to the position of the functional group (in this case the hydroxyl) along the backbone of the carbon chain. In the case of propan-1-ol, the hydroxyl is attached to carbon 1, while in propan-2-ol the hydroxyl group is attached to carbon 2. The carbon with the hydroxyl group is always given the lowest possible number. These compounds are both isomers of propanol.

Compounds containing more than one carbon atom can contain more than one hydroxyl group attached to the carbons. Some examples are shown below:

ethane-1,2-diol $H-C-C-O-H$ CH_2CH_2 with $\overset{OH}{|}\ \overset{OH}{|}$

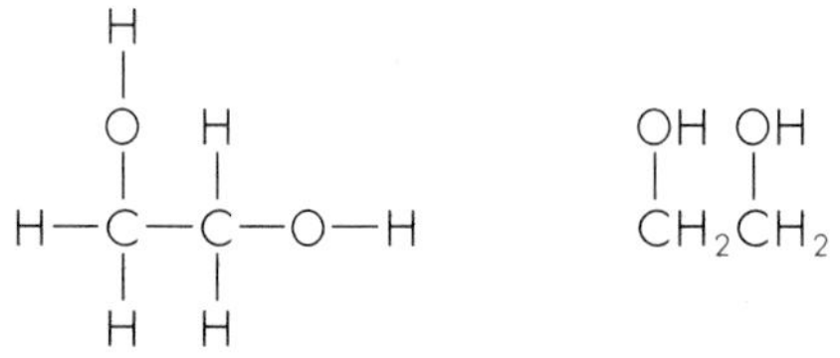

propane-1,2-diol $H-C-C-C-O-H$ CH_3CHCH_2OH

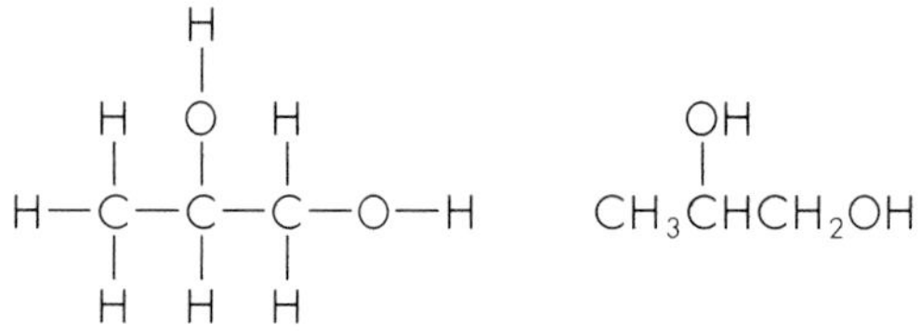

propane-1,3-diol $H-C-C-C-O-H$ $CH_2CH_2CH_2OH$

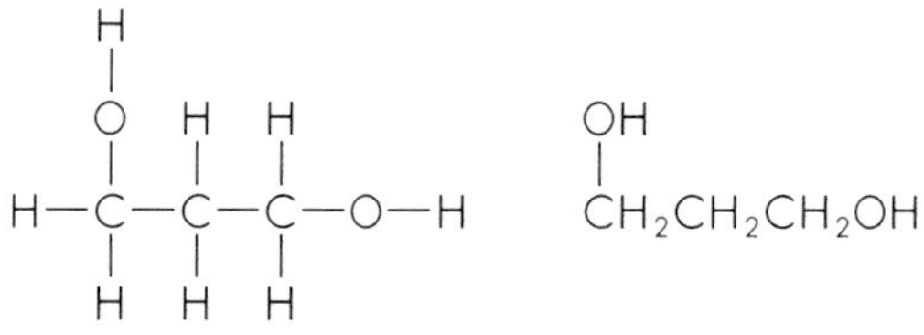

propane-1,2,3-triol or glycerol $H-C-C-C-O-H$ CH_2CHCH_2OH

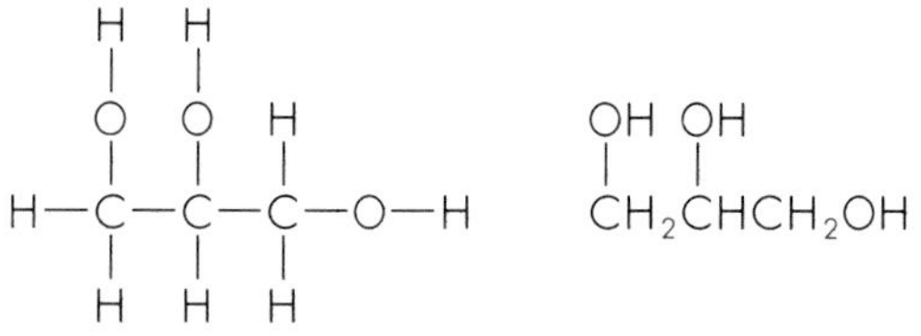

name   *structural formulae*   *condensed formulae*

Examples of diols (two hydroxyls), triols (three hydroxyls), and polyols (many hydroxyls) will be found in Chapter 13 on carbohydrates and Chapter 14 on fats.

9.2 The carbonyl group

The valencies of carbon (4) and oxygen (2) mean that both arms of the oxygen can be shared with carbon as seen already with carbon dioxide (see Chapter 2, page 15). Examples of two compounds in which this happens are shown below:

name	structural formulae	condensed formulae
propanal	$\begin{array}{ccc} H & H & O \\ | & | & \parallel \\ H-C-C-C \\ | & | & \backslash \\ H & H & H \end{array}$	CH_3CH_2CH
propanone	$\begin{array}{ccc} H & O & H \\ | & \parallel & | \\ H-C-C-C-H \\ | & & | \\ H & & H \end{array}$	CH_3CCH_3

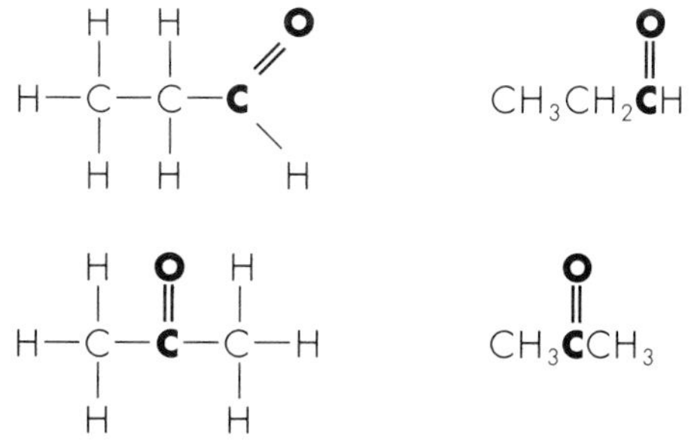

In each case the 'functional' group is shown in bold. The group $C{=}O$ is known as the carbonyl group. When the carbonyl group is positioned at the end of the carbon chain the resulting compound is called an aldehyde; if the carbonyl group is in the middle, it is a ketone. Propanal is an aldehyde and propanone is a ketone. The carbonyl group is an example of a functional group. Aldehydes and ketones are named in the same way as alcohols. Aldehydes have the suffix -al added to the stem of the related alkane. Thus propanal derives from propane ($CH_3CH_2CH_3$). Ketones have the suffix -one. In larger compounds, the position of the ketone carbonyl is identified by numbering in a similar way to that used for alcohols. This is shown below:

name	structural formulae	condensed formulae
pentan-2-one	$\begin{array}{ccccc} H & H & H & O & H \\ | & | & | & \parallel & | \\ H-C-C-C-C-C-H \\ | & | & | & & | \\ H & H & H & & H \end{array}$	$CH_3CH_2CH_2CCH_3$
pentan-3-one	$\begin{array}{ccccc} H & H & O & H & H \\ | & | & \parallel & | & | \\ H-C-C-C-C-C-H \\ | & | & & | & | \\ H & H & & H & H \end{array}$	$CH_3CH_2CCH_2CH_3$

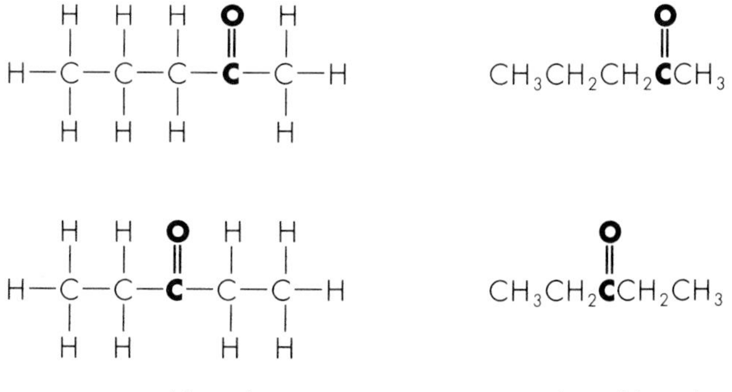

Pentan-2-one is compound (iv) shown in Q9.1. The general formula for aldehydes and ketones are generated in the same way as the general formula for alcohols. Aldehydes have the general formula $R\overset{\displaystyle O}{\overset{\parallel}{C}}H$ and ketones are $R\overset{\displaystyle O}{\overset{\parallel}{C}}R$.

9.3 Compounds containing more than one functional group

Many biological compounds are not simple alcohols, aldehydes or ketones but contain two or more functional groups. Two examples are D-glyceraldehyde and dihydroxyacetone:

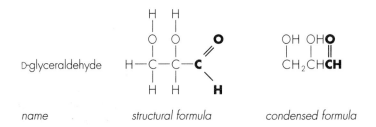

| name | structural formulae | condensed formulae |

D-Glyceraldehyde is also shown in Q9.1(v). The phosphate esters of these compounds (D-glyceraldehyde-3-phosphate and dihydroxyacetone-3-phosphate) are formed during the breakdown of glucose to carbon dioxide and water by nearly all living organisms (see later in this chapter). Both these compounds contain hydroxyl groups. D-Glyceraldehyde also contains an aldehyde group while dihydroxyacetone also contains a ketone. We shall examine D-glyceraldehyde in more detail in Example 9.1.

Example 9.1
Indicate the aldehyde group in D-glyceraldehyde.
Write the formula for the compound with the aldehyde group shown in bold:

D-glyceraldehyde

name   structural formula   condensed formula

The part of the molecule not shown in bold could be replaced by R, in which case the formula

$$O$$
$$\|$$

becomes RCH, the general formula for an aldehyde.

Example 9.2
Indicate the hydroxyl group attached to carbon 2 in D-glyceraldehyde. Write D-glyceraldehyde using the stick method with the OH groups shown in bold.

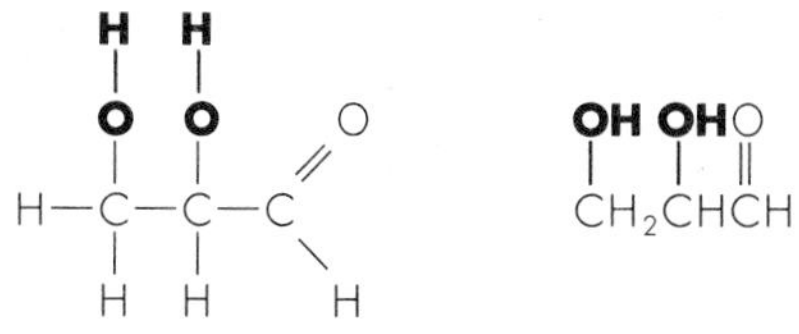

$$H-\overset{\overset{\displaystyle H}{|}}{\underset{\underset{\displaystyle H}{|}}{C}}-\overset{\overset{\displaystyle H}{|}}{\underset{\underset{\displaystyle H}{|}}{C}}-C\overset{\nearrow O}{\underset{\searrow H}{}}$$

structural formula

$$\underset{CH_2CHCH}{\overset{OH\ OH\ O}{|\ \ |\ \ ||}}$$

condensed formula

Now identify the OH group attached to carbon 2:

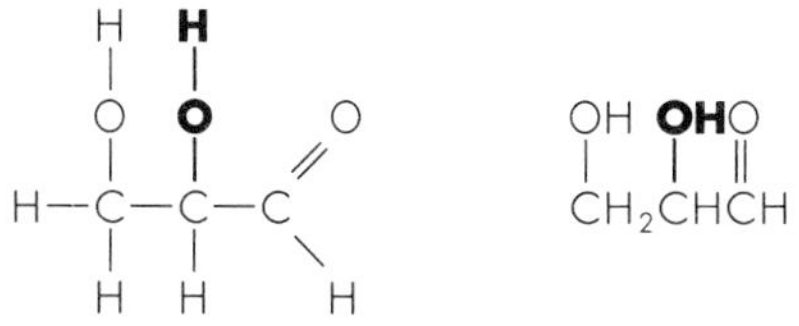

$$H-\overset{\overset{\displaystyle H}{|}}{\underset{\underset{\displaystyle H}{|}}{C}}-\overset{\overset{\displaystyle \mathbf{H}}{|}}{\underset{\underset{\displaystyle H}{|}}{\mathbf{C}}}-C\overset{\nearrow O}{\underset{\searrow H}{}}$$

structural formula

$$\underset{CH_2CHCH}{\overset{OH\ \mathbf{OH}\ O}{|\ \ \mathbf{|}\ \ ||}}$$

condensed formula

The part of the molecule not shown in bold will be called R; the formula for D-glyceraldehyde then becomes ROH, the general formula for an alcohol.

Compounds that contain both an aldehyde and a hydroxyl group can be called aldols. Thus glyceraldehyde is an example of an aldol as it contains both aldehyde and hydroxyl groups. You should now be able to answer Q9.1(d).

9.4 Hemiacetals and hemiketals

The general formulae of aldehydes and ketones are $R\overset{\overset{\displaystyle O}{||}}{C}H$ and $R\overset{\overset{\displaystyle O}{||}}{C}R$, respectively. An aldehyde can react chemically with an alcohol to form a hemiacetal as shown in the reaction scheme below:

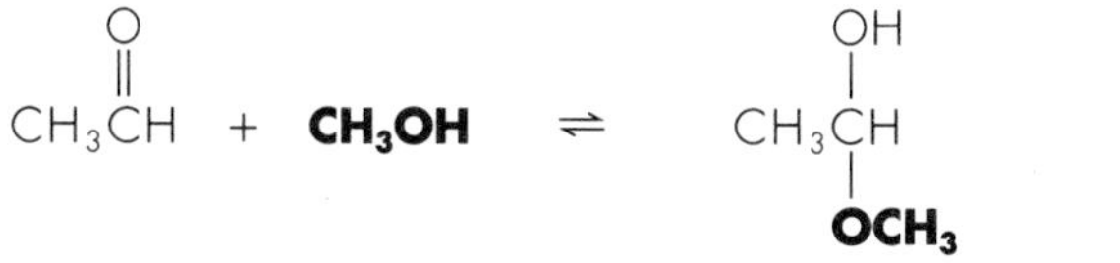

$$CH_3\overset{\overset{\displaystyle O}{||}}{C}H \quad + \quad \mathbf{CH_3OH} \quad \rightleftharpoons \quad CH_3\underset{\underset{\displaystyle \mathbf{OCH_3}}{|}}{\overset{\overset{\displaystyle OH}{|}}{C}}H$$

| ethanal | methanol | ethanal methyl hemiacetal or 1-methoxyethanol |

The position of the methanol in the hemiacetal, 1-methoxyethanol, is shown in bold. The product is the compound shown in Q9.1(vi). Similar reactions between ketones and alcohols yield hemiketals:

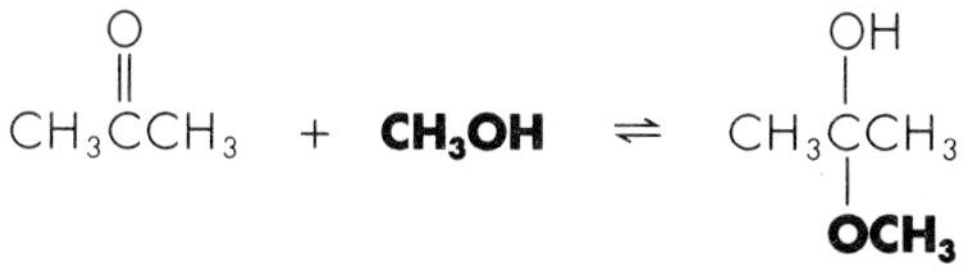

$$CH_3\overset{\overset{\displaystyle O}{||}}{C}CH_3 \quad + \quad \mathbf{CH_3OH} \quad \rightleftharpoons \quad CH_3\underset{\underset{\displaystyle \mathbf{OCH_3}}{|}}{\overset{\overset{\displaystyle OH}{|}}{C}}CH_3$$

| propan-2-one | methanol | 2-methoxypropan-2-ol |

Again the position of the methanol in the hemiketal, 2-methoxypropan-2-ol, is displayed in bold; this is the compound shown in Q9.1(i). The reactions of alcohols with aldehydes or ketones can be written using the general formulae for those compounds:

$$
\underset{\text{aldehyde}}{\overset{\overset{\displaystyle O}{\|}}{R C H}} + \underset{\text{alcohol}}{\textbf{ROH}} \rightleftharpoons \underset{\text{hemiacetal}}{\overset{\overset{\displaystyle OH}{|}}{R C H}}
$$

OR

$$
\underset{\text{ketone}}{\overset{\overset{\displaystyle O}{\|}}{R C R}} + \underset{\text{alcohol}}{\textbf{ROH}} \rightleftharpoons \underset{\text{hemiketal}}{\overset{\overset{\displaystyle OH}{|}}{R C R}}
$$

OR

Hemiacetals and hemiketals are similar in structure, with the aldehyde —H group being replaced by an —R group in the hemiketal (see also Q9.3, page 71). The formation of hemiacetals and hemiketals is important in the formation of ring sugars such as glucose and fructose. This will be discussed in more detail in Chapter 13.

Tables 9.1, 9.2 and 9.3 (pages 77–79) give examples of biologically important alcohols, aldehydes and ketones. Examination of Table 9.1 will reveal that most alcohols have either the prefix hydroxy- or the suffix -ol. Table 9.2 shows that many aldehydes have the prefix aldo- or suffix -al. Table 9.3 shows that ketones are usually prefixed keto- or suffixed -one. Reference to these tables will allow you to answer Q9.4.

9.5 The aldolase reaction

Aldolase is an enzyme that is important in the breakdown pathway of glucose to pyruvate. It is responsible for accelerating (catalysing) the reaction in a reversible manner:

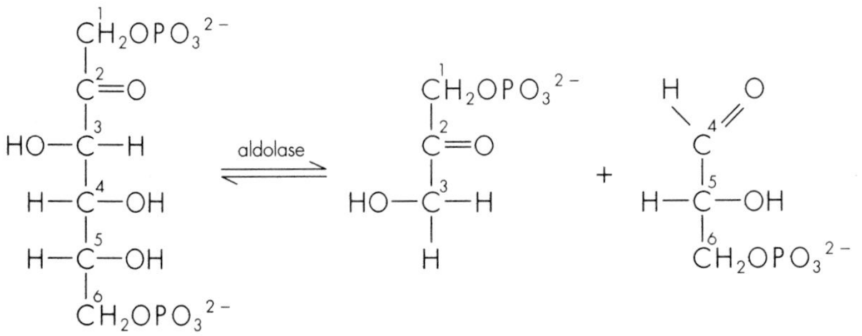

D-fructose-1,6-diphosphate   dihydroxyacetone   D-glyceraldehyde-3-phosphate
phosphate

We can also depict the chemical reaction catalysed by aldolase using only the names of the compounds involved:

$$
\text{D-fructose-1,6-diphosphate} \underset{}{\overset{\text{aldolase}}{\rightleftharpoons}} \text{D-glyceraldehyde-3-phosphate} + \text{dihydroxyacetone-3-phosphate}
$$

Table 9.1 Alcohols of biological importance

Name	Structural formula	Biological importance
Ethanol	CH_3CH_2OH	Products of bacterial fermentation
Propanol	$CH_3CH_2CH_2OH$	
Butanol	$CH_3CH_2CH_2CH_2OH$	
5-hydroxytryptamine	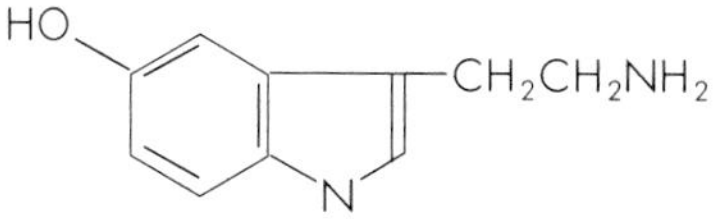	Hormone/neurotransmitter
Adrenaline	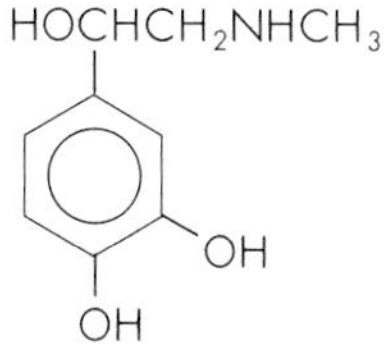 $HOCHCH_2NHCH_3$	
Noradrenaline	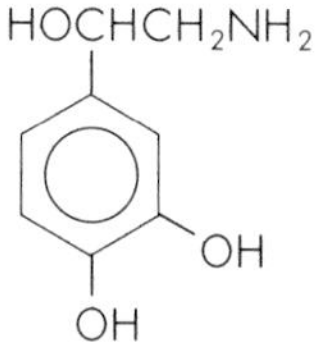 $HOCHCH_2NH_2$	
Cholesterol	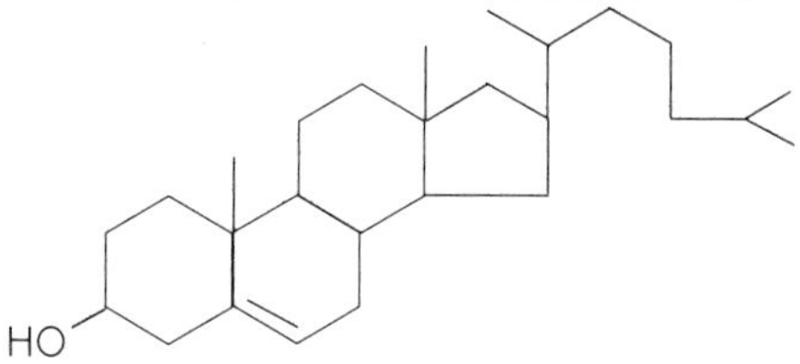	Component of biological membranes
Retinol	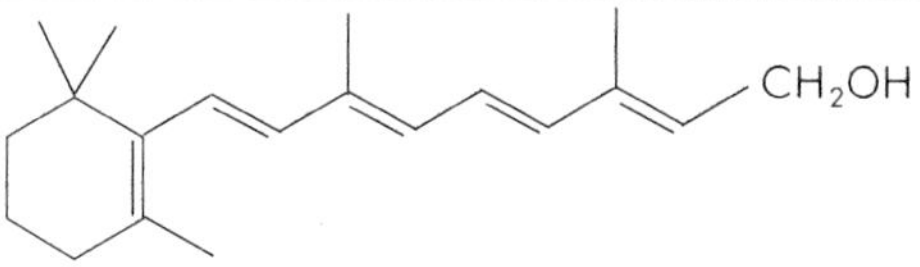 CH_2OH	Vitamin A
Sugars and carbohydrates, for example β-D-glucose	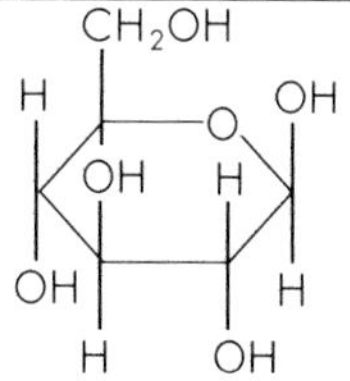	Store of cellular energy. Building block of structural cellular components

In this reaction, a hemiketal (D-fructose-1,6-diphosphate) is cleaved to form an aldehyde (D-glyceraldehyde-3-phosphate) and a ketone (dihydroxyacetone-3-phosphate). In living cells, this reaction can proceed in either direction and it is therefore called a reversible or equilibrium process. D-Glyceraldehyde-3-phosphate is broken down further in glycolysis to pyruvate and then by the tricarboxylic acid (TCA, Krebs, or citric acid) cycle to carbon dioxide and water, which releases energy for living systems to use. The dihydroxyacetone-3-phosphate is not wasted as it is converted into D-glyceraldehyde-3-phosphate by another enzyme. The aldolase reaction is only one of many thousands of chemical reactions that living organisms,

Table 9.2 Some aldehydes of biological importance

Name	Structural formula	Biological importance
D-Glucose	$\begin{array}{cccc} OH & OHOH & OHO \\ | & | & | & | & \| \\ CH_2CHCHCHCHCH \\ & & | \\ & & OH \end{array}$	Store of cellular energy. Building block of structural cellular components
D-Mannose	$\begin{array}{ccc} OH & OH & OHO \\ | & | & | & \| \\ CH_2CHCHCHCHCH \\ & | & | \\ & OH & OH \end{array}$	
D-Ribose	$\begin{array}{c} OH\ OHOHOHO \\ | \ | \ | \ | \ \| \\ CH_2CHCHCHCH \end{array}$	
D-Deoxyribose	$\begin{array}{cc} OH\ OHOH & O \\ | \ | \ | & \| \\ CH_2CHCHCH_2CH \end{array}$	
Aldosterone	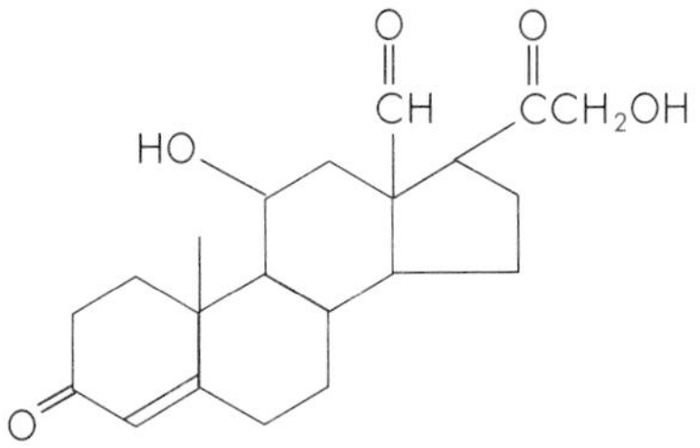	Steroid hormone
Benzaldehyde	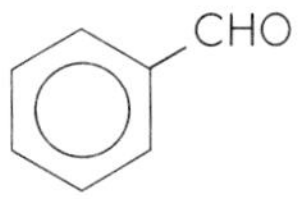	Woody tissue building block

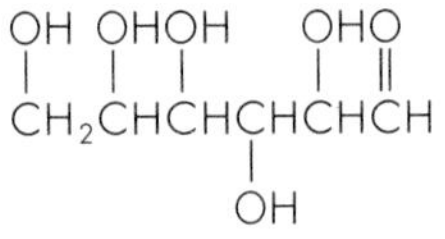

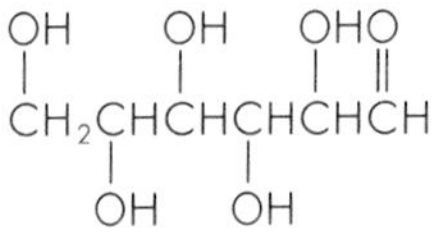

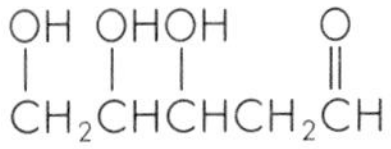

such as bacteria, plants and animals, use to make complex molecules, such as DNA, or to provide energy to grow and move. In all of these reactions molecules such as aldehydes, ketones and alcohols are constantly being synthesised and broken down.

Table 9.3 Ketones of biological importance

Name	Structural formula	Biological importance
Keto sugars, e.g. D-fructose	OH OHOH O $\|$ $\|$ $\|$ $\|$ $CH_2CHCHCHCCH_2OH$ $\|$ OH	Store of cellular energy. Building block of structural cellular components
Progesterone	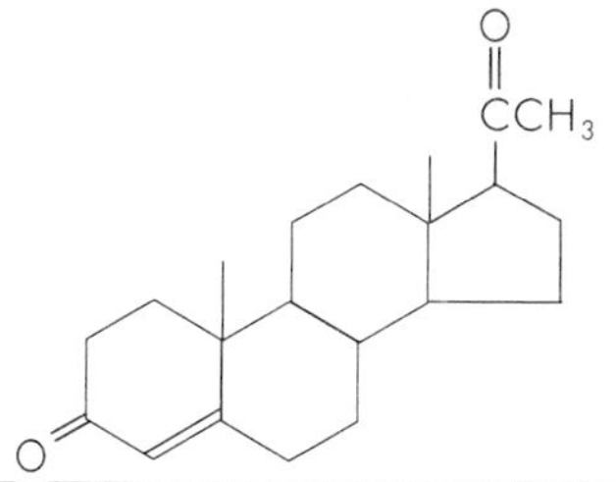	Steroid hormones
Corticosterone	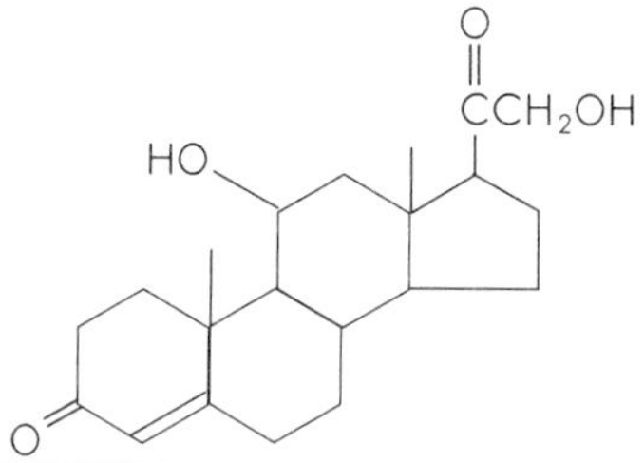	
Testosterone	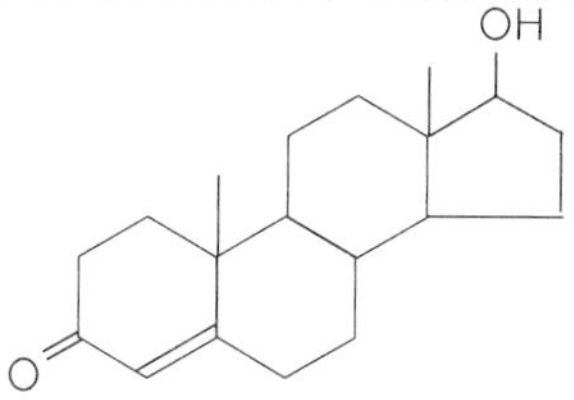	
α-Ketoglutarate	O $\|$ $^-OOCCCH_2CH_2COO^-$	Tricarboxylic acid intermediates
Oxaloacetate	O $\|$ $^-OOCCCH_2COO^-$	
Quinones such as ubiquinone	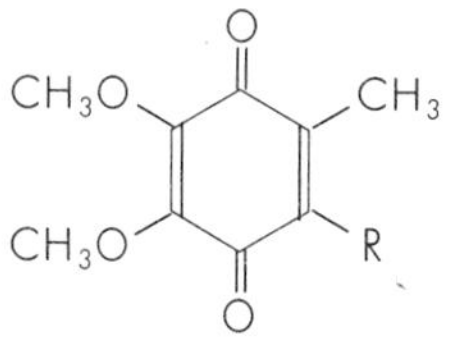	Used to carry electrons in nearly all living organisms

Summary

Alcohols have the general formula ROH and are named by adding the suffix -ol to the related alkane. In larger compounds a number will further define the position of the hydroxyl group. Diols, triols and polyols contain two, three, and many hydroxyl groups; these compounds are named in the same way as simple

$$\overset{O}{\overset{\|}{}}$$

alcohols. Aldehydes have the general formula RCH. The suffix -al is used to name aldehydes, the name deriving from the 'parent' alkane. Aldols contain both a hydroxyl and an aldehyde group. Ketones have the

$$\overset{O}{\overset{\|}{}}$$

general formula RCR. They are named by adding the suffix -one to the appropriate alkane. Reactions between ketones or aldehydes and alcohols yield hemiketals and hemiacetals, respectively. Hemiketals and hemiacetals are related in structure. Many compounds of biological importance are alcohols, aldehydes or ketones. In living organisms, compounds such as alcohols, aldehydes, ketones, hemiacetals and hemiketals are constantly being made or broken down. This can be demonstrated using the aldolase reaction.

Self-assessment questions

Try these questions. The answers will allow you to assess your understanding of Chapter 9.

Q9.6 Draw structures for these compounds:
- (a) butane-1,3-diol;
- (b) 4-hydroxypentan-2-one;
- (c) butanone;
- (d) the hemiacetal formed from ethanol and ethanal.

Q9.7 Name these compounds:

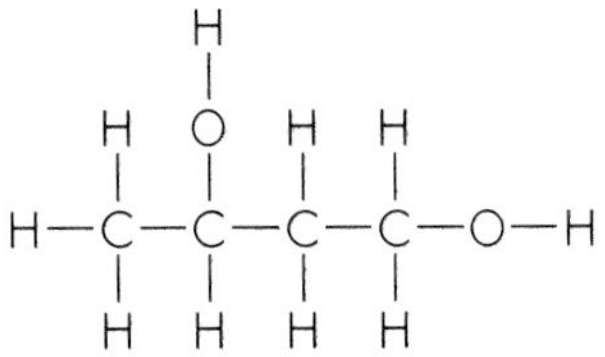

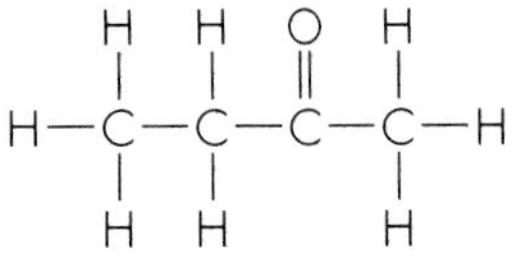

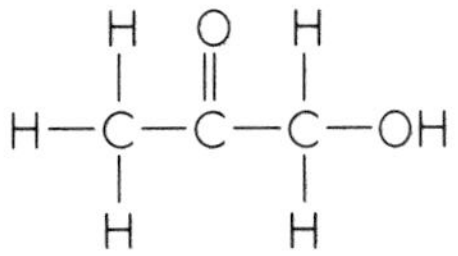

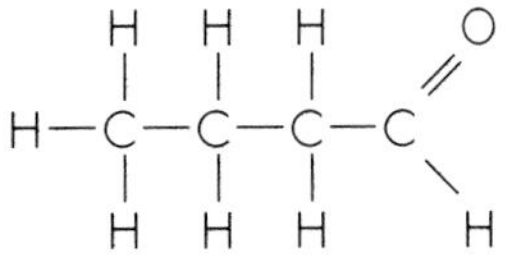

Q9.8 Classify each of the following biological compounds as
- (a) an alcohol
- (b) an aldehyde
- (c) a ketone:
  - (i) pregnenolone;
  - (ii) ubiquinone;
  - (iii) cholesterol;
  - (iv) D-glyceraldehyde-3-phosphate;
  - (v) retinol;
  - (vi) retinal;
  - (vii) estradiol.

Even if you have not met the compound before you should be able to assign it to one of groups (a), (b), or (c).

Carboxylic Acids and Esters

Introduction

This chapter deals with the structure and properties of carboxylic acids and esters.

Objectives

After completing this chapter you should be able to:
- describe the structure of the carboxyl group;
- name simple carboxylic acids;
- know the important carboxylic acids;
- explain the acidity of carboxylic acids;
- understand the role of the carboxyl group in forming hydrogen bonds;
- recall the reaction of carboxylic acids with hydroxyl groups to form organic esters;
- understand the structures of phosphate and thiol esters;
- explain the decarboxylation of 3-keto carboxylic acids.

Questions

If the areas covered in this chapter are familiar, try the questions below. If you can answer them correctly, you could move on to the next chapter.

Q10.1 Name the following compounds containing carboxyl groups:

(a) $CH_3CH_2CH_2COOH$;

(b) $HOOCCH_2CH_2COOH$;

(c) CH_3COOH;

(d) $CH_3(CH_2)_6COOH$.

Q10.2 Write out the abbreviated structure for decanoic acid $CH_3(CH_2)_8COOH$.

Q10.3 The pK_a of *p*-hydroxybenzoic acid is 4.55. What is the major form (ion or acid) at pH 7?

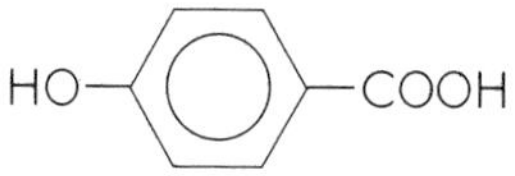

$$HO-\langle\bigcirc\rangle-COOH$$

Q10.4 Draw a hydrogen bond between the hydroxyl hydrogen of a carboxyl group and a carbonyl oxygen of a ketone.

Q10.5 What two compounds react to form an organic ester?

Q10.6 Draw the general structure of:

(a) a thioester;

(b) a phosphate ester.

10.1 Carboxylic acid structure and naming

Carboxylic acids and their derivatives are amongst the most important biological building block molecules and a knowledge of their structure, properties and reactions is of vital importance. The simplest carboxylic acid is methanoic acid (formic acid):

name	structural formula	condensed formula
methanoic acid or formic acid	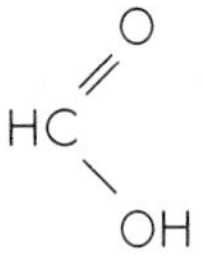 HC⟨=O, OH⟩	HCOOH

The carboxyl functional group is made up of a carbonyl and a hydroxyl functional group bound to the same carbon. The functional groups of a carboxylic acid are shown below:

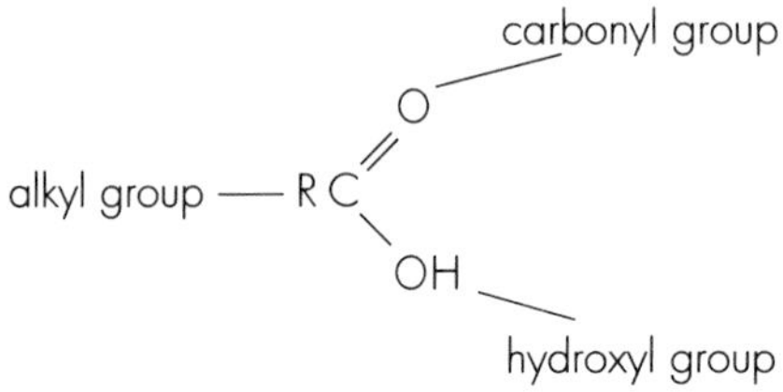

carbonyl group

alkyl group — R C ⟨=O, OH⟩

hydroxyl group

The three bonds (R—C, C—O—H, C=O) of the carboxyl group lie in the same plane and are separated by angles of approximately 120°:

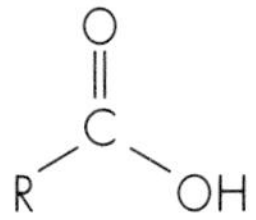

The names of carboxylic acids are based on those of the parent alkanes. The -e at the end of the alkane is replaced by -oic acid. In the example shown below, the -e at the end of propane was removed and replaced with -oic acid to give propanoic acid.

parent alkane

carboxylic acid

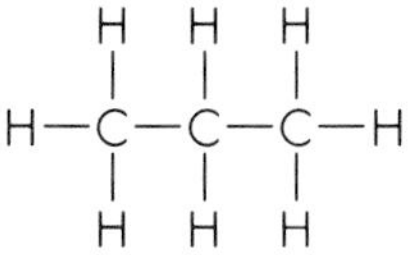

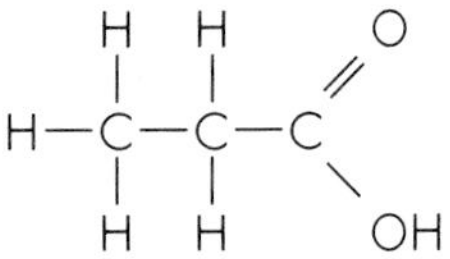

$CH_3CH_2CH_3$
propane

CH_3CH_2COOH
propanoic acid

Example 10.1

Name the carboxylic acids: **(a)** $CH_3CH_2CH_2COOH$; **(b)** $HOOCCH_2CH_2COOH$.

- Replace the —OOH by —H.
- Both parent compounds are butane.
- Compound (a), remove the -e and add -oic acid to give butanoic acid.
- Compound (b), remove the -e and add -dioic acid to give butandioic acid. Butandioic acid sounds clumsy and so compounds of this type normally add the -e back in as in butanedioic acid.

It should be noted that, like the aldehyde group, the carboxyl group must occur at the end or as a branch of an alkyl chain. It is therefore usually unnecessary to number the position of the carboxyl group of a simple carboxylic acid. The carboxyl group may be part of a more complicated molecule. In this case the prefix carboxyl- or the suffix -carboxylic acid may be added to the name of the corresponding structure:

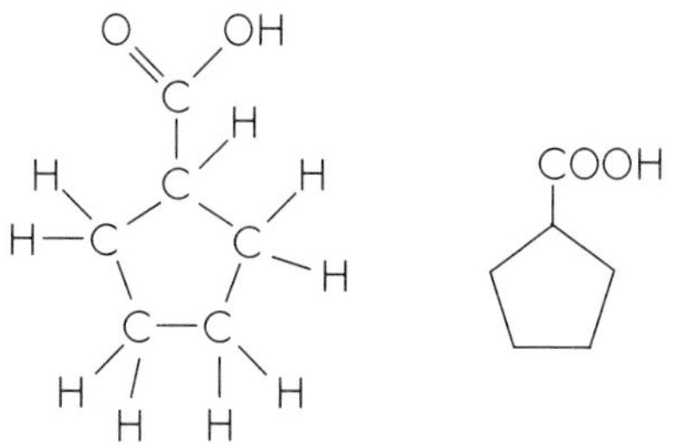

cyclopentane carboxylic acid

You may have already recognised the compound in Example 10.1(b) as succinic acid from work done on the tricarboxylic acid cycle (TCA or Krebs cycle) or elsewhere. Historically, organic acids were among the first biomolecules to be purified and characterised and they are given names that relate to their source of isolation. For example, pelargonic acid (nonanoic acid) was originally isolated from the pelargonium. Thus many commonly used names are recognised as proper names for carboxylic acids. Although we shall use systematic names where possible, the more common name is also given. Some commonly occurring carboxylic acids are shown in Table 10.1 overleaf.

Question

Q10.7 Name the carboxylic acids: (a) $HOOCCH=CHCOOH$; (b) CH_3COOH.

Carboxylic acids containing long carbon chains are usually called fatty acids. As you can see in Table 10.1, these chains are sometimes very long. Writing these out can be tedious as shown below for dodecanoic (lauric) acid. For this reason, an abbreviated version for writing down complex carboxylic acids (and many other complicated compounds) is often used, as shown for dodecanoic acid:

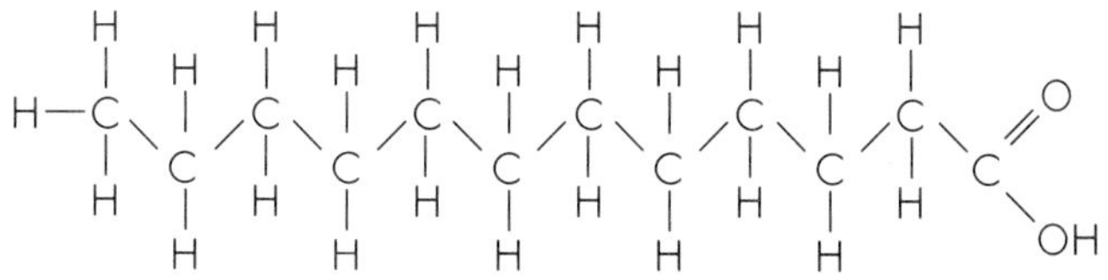

full structure of dodecanoic acid

abbreviated structure of dodecanoic acid

The method for writing these structures is:

(i)   leave out all hydrogen atoms;
(ii)   mark each carbon as a change in the direction of a line;
(iii)   put in double bonds as double lines.

This is shown step by step below. The abbreviated structure is much easier to write.

Table 10.1 Some commonly occurring carboxylic acids

Systematic name	Common name	Structure
Methanoic acid	Formic acid	HCOOH
Ethanoic acid	Acetic acid	CH_3COOH
Propanoic acid	Propionic acid	CH_3CH_2COOH
Butanoic acid	Butyric acid	$CH_3CH_2CH_2COOH$
Pentanoic acid	Valeric acid	$CH_3CH_2CH_2CH_2COOH$
Dodecanoic acid	Lauric acid	$CH_3(CH_2)_{10}COOH$
Hexadecanoic acid	Palmitic acid	$CH_3(CH_2)_{14}COOH$
Octadecanoic acid	Stearic acid	$CH_3(CH_2)_{16}COOH$
n-Eicosanoic acid	Arachidic acid	$CH_3(CH_2)_{18}COOH$
cis,cis-9,12-Octadecadienoic acid	Linoleic acid	$CH_3(CH_2)_4CH{=}CHCH_2CH{=}CH(CH_2)_7COOH$
Ethanedioic acid	Oxalic acid	HOOCCOOH
Propanedioic acid	Malonic acid	$HOOCCH_2COOH$
Butanedioic acid	Succinic acid	$HOOCCH_2CH_2COOH$
Pentanedioic acid	Glutaric acid	$HOOCCH_2CH_2CH_2COOH$
3-Carboxypentan-3-oldioic acid	Citric acid	OH | $HOOCCH_2CCH_2COOH$ | COOH
Pentan-2-onedioic acid	2-Ketoglutaric acid	O || $HOOCCH_2CH_2CCOOH$

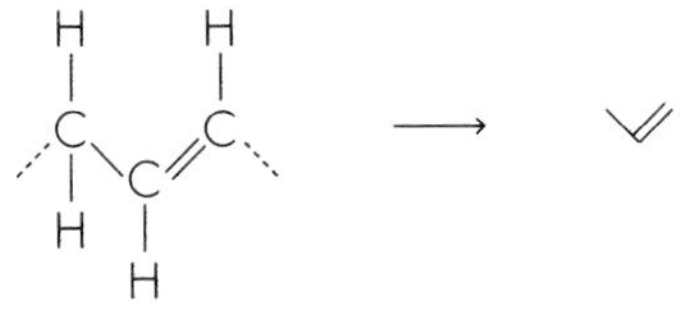

full structure   abbreviated structure

Question

Q10.8 Draw abbreviated structures for: (a) hexadecanoic acid; (b) pentanedioic acid.

10.2 Hydrogen bonding of carboxylic acids

Hydrogen bonding is very important in stabilising the structure of many biological molecules. A brief explanation of hydrogen bonding will be given. Functional groups such as the carbonyl oxygen contain electrons that are not shared with other atoms in the molecule's structure. These electrons are called unshared or lone pair electrons (see Chapter 8, page 63). The unshared electrons give the carbonyl group an overall negative charge. Other groups containing lone pair electrons are the amine nitrogen, and the hydroxyl oxygen. The size of this charge is much much smaller than the charge carried by an ion. The hydrogen atoms of sulphydryl, hydroxyl and amine groups bear a slight positive charge. In many biomolecules the slightly positive hydrogens are attracted to the slightly negative charge of amine nitrogens, or carbonyl or hydroxyl oxygens. This forms a very weak bond which is called a hydrogen bond. Typically, a hydrogen bond has less than 5 per cent of the strength of a covalent bond. The diagram below shows a hydrogen bond between a carbonyl oxygen and a hydroxyl hydrogen:

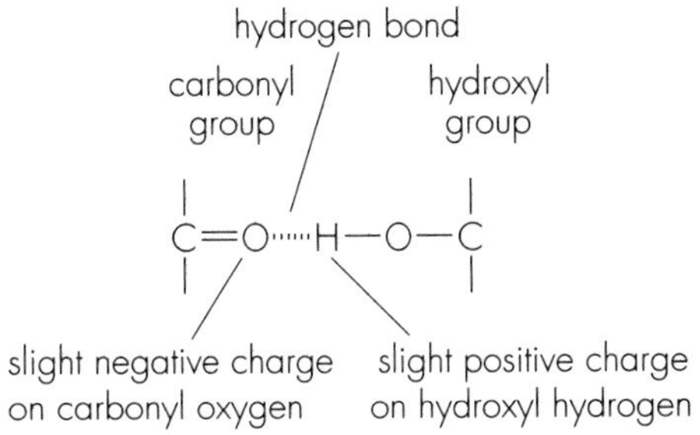

Solutions of carboxylic acids can participate in hydrogen bonding. The 'carbonyl' oxygen of one carboxylic acid is hydrogen bonded to the hydrogen of the hydroxyl group of an adjacent carboxyl residue:

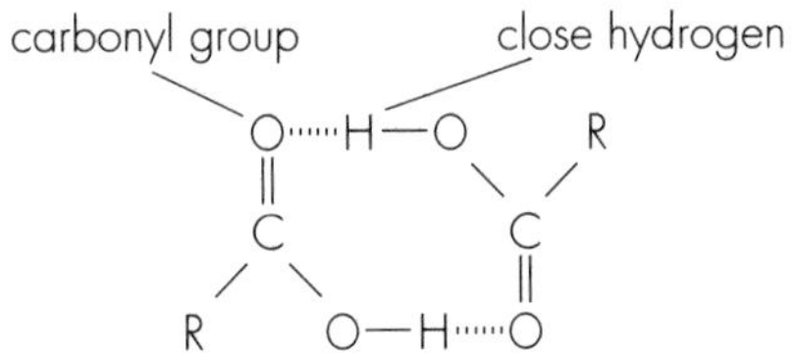

Carboxyl carbonyl oxygens can also make hydrogen bonds with the hydrogens of sulphydryl, hydroxyl, and amine groups, while the hydroxyl proton of carboxyl groups can form hydrogen bonds with amino nitrogen atoms, carbonyl groups and hydroxyl oxygen atoms.

Question

Q10.9 Draw a diagram of a hydrogen bond between a hydroxyl hydrogen and the carboxyl carbonyl group.

10.3 Acid–base properties of carboxyl groups

The carboxyl group can act as an acid by reaction with a base as shown below. The lone pair electrons (first described in Chapter 8, page 63) that are part of the base are represented by using two dots instead of a 'balloon': one dot is used for each unshared electron. This is another way of showing lone pair (unshared) electrons as part of a molecule.

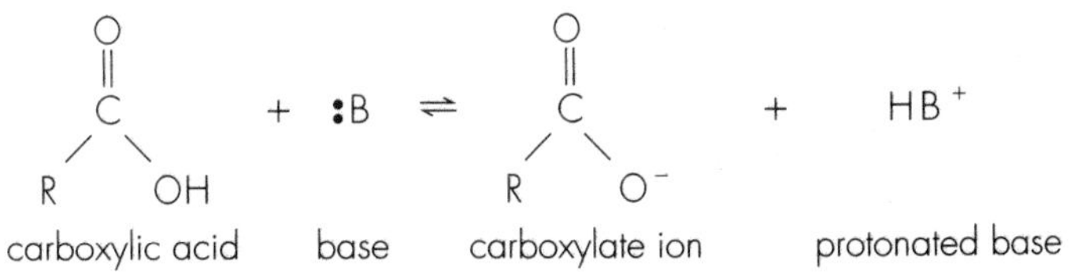

Donation of a proton to a base gives the carboxylate anion. For example ethanoic (acetic) acid will form the ethanoate (acetate) anion. The measure of how good an acid a carboxyl group is can be related to the pH value in water at which the carboxyl group is 50 per cent ionised. We call this pH the **pK_a**. Ethanoic acid has a pK_a of 4.72 as at this pH half of the acid is in the CH_3COOH (acid) form and half in the CH_3COO^- (ion) form. A smaller pK_a value indicates a stronger acid. The pK_a can tell us which of the acid or ion is the predominant form at the pH of the solution. The relationship between pK_a, pH and form is shown in Table 10.2. If the pH and pK_a are known, the values in this table can be used to work out the major form of any compound containing a carboxyl group in solution.

Table 10.2 The relationship between pH, pK_a and form

pH units away from pK_a	Concentration ratio (%)	
	Ion (RCOO⁻)	Acid (RCOOH)
≥−3	100	0
−2	99	1
−1	91	9
0	50	50
+1	9	91
+2	1	99
≥+3	0	100

Example 10.2
The pK_a of the carboxyl group of glycine is 2.3. What is the major form (ion or acid) at pH 5.3?

glycine (carboxylic acid) $NH_3^+CH_2COOH$
glycine (carboxylate ion) $NH_3^+CH_2COO^-$

- Essential information: $pK_a = 2.3$; pH = 5.3
- Subtract the pH from the pK_a: $pK_a - pH = 2.3 - 5.3 = -3$
- Look up the value in Table 10.2. A value of −3 tells us that the carboxyl group of glycine is nearly all in the ionic (RCOO⁻) form.

Table 10.3 The pK_a values of some biologically important carboxyl groups (relevant carboxyl shown in bold)

Group	Structure	pK_a
Amino acid α-carboxyl	NH_3^+CHR**COO**⁻	2.0–2.6
Glutamate side-chain	COO⁻ | $NH_2CHCH_2CH_2$**COO**⁻	4.2
Aspartate side-chain	COO⁻ | NH_2CHCH_2**COO**⁻	3.9
Methanoic acid	H**COOH**	3.85
Ethanoic acid	CH_3**COOH**	4.72
Propanoic acid to decanoic acid	CH_3CH_2**COOH** to $CH_3(CH_2)_8$**COOH**	4.82–4.95
Salicylic acid	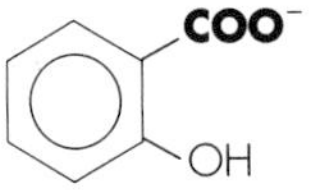 **COO**⁻ / OH (benzene ring)	2.96

The values of the pK_a of some biologically important carboxyl groups are shown in Table 10.3.

Question

Q10.10 What is the major form of the aspartate carboxyl side-chain at pH 7.0?

10.4   Reactions of carboxylic acids

Carboxylic acids can undergo a variety of biologically important reactions. These include decarboxylation, amidation and acyl substitution. Amidation will be covered in Chapter 11. The other reactions are shown below:

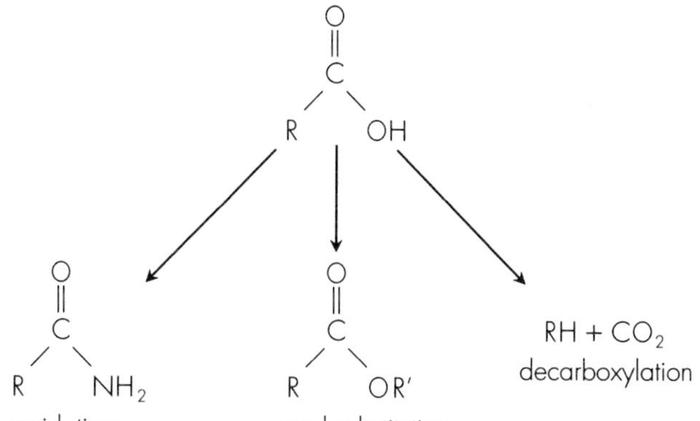

amidation   acyl substitution   decarboxylation

Acyl substitution

Only one type of acyl substitution is considered in this chapter, the formation of organic esters. An ester is the product of a reaction between an organic acid and an organic base.

general structure of an organic ester

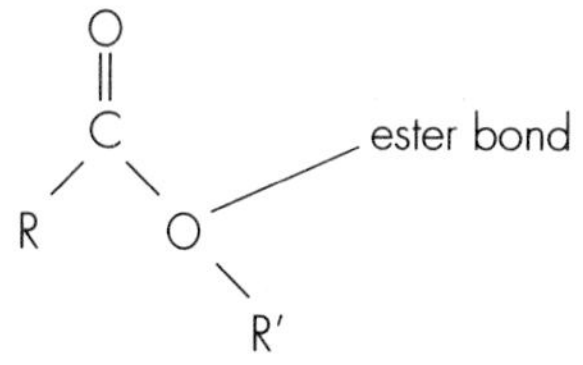

ester bond

The most commonly occurring base in biology is the hydroxyl group. A reaction between a hydroxyl of an alcohol and a carboxyl group is:

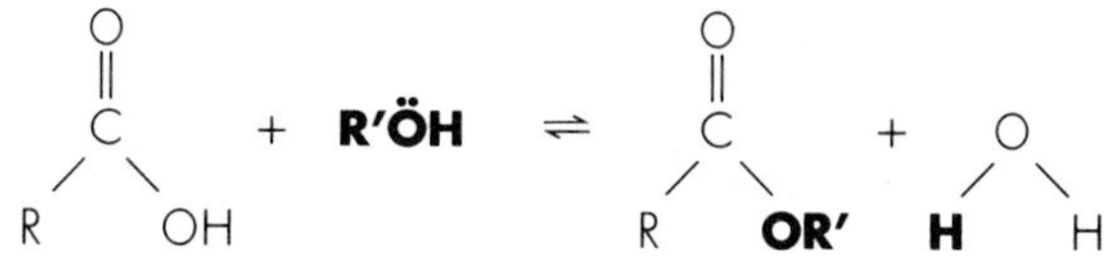

acid   alcohol   ester   water

This reaction requires strong acids (such as concentrated hydrochloric acid) and heating (100 °C) in order to proceed. It is not carried out by living cells, most of which can only work at mild temperatures and pH. As a result, most living cells use **thioesters** as intermediates in ester formation. The thiol group (RSH) is similar to the hydroxyl group (ROH) except that thiols are more reactive and less harsh conditions are required to form thioesters. A general reaction between carboxyl groups and thiols is:

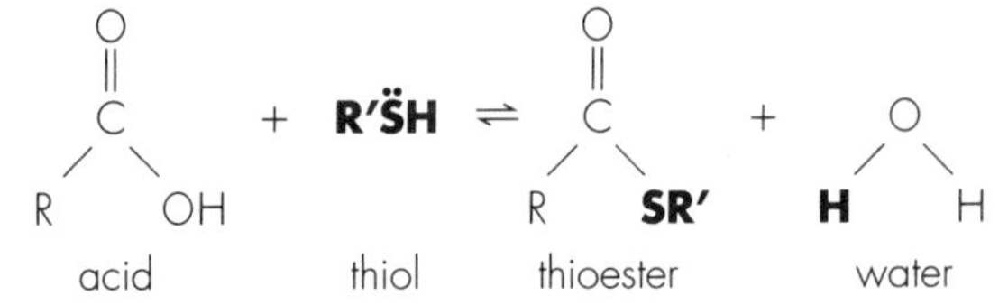

The thioesters used in many biological reactions are esters of the thiol Coenzyme A (abbreviated to CoA):

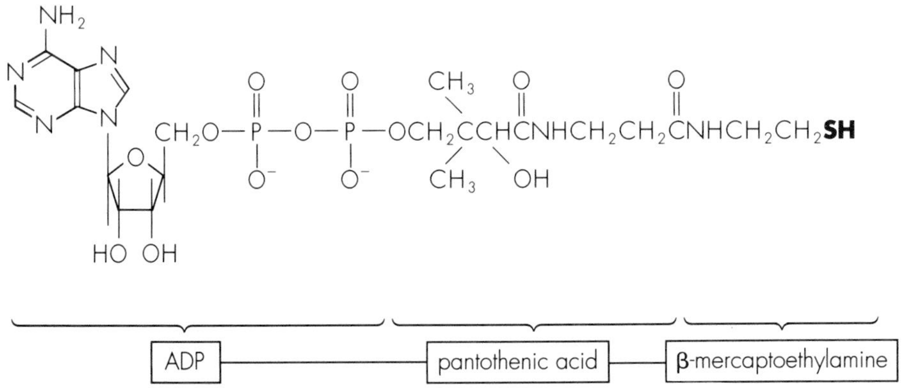

Coenzyme A esters are important in the esterification of intermediates in both carbohydrate and fatty acid metabolism.

Phosphate esters

A third class of esters are important in living organisms. These are the esters of phosphoric, diphosphoric and triphosphoric acids with organic bases. These acids' structures are:

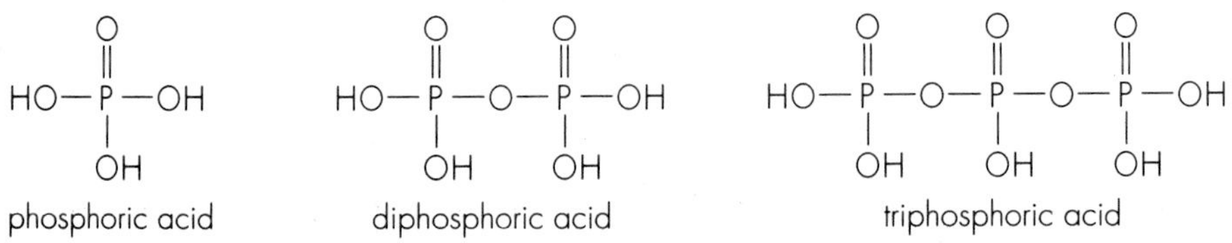

Comparison of phosphoric acid with carboxylic acids and their esters shows their similarity:

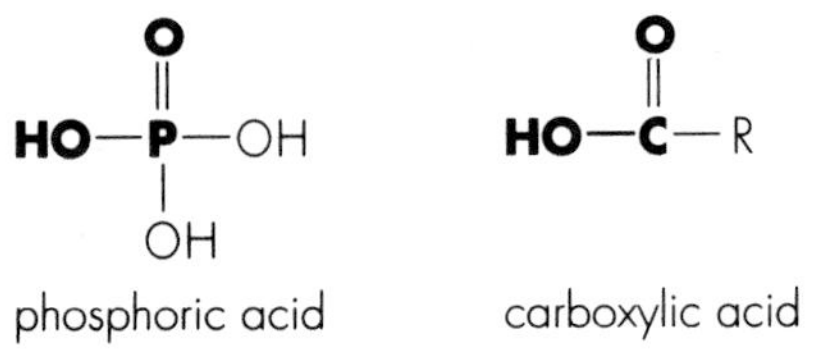

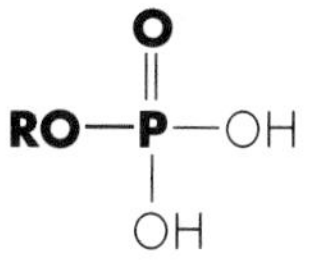

$$RO-\overset{\overset{\displaystyle O}{\|}}{\underset{\underset{\displaystyle OH}{|}}{P}}-OH \qquad RO-\overset{\overset{\displaystyle O}{\|}}{C}-R$$

phosphate ester 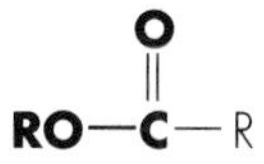   carboxylic acid ester

The phosphate esters are formed in many parts of the cell, from adenosine-5'-triphosphate (ATP), which acts as the energy currency of the cell, to the backbone structure of nucleotides, which are of the greatest importance.

Decarboxylation

Simple carboxylic acids can lose their carboxyl groups when treated in the presence of heavy metals and iodine or bromine. This reaction is not feasible in living systems, as the reaction conditions are too harsh for the viability of most cells. The 3-keto acids and 1,3-dioic acids can be decarboxylated without such vigorous conditions to yield a ketone. This reaction is used in the decarboxylation of isocitrate to form 2-oxoglutarate (α-ketoglutarate) in the citric acid (TCA or Krebs) cycle. It is an example of the decarboxylation of a 3-keto acid. Isocitrate is not a 3-keto acid, and the enzyme responsible for accelerating the reaction first forms a 3-keto acid, oxalosuccinic acid. Oxalosuccinic acid can then readily decarboxylate to yield α-ketoglutarate:

isocitrate $\xrightarrow{\text{on surface of enzyme}}$ oxalosuccinate $\longrightarrow$ α-ketoglutarate + CO_2
(not a 3-keto acid)   (a 3-keto acid)

Isocitrate is a 6-carbon compound, while α-ketoglutarate is a 5-carbon compound. Other decarboxylation reactions in the citric acid cycle and elsewhere, although similar to this one, are carried out by complex enzymes containing the cofactor thiamine pyrophosphate. They are beyond the scope of this book.

Summary

The structure of the carboxyl group, formula —COOH, can be viewed as containing both hydroxyl and carbonyl functional groups bound to the same carbon. Simple carboxylic acids are named by reference to the parent alkane; the terminal -e is replaced by -oic acid. In more complex biomolecules, the prefix carboxy- may be used. Important carboxylic acids are found universally and were amongst the first biomolecules to be purified. Carboxylic acids can dissociate to form the carboxylate anion and H^+. They are thus acids; typically with pK_a of 2.0–3.5. Carboxyl groups can form hydrogen bonds with both electron-rich and electron-poor centres. Carboxylic acids react with hydroxyl groups to form organic esters, with sulphydryl groups to form thioesters, and with phosphoric acids to form phosphate esters. Decarboxylation of 3-keto carboxylic acids and 1,3-dioic acids proceeds readily. This is used in biology to carry out some important decarboxylation reactions.

Self-assessment questions

Try these questions to test your understanding of carboxylic acids and esters.

Q10.11 Name these carboxylic acids:

(a)
$$\begin{array}{c} \text{OH} \\ | \\ \text{CH}_3\text{CH}_2\text{CHCOOH} \end{array}$$

(b) $\text{HOOCCH}_2\text{CH}_2\text{CH}_2\text{CH}_2\text{COOH}$

(c)
$$\begin{array}{c} \text{CH}_3 \\ | \\ \text{CH}_3\text{CHCOOH} \end{array}$$

(d) 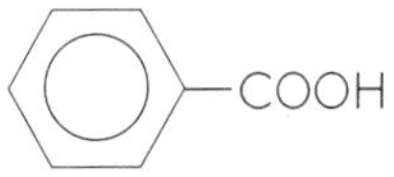 —COOH

Q10.12 Give the common name of hexadecanoic acid.

Q10.13 What is the major form of the carboxyl group of nonanoic acid at pH 6.5?

Q10.14 (a) Draw the reaction between methanoic acid and methanol.
(b) What is the product of this reaction called?

Q10.15 (a) Why is the cell unable to carry out direct esterification?
(b) What type of compound does the cell normally use to help carry out esterification reactions?

Q10.16 Name two important biomolecules that contain phosphate esters.

Nitrogen-containing Molecules

Introduction

This chapter deals with the structure, names, properties and reactivity of biologically important nitrogen-containing biomolecules. Nitrogen is one of the most important elements of life (reviewed in Chapter 7, page 47). It forms an essential part of most of the molecules of the cell. It is a constituent part of proteins and the genetic molecules of the cell nucleus. It is also an important part of some molecules of the cell membrane and some complex carbohydrates. In addition, many hormones and drugs are nitrogen-containing molecules.

Objectives

After completing this chapter you should be able to:
- differentiate between primary, secondary and tertiary amines;
- name simple amines;
- understand the geometry of amines;
- know the structure of the biologically important nitrogen-containing ring structures such as pyrrolidines, imidazoles, pyridines, pyrimidines, purines, indoles and flavins;
- understand the importance of amines in forming hydrogen bonds;
- recall the ability of amines to act as bases, and to work out which of the forms, base or ion, is the major species at a given pH value;
- describe the structure of amides, understand the important properties of the amide bond, and know of the importance of amides in nitrogen metabolism.

Questions

Test your understanding of these topics by answering the questions given below. If you can answer them correctly, you could move on to Chapter 12.

Q11.1 Classify the following nitrogen-containing compounds as:
(a) a primary amine; (b) a secondary amine; (c) a tertiary amine.

(i) 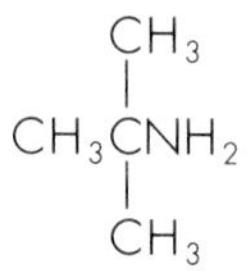
$$CH_3$$
$$|$$
$$CH_3CNH_2$$
$$|$$
$$CH_3$$

(ii) CH_3NHCH_3

(iii) 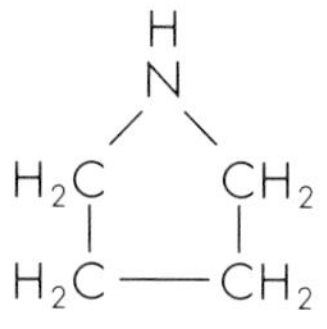
$$\begin{array}{c} H \\ N \\ / \ \backslash \\ H_2C \quad CH_2 \\ | \quad\quad | \\ H_2C - CH_2 \end{array}$$

(iv) 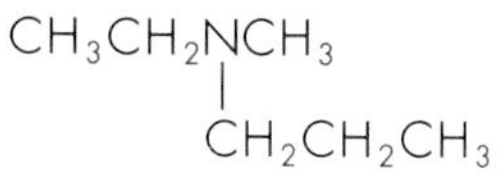
$$CH_3CH_2NCH_3$$
$$|$$
$$CH_2CH_2CH_3$$

Q11.2 Name compound (i) in Q11.1.

Q11.3 Give the names of amino acids that contain:

(a) a pyrrolidine ring;   (b) an imidazole ring;   (c) an indole ring.

Q11.4 (a) Draw the structure of a pyridine ring.

(b) Name an important group of biomolecules that contain a pyridine ring.

(c) What is the major biological function of the compound identified in (b)?

Q11.5 The pK_a of the amine in aniline (shown below) is 4.63. What is the major form of the molecule at pH 7? aniline (phenylamine)

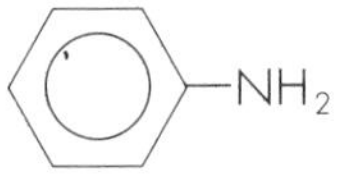

Q11.6 What property of amines and amides is important in stabilising the structure of proteins and nucleic acids?

11.1 Amines

Most nitrogen-containing biomolecules behave chemically like ammonia (NH_3):

name	structural formula	condensed formula
ammonia	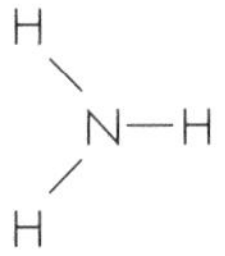 $\begin{array}{c} H \\ \diagdown \\ N{-}H \\ \diagup \\ H \end{array}$	NH_3

Many biological molecules have one or more of the hydrogens covalently bonded to the nitrogen replaced by a carbon-containing compound. The simplest example of such a compound, methylamine, is formed by replacing one of the hydrogens of ammonia by a methyl group:

name	structural formula	condensed formula
methylamine or aminomethane	$\begin{array}{c} H \quad H \\ | \quad \diagup \\ H{-}C{-}N \\ | \quad \diagdown \\ H \quad H \end{array}$	CH_3NH_2

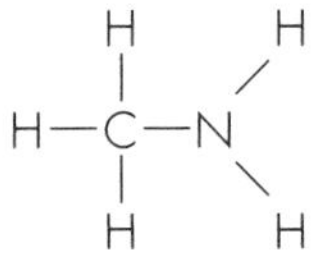

The $-NH_2$ part of methylamine is called the **amine** group. The $-NH_2$ part of a molecule can also be called an **amino** group. Amines where only one of the hydrogens of ammonia has been replaced by a carbon are known as **primary** amines. The general formula for a primary amine is RNH_2. Two or three of the hydrogens in ammonia can be replaced by organic groups, yielding **secondary** (R_2NH) and **tertiary** (R_3N) amines respectively:

	secondary amine	tertiary amine
structural formulae	$\begin{array}{c} H \quad H \quad H \\ | \quad | \quad | \\ H{-}C{-}N{-}C{-}H \\ | \qquad | \\ H \qquad H \end{array}$	$\begin{array}{c} H \ H \ H \\ \diagdown | \diagup \\ H \ C \ H \\ | \ | \ | \\ H{-}C{-}N{-}C{-}H \\ | \qquad | \\ H \qquad H \end{array}$
condensed formulae	CH_3NHCH_3	$\begin{array}{c} CH_3 \\ | \\ CH_3NCH_3 \end{array}$
names	*N,N*-dimethylamine	*N,N,N*-trimethylamine

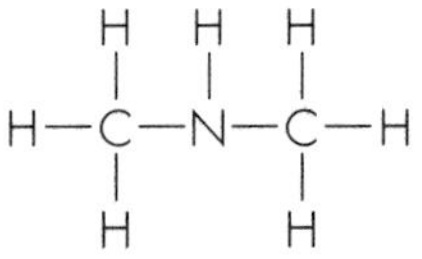

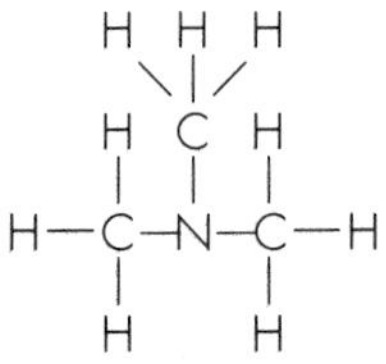

Example 11.1

Categorise the following amine as: **(a)** primary; **(b)** secondary; **(c)** tertiary.

$$
\text{(i)} \qquad
\begin{array}{c}
CH_3 \\
| \\
H_3C-C-NH_2 \\
| \\
CH_3
\end{array}
\qquad
\text{(ii)} \qquad
\begin{array}{c}
CH_3 \\
| \\
H_3C-\mathbf{C-NH_2} \\
| \\
CH_3
\end{array}
$$

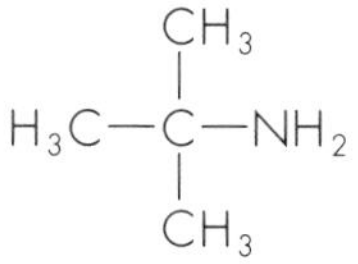

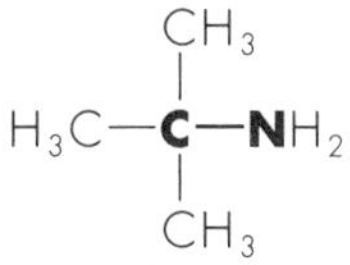

Count the number of nitrogen–carbon (C—N) bonds. The C—N bond is shown in bold in structure (ii). There is only one C—N bond and so the molecule shown is a primary amine. The method for categorising the type of amine from the number of C—N bonds is shown in Table 11.1.

Table 11.1 The relationship between number of C–N bonds and type of amine

Type of amine	Number of C–N bonds
Primary	1
Secondary	2
Tertiary	3

Question

Q11.7 Examine the nitrogen-containing compounds below and classify them as either:

(a) primary amine;   (b) secondary amine;   (c) tertiary amine.

$$
\text{(i)} \qquad
\begin{array}{c}
H \\
| \\
H_3C-N-CH_3
\end{array}
\qquad\qquad
\text{(ii)} \qquad \bigcirc\!\!-NH_2
$$

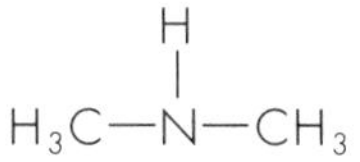

$$
\text{(iii)} \qquad
\begin{array}{c}
CH_3 \\
| \\
H_3C-N-CH_2CH_2CH_3
\end{array}
\qquad
\text{(iv)} \qquad
H_2N-CH_2-C
\begin{array}{c}
O \\
\| \\
\\
\backslash OH
\end{array}
$$

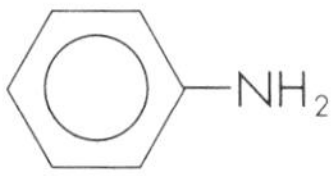

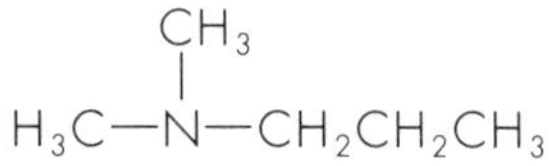

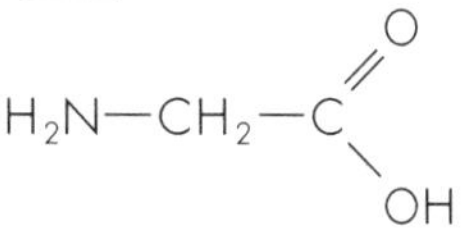

Naming amines

Primary amines are normally named by replacing the -ane at the end of the corresponding alkane by **-ylamine**. Alternatively the -e at the end of the parent alkane can be replaced by **-amine**:

ethane	$\begin{array}{c} H\ \ H \\ |\ \ \ | \\ H-C-C-H \\ |\ \ \ | \\ H\ \ H \end{array}$	CH_3CH_3
ethylamine or ethanamine	$\begin{array}{c} H\ \ H \\ |\ \ \ | \\ H-C-C-NH_2 \\ |\ \ \ | \\ H\ \ H \end{array}$	$CH_3CH_2NH_2$
names	structural formulae	condensed formulae

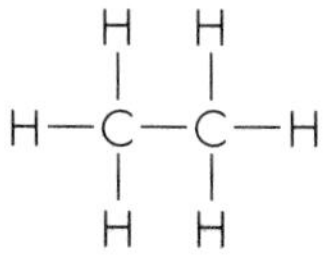

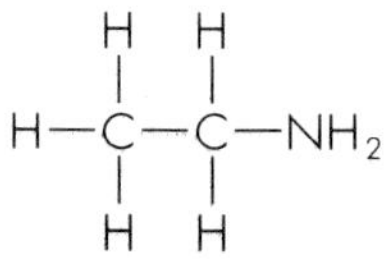

Molecules that are not simple alkanes because they contain other functional groups, such as a hydroxyl, carbonyl, or carboxyl group, and also contain an amine can be named by adding the prefix **amino-** to the name of the parent molecule. This is shown below:

aminoacetic acid
or aminoethanoic acid
or glycine

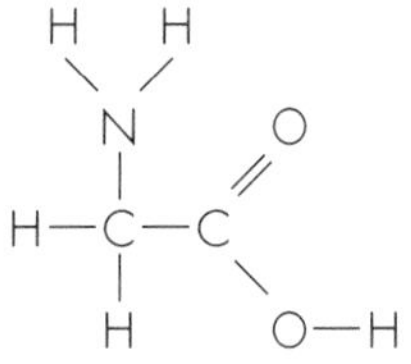

NH_2CH_2COOH

names structural formula condensed formula

In some molecules, the position of the amino group will need to be identified. This is done by referring to the number of the carbon atom to which the amino group is attached:

2-aminopropanoic acid
or alanine

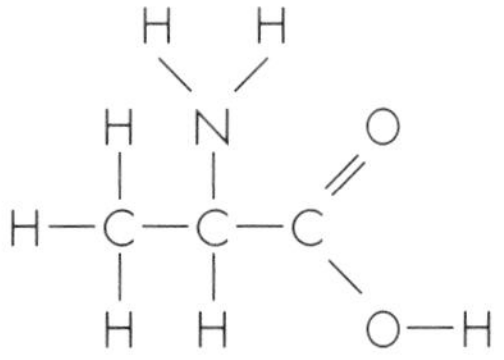

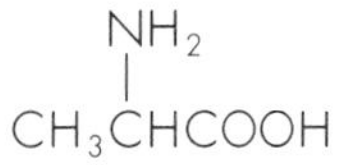

$CH_3CHCOOH$

lysine
or 2,6-diaminohexanoic acid

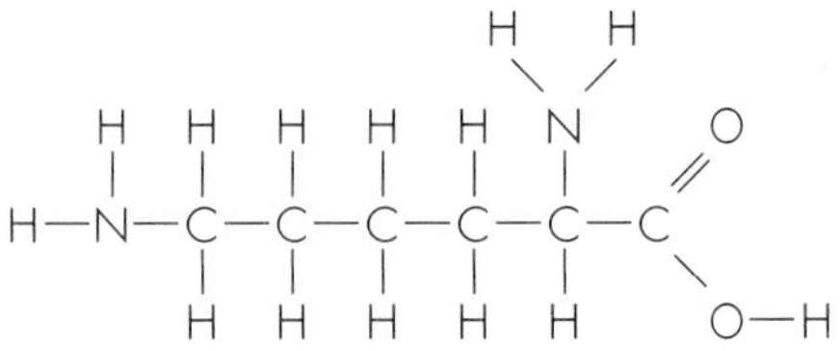

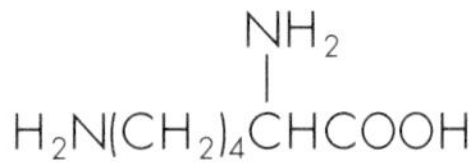

$H_2N(CH_2)_4CHCOOH$

names structural formulae condensed formulae

Glycine, alanine and lysine are examples of amino acids. Amino acids are the building blocks of proteins and will be discussed further in Chapter 12.

Example 11.2

Name the amine:

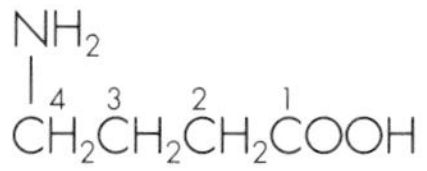

$$\overset{NH_2}{\underset{\overset{4}{CH_2}\overset{3}{CH_2}\overset{2}{CH_2}\overset{1}{COOH}}{|}}$$

The first step is to name the parent compound. Do this by replacing the —NH_2 group with an —H. This is:

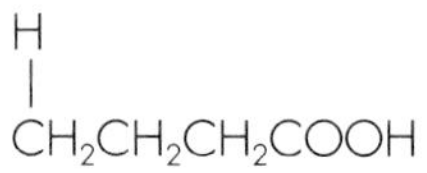

$$\overset{H}{\underset{CH_2CH_2CH_2COOH}{|}}$$

It can be seen that the molecule shown is butanoic acid.
The above numbering shows that the molecule has the amino group attached to the C^4 carbon of butanoic acid. Therefore the molecule is 4-aminobutanoic acid (sometimes referred to as γ-aminobutyric acid, which is a neurotransmitter).

Question

Q11.8 Name the following amines:

(i) 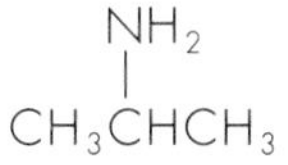   CH$_3$CHCH$_3$
              |
              NH$_2$

(ii)   CH$_3$CH$_2$CH$_2$NH$_2$

(iii) 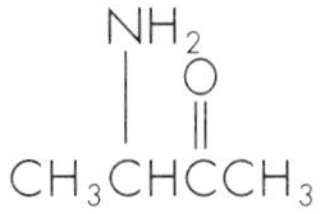   CH$_3$CHCCH$_3$
              | ||
              NH$_2$ O

(iv)   NH$_2$CH$_2$CH$_2$CHO

Secondary and tertiary amines are named by referring to the groups that are bound to the nitrogen. The example given below shows how the quaternary amine choline, an important part of membrane phospholipids, is named, although the naming of these compounds is beyond the scope of this book.

$$(CH_3)_3N^+CH_2CH_2OH$$

2-hydroxyethyltrimethylamine
or choline

11.2   Ring structures containing nitrogen

The nitrogen in many biomolecules is part of a ring. In such rings the nitrogen atom is given the number 1. The simplest biologically important nitrogen-containing ring structure is **pyrrolidine**, a five-membered ring with one nitrogen:

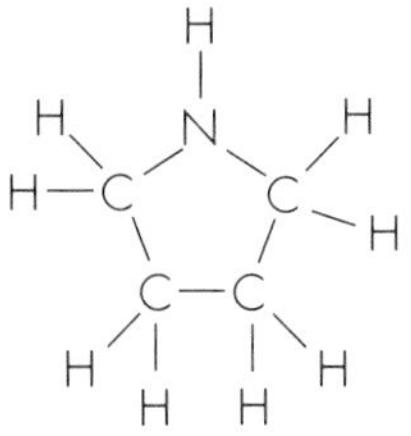

pyrrolidine

This ring is part of the unusual amino acids proline and hydroxyproline:

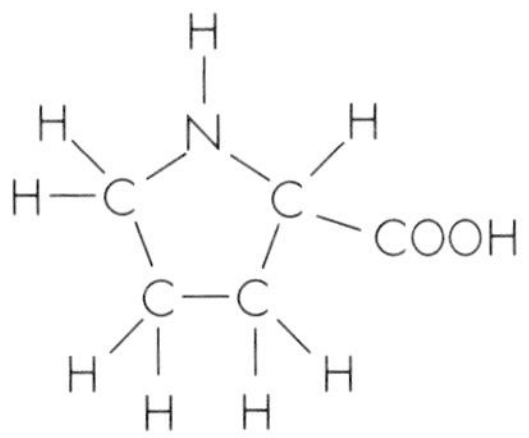

proline 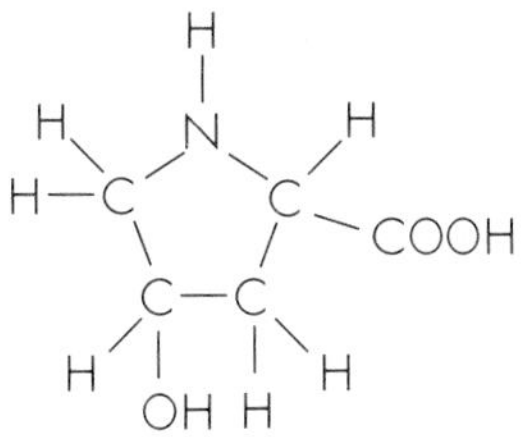   hydroxyproline

Proline and hydroxyproline should more properly be called imino acids as the nitrogen is present as an imine. Pyrrolidine rings are relatively inflexible, and this means that proline and hydroxyproline cannot fold into some of the regular three-dimensional shapes that a polypeptide can assume, such as an α-helix (see Section 12.4, page 109).

The other five-membered ring of importance is the **imidazole** ring. This ring structure is the side-chain of the amino acid histidine:

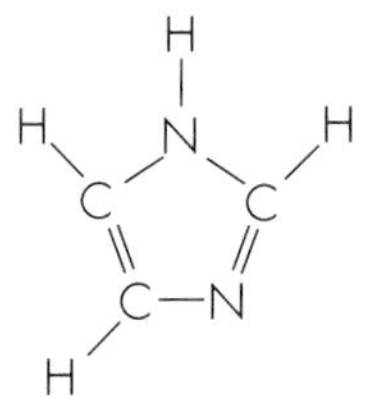

imidazole 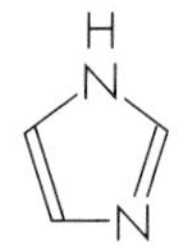   abbreviated structure

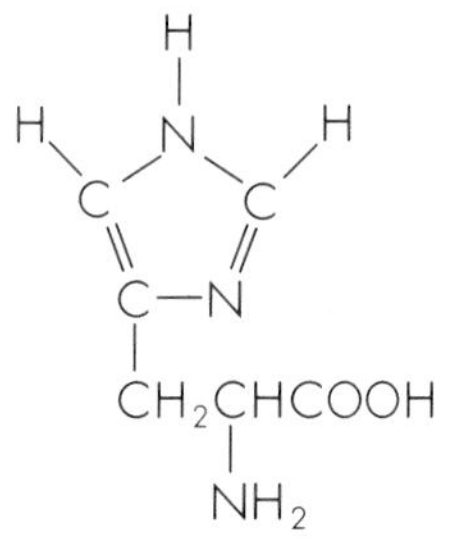

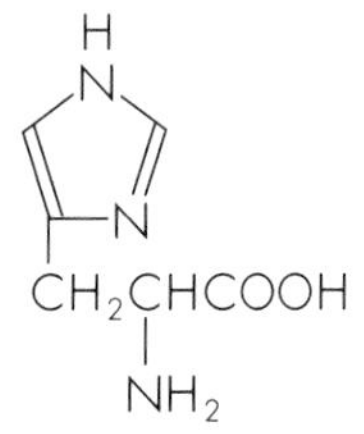

The important six-membered nitrogen-containing rings are the pyridine and pyrimidine rings:

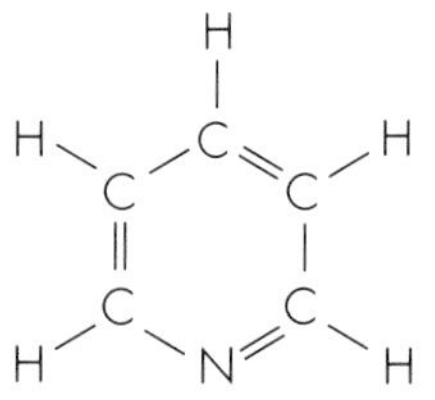

pyridine 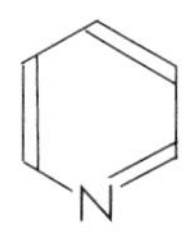   abbreviated structure 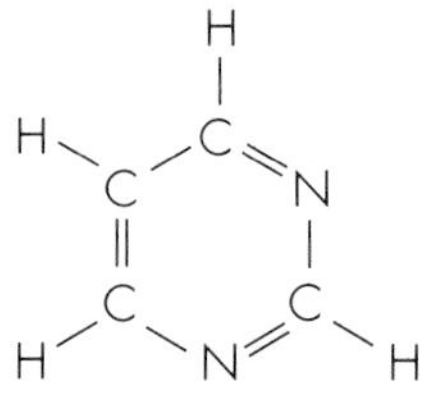   pyrimidine 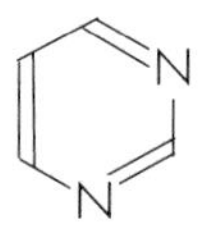   abbreviated structure

Pyridine rings are the functional part of the molecule NAD^+ (nicotinamide adenine dinucleotide), which used to be called DPN (diphosphopyridine nucleotide). This molecule is important in catalysing biological redox reactions, and is used by the cell to move and store the hydrogen atoms released from the breakdown of foods. The reduced (NADH) and oxidised forms (NAD^+) with the changes in the pyridine ring as this reaction takes place are shown below. This will be discussed further in Chapter 17, which focuses on redox reactions.

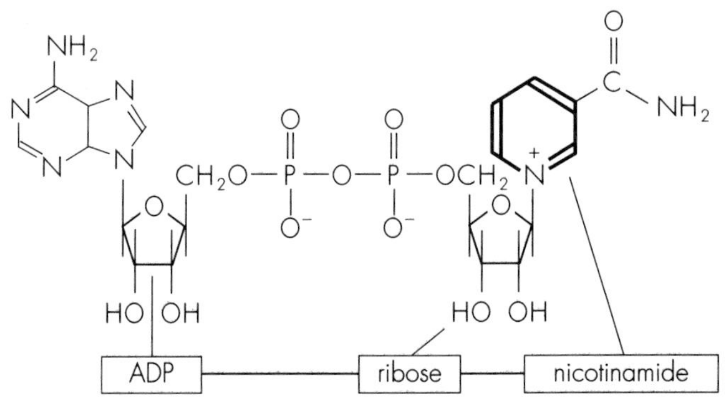

nicotinamide adenine dinucleotide (pyridine ring shown in bold)

reduced and oxidised forms of the nicotinamide part of NADH

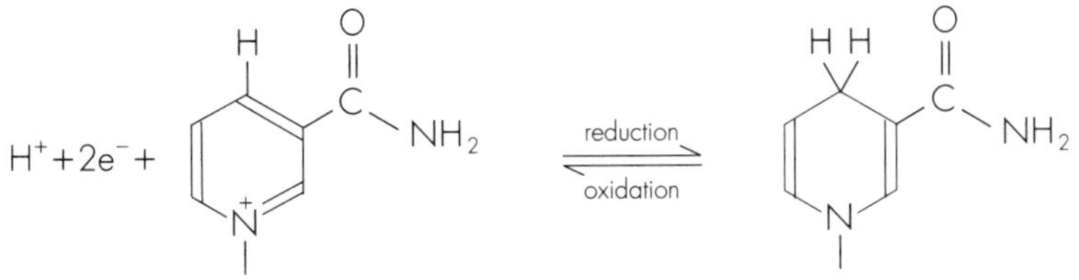

The molecule NADPH is identical to NADH except that an extra phosphate is attached to one of the ribose hydroxyl groups.

Substituted **pyrimidine** rings are one of the two types of bases found in RNA and DNA, the other being purines. The commonly occurring pyrimidine bases found in DNA and RNA are uracil, thymine and cytosine (see Chapter 15, page 141), in which the bond of N^1 is joined to the sugar ribose or deoxyribose. This is discussed later in Chapter 15 on the formation and structure of nucleotides.

Several important biomolecules have more complex nitrogen-containing ring structures. The amino acid tryptophan and the plant auxin indole-3-acetic acid both contain the **indole** ring (shown in bold below).

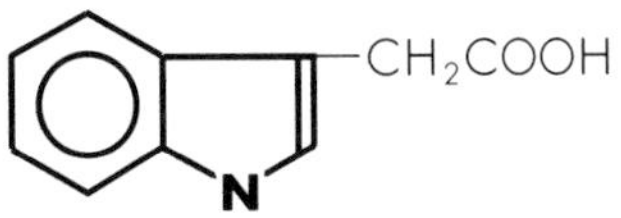

indole-3-acetic acid 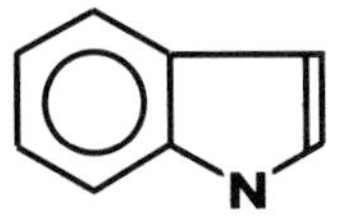   indole 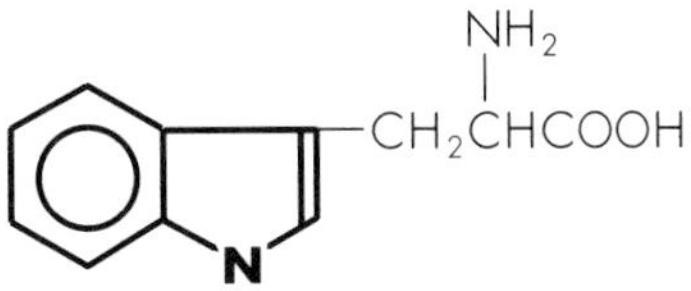   tryptophan

Substituted **purine** rings are the other common type of base found in DNA and RNA. These bases are called guanine and adenine (shown below).

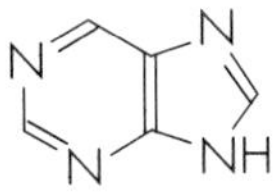

purine 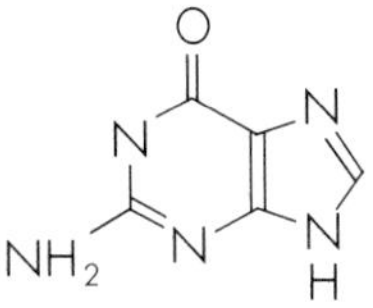   guanine 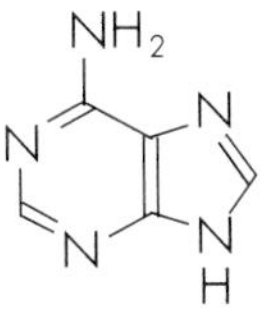   adenine

The other important nitrogen-containing ring, the **flavin** ring, is a part of the cofactors FAD and FMN (flavin adenine dinucleotide and flavin mononucleotide, see below) of some enzymes, where it carries out a similar redox function to NADH (see below). The body cannot synthesise flavins and so flavins such as riboflavins are vitamins.

oxidation and reduction of flavin

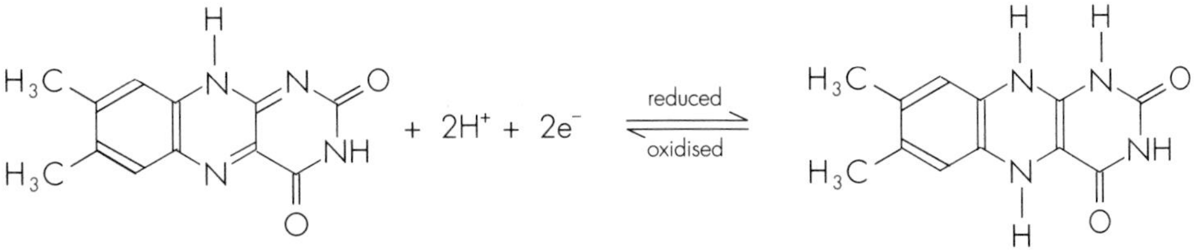

structure of flavin coenzymes

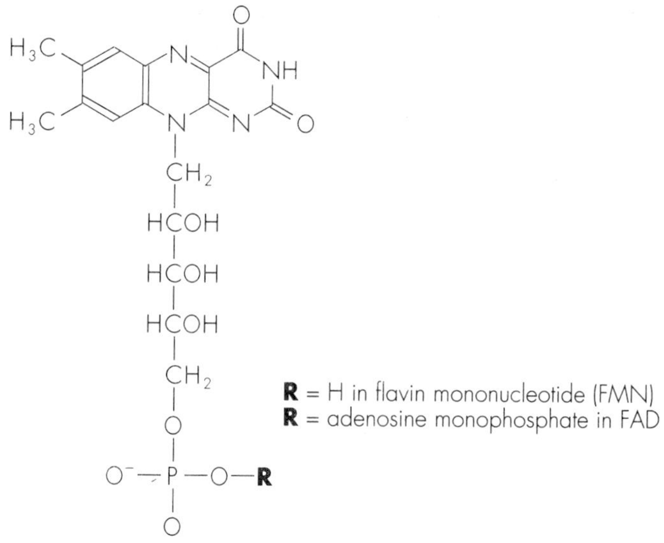

R = H in flavin mononucleotide (FMN)
R = adenosine monophosphate in FAD

11.3 Properties of amines

The importance of amines in biology can clearly be related to their properties. The simplest property is the three-dimensional conformation (geometry) of the bond joining the amino nitrogen. Like alkanes, amines have a tetrahedral (three-sided pyramid) geometry with the nitrogen atom in the centre of the molecule. Three of the corners of the tetrahedron are occupied by atoms, while the fourth is occupied by electrons. The electrons are important in the way in which the amines behave.

Hydrogen bonding

The electrons of the amino nitrogen can form hydrogen bonds with some neighbouring hydrogen atoms such as those of the hydroxyl, amine and thiol (sulphydryl) groups. The hydrogen bonding between the electrons of an amino nitrogen and hydrogen is shown below.

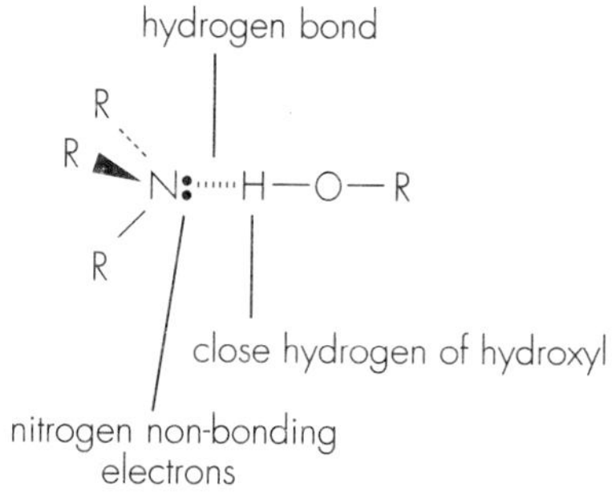

The amine hydrogens can also participate in hydrogen bonding with a variety of functional groups such as carbonyl oxygen, carboxyl oxygen, and amino nitrogen:

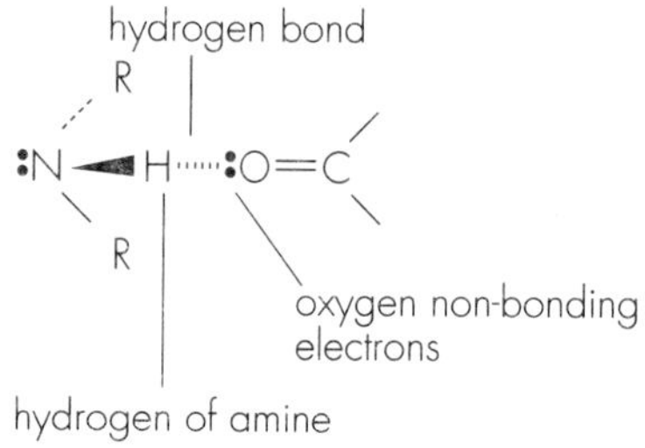

Hydrogen bonding is particularly important in stabilising the folded structures of proteins and nucleic acids, where it is the major type of bond holding these macromolecules in their three-dimensional conformation. The hydrogen bonding in nucleic acids and proteins will be examined later.

Basicity of amines

Ammonia can act as a base by accepting a proton from an acid:

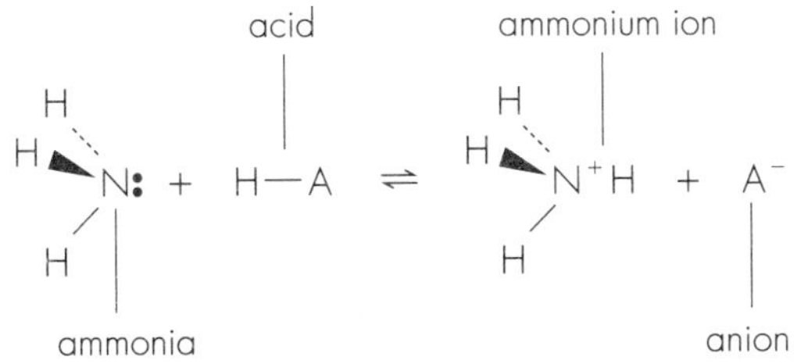

In accepting a proton, the ammonia becomes positively charged and is called an ammonium ion. Amines, such as the side-chain of lysine, can also act as bases:

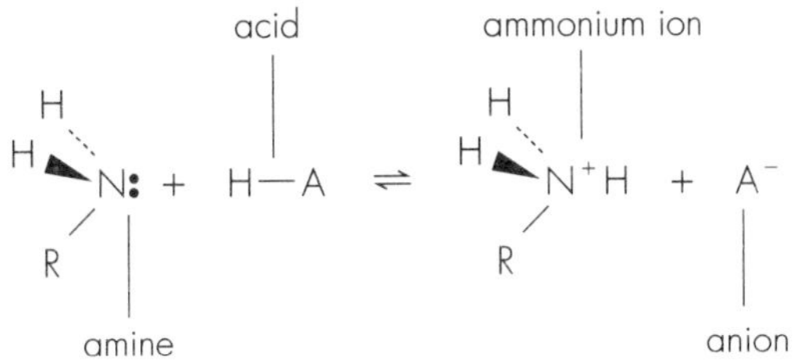

The measure of how good a base an amine is can be related to the pH value in water at which the amine is 50 per cent ionised. We call this pH the pK_a. Ammonia has a pK_a of 9.26 as at this pH value half of the ammonia is in the NH_3 (base) form and half in the NH_4^+ (ion) form. A bigger pK_a value indicates a stronger base. It can tell us whether the base or the ion is the predominant form at the pH of a solution. The relationship between pK_a, pH and form is shown in Table 11.2.

Table 11.2 The relationship between pH, pK_a and molecular species in solution

pH units away from pK_a	Concentration ratio (%)	
	Base (RNH_2)	Ion (RNH_3^+)
≥ -3	100	0
-2	99	1
-1	91	9
0	50	50
$+1$	9	91
$+2$	1	99
$\geq +3$	0	100

Example 11.3

The pK_a of the amino group of glycine (aminoethanoic acid) is 9.9. What is the major form of the amino nitrogen at pH 7.6?

glycine (amino base) $NH_2CH_2COO^-$
glycine (amino ion) $NH_3^+CH_2COO^-$

- Essential information $pK_a = 9.6$; pH = 7.6
- Subtract the pH from the pK_a: $pK_a - pH = 9.6 - 7.6 = +2$
- Look up the value in Table 11.2. A value of +2 tells us that the amino group of glycine is nearly all in the ionic ($NH_3^+CH_2COO^-$) form. The pK_a values of some biologically important amines are shown in Table 11.3.

Question

Q11.9 What is the major form of the following nitrogen-containing bases at pH 7.4 (the normal cell pH):

(i)   arginine side-chain;
(ii)   imidazole;
(iii) cytosine amino group;
(iv) imino acid imine?

11.4 The amide – structure and properties

The structure of an amide is:

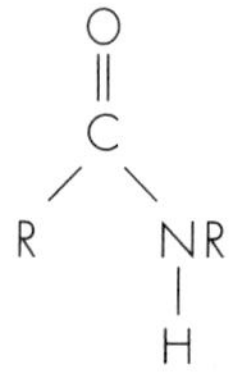

$$\underset{\displaystyle \overset{\displaystyle R}{\diagup} \overset{\displaystyle C}{\underset{\displaystyle \overset{|}{H}}{\diagdown}} \overset{\displaystyle NR}{}}{\overset{\displaystyle O}{\overset{||}{C}}}$$

Amides in biology are the product of the reaction of an amine group (or ammonia) with the carboxyl group of a carboxylic acid. This reaction is not favoured under physiological conditions (pH 7.0, 37 °C), as both the carboxyl and amine groups are in their ionic form. The reaction of an amine and carboxyl to form a salt is the favoured reaction:

$$\underset{\text{amine ion}}{R'NH_3^+} + \underset{\text{carboxyl ion}}{R''COO^-} \rightleftharpoons \underset{\text{salt}}{R'NH_3^+R''COO^-}$$

Table 11.3 The pK_a values of some commonly occurring amino groups in biology

Group	pK_a
Amino acid amino terminal	9.32
Imidazole	6.0
Arginine side-chain	12.48
Lysine side-chain	10.53
Imino nitrogen of proline	10.6
Cytosine amino	4.0
Adenosine amino	3.45
Guanosine amino	1.6

Amides are therefore formed from derivatives of carboxylic acids, the most important being a carboxylic acid ester as in ribosomal polypeptide synthesis:

$$\begin{array}{ccccccc} & O & & & & O & \\ & \parallel & & & & \parallel & \\ \underset{\substack{\text{carboxylic acid}\\\text{ester}}}{RC-OR'} & + & \underset{\text{amine}}{H_2NR''} & \rightleftharpoons & \underset{\substack{\text{peptide}\\\text{(contains amide}\\\text{bond)}}}{RC-NHR''} & + & \underset{\text{alcohol}}{R'OH} \end{array}$$

This reaction is catalysed by peptidyl transferase, an enzyme associated with the 50s ribosomal subunit. This enzyme accelerates the formation of a peptide bond in the growing peptide chain in translation of mRNA by ribosomes (see Chapter 15).

In contrast to amines, amides do not act as bases; they are neutral in aqueous solutions. The amide is neutral because the non-bonding electrons of the nitrogen atom are shared with the carbonyl oxygen. This increases the stability of the amide bond. The flexibility around the amide bond is reduced because of the partial double-bond character of the amide bond (see Chapter 12, page 108). This affects the folding of a polypeptide chain. The amide nitrogen and proton can both participate in hydrogen-bond formation. This is important in stabilising the secondary structures that are formed when polypeptides fold up.

Amides are important in the formation and breakdown of biomolecules containing nitrogen. The amide-containing amino acids asparagine and glutamine are nitrogen-rich compounds acting as the nitrogen store of the cell (see below).

$$\begin{array}{cc} \text{COOH} & \text{COOH} \\ | & | \\ NH_2CHCH_2\mathbf{CONH_2} & NH_2CHCH_2CH_2\mathbf{CONH_2} \\ \text{asparagine} & \text{glutamine} \end{array}$$

(transferable amides are shown in bold)

They can pass on the amide nitrogen to other biomolecules involved in the manufacture of amino acids and nucleotides, yielding the amino acids aspartate and glutamate. The body uses the carbons of amino acids as an energy source, but it is unable to use the nitrogens. The simplest waste product from amino acid breakdown would be ammonia. Ammonia is quite basic, a property that renders it toxic to the workings of the cell. A safe compound needs to be found to store this nitrogen. The body therefore makes the nitrogen-rich but stable compound urea as a waste product (see below). The amide groups of urea are not bases and are not poisonous to the cell.

$$\begin{array}{c} O \\ \parallel \\ C \\ \diagup \quad \diagdown \\ H_2N \qquad NH_2 \\ \text{urea} \end{array}$$

Summary

Amines are important biomolecules in which the hydrogens in ammonia are replaced by one or more organic groups. This results in the formation of primary, secondary or tertiary amines. Simple amines are named by reference to the parent alkane; by having either the terminal -ane replaced by -ylamine or the terminal -e replaced by -amine. Amines may also be named by using the prefix amino-, numbering if necessary. Nitrogen is an important part of biologically significant ring-containing molecules such as pyrrolidines, imidazoles, pyridines, pyrimidines, purines, indoles and flavins. The nitrogen and hydrogens of amines can participate in hydrogen-bond formation. Amines can act as bases by accepting protons. Amides are formed by the reaction of amines with carboxylic acids. The amide bond has limited flexibility because of electron sharing between the carbonyl oxygen and the amide nitrogen. Amides are important in nitrogen metabolism owing to their unreactive nature.

Self-assessment questions

Try these questions to test your knowledge.

Q11.10 Decide whether the following compounds are

(a) primary amine;   (b) secondary amine;   (c) tertiary amine:

(i) $CH_3\overset{\overset{\displaystyle O}{\|}}{C}CH_2NH_2$ (ii) $CH_3\overset{\overset{\displaystyle O}{\|}}{C}CH_2\overset{\overset{\displaystyle CH_2CH_3}{|}}{\underset{\underset{\displaystyle CH_2CH_2CH_3}{|}}{N^+}}H$

(iii) $((CH_3)_3C)_2NH$ (iv) $CH_3\overset{\overset{\displaystyle CH_3}{|}}{C}\underset{\underset{\displaystyle CH_3 \quad CH_3}{}}{CHNH_2}$

Q11.11 Name the following amines:

(a) $CH_3\overset{\overset{\displaystyle O}{\|}}{C}CH_2NH_2$;   (c) $NH_2CH_2CH_2NH_2$;   (e) $NH_2CH_2CH_2COOH$.

(b) $CH_3CH_2CH_2CH_2NH_2$;   (d) $NH_2CH_2CH_2OH$;

Q11.12 Identify the following biologically important ring structures choosing from these names:

(a) pyrrolidine;   (d) pyrimidine;   (f) indole;

(b) imidazole;   (e) purine;   (g) flavin.

(c) pyridine;

(i)   (ii)

(iii)   (iv)

(v)   (vi)

Q11.13 What is the major biological function of the pyridine and flavin ring systems?

Q11.14 Using this method:

atom1   bond   atom2

N .... H

hydrogen bond as a dashed line

draw hydrogen bonds between
(a) a carbonyl oxygen and amide hydrogen (attached to a nitrogen);
(b) hydroxyl hydrogen and amine nitrogen.

Q11.15 Explain why there is a limited amount of flexibility around the amide C—N bond.

Q11.16 The pK_a of p-methoxyaniline (shown below) is 5.34. What is the major form of the ion at pH 7?

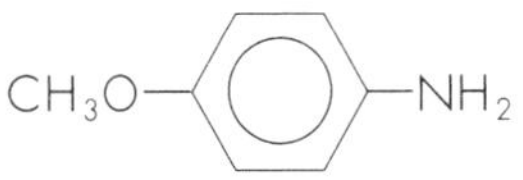

CH_3O—⟨◯⟩—NH_2

p-methoxyaniline

Amino Acids, Peptides and Proteins

Introduction

This chapter concentrates on proteins, from the amino acid building blocks that make up polypeptide chains to the three-dimensional structure of complex proteins. Proteins are among the most important biomolecules and carry out a diverse range of functions from acting as the body's elastic to accelerating many of the complex chemical reactions that form the build up and breakdown of the molecules of life.

Objectives

After completing this chapter you should:
- know the structure of amino acids;
- be able to name the common amino acids;
- understand the peptide bond, structure and conformation;
- know what is meant by the secondary structure of proteins;
- know what is meant by the tertiary structure of proteins;
- know what is meant by the quaternary structure of proteins;
- understand the different functions of proteins, from biological catalyst to biological elastic.

Questions

If these topics are familiar, try answering the questions given below. If your answers are correct, you may move onto the next chapter.

Q12.1 Name two common features of L-amino acids.

Q12.2 Choose from the L-amino acids alanine, valine, histidine, cysteine, glycine, aspartic acid, lysine, serine, the following:
- (a) an amino acid with a hydrophobic side-chain;
- (b) an amino acid with an acidic side-chain;
- (c) an amino acid with a basic side-chain;
- (d) amino acids with abbreviations (i) D, (ii) Val, (iii) A, (iv) Ser.

Q12.3 List two types of secondary structure found in proteins.

Q12.4 Give two differences between the structures named in Q12.3.

Q12.5 Name the bond responsible for stabilising the secondary structure of proteins.

Q12.6 Choose from the amino acids alanine, arginine, aspartate, cysteine, glutamine and phenylalanine, those that can form the four main types of forces stabilising tertiary structure:
- (a) hydrophobic interactions;
- (b) salt links;
- (c) covalent bonds;
- (d) hydrogen bonds.

12.1 Amino acids

Although many proteins are very complex structures that can have molecular weights of 100 000 they are all made out of around 20 different L-amino acid monomers [the prefixes L- and D- are discussed in Section 13.3 (page 120) for sugars but the idea of isomers applies also to amino acids]. The amino acids are joined together by one type of covalent bond. They can combine in a variety of sequences to make an infinite diversity of polymers. α-Amino acids are the monomers joined by peptide bonds to form a chain, called a polypeptide. There are 20 common amino acids found in proteins. The amino acids all have parts of their structure in common. These parts are a central 2-carbon, normally described as an α-carbon, attached to which are a variable side-chain (shown in the structure below as —R), a carboxyl group (—COOH), an amino group (—NH$_2$) and a hydrogen (—H). The side-chain (—R) can be one of four major groups, defined by the structure and consequent property of the side-chain. The common features of L-amino acids can be depicted as:

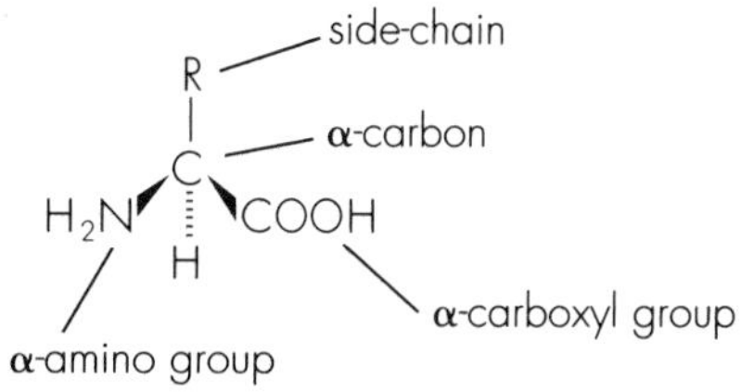

infinitive

Example 12.1

The α-carbon of most L-amino acids has four different functional groups attached. Give:

(a) the name of the acidic group;

(b) the general symbol for the side-chain.

Look at the structure of L-amino acids. The carboxyl group is the acidic group (see Chapter 10) and the side-chain is normally given the symbol —R.

Question

Q12.7 Give the part of the amino acid alanine that can contain a positive charge.

The four major groups are **nonpolar**, **neutral polar**, **acidic** (anionic polar), and **basic** (cationic polar). The commonly occurring amino acids are shown in Table 12.1, page 106. The Table sub-divides the amino acids into the four functional types and gives the two forms of commonly used abbreviation, the three-letter and one-letter code. You will need to learn the group an amino acid is in, as well as both of the abbreviated forms as they are in common use.

Example 12.2

... Cys-Gly-Pro-Ala-Glu-Asp-Val-Arg-Asn ... is a sequence of amino acids in a polypeptide. Answer the following questions based on that sequence:

(a) Give the full name of each amino acid in the sequence shown.

(b) Write out the sequence using the single letter code for amino acids.

(c) Which amino acid has a basic side-chain?

(d) Name a cationic polar amino acid.

Use Table 12.1 to find the information.

(a)

Cys	L-Cysteine	Ala	L-Alanine	Gly	Glycine
Glu	L-Glutamic acid	Pro	L-Proline	Asp	L-Aspartic acid
Val	L-Valine	Arg	L-Arginine	Asn	L-Asparagine

(b) CGPAEDVRN.

Table 12.1 The comman amino acids

Name	Abbreviations		Side-chain structure
	one-letter	three-letter	
(a) Nonpolar			
L-Alanine	A	Ala	$-CH_3$
L-Valine	V	Val	CH_3 $\|$ $-CHCH_3$
L-Leucine	L	Leu	CH_3 $\|$ $-CH_2CHCH_3$
L-Isoleucine	I	Ile	CH_3 $\|$ $-CHCH_2CH_3$
L-Proline	P	Pro	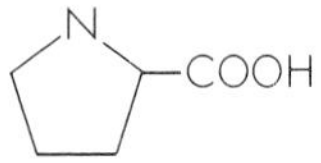
L-Phenylalanine	F	Phe	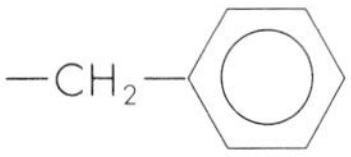
L-Tryptophan	W	Trp	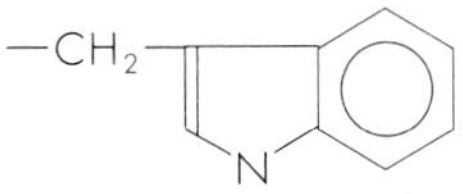
L-Methionine	M	Met	$-CH_2CH_2SCH_3$
(b) Neutral polar			
Glycine	G	Gly	$-H$
L-Serine	S	Ser	$-CH_2OH$
L-Threonine	T	Thr	OH $\|$ $-CHCH_3$
L-Cysteine	C	Cys	$-CH_2SH$
L-Asparagine	N	Asn	$-CH_2CONH_2$
L-Glutamine	Q	Gln	$-CH_2CH_2CONH_2$
L-Tyrosine	Y	Tyr	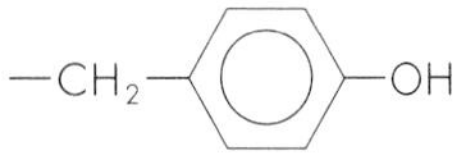
(c) Basic (cationic polar)			
L-Histidine	H	His	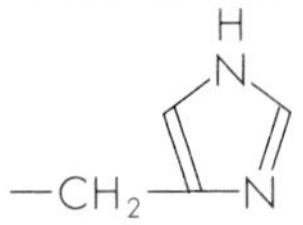
L-Lysine	K	Lys	$-CH_2CH_2CH_2CH_2NH_2$
L-Arginine	R	Arg	$\overset{+}{N}H_2$ $\|\|$ $-CH_2CH_2CH_2NHCNH_2$
(d) Acidic (anionic polar)			
L-Aspartic acid	D	Asp	$-CH_2COOH$
L-Glutamic acid	E	Glu	$-CH_2CH_2COOH$

(c) The basic amino acids are L-histidine, L-lysine and L-arginine. The only one that occurs in the above sequence is L-arginine.

(d) The cationic polar (acidic) amino acids are L-glutamic acid and L-aspartic acid. Both occur in the above sequence.

Question

Q12.8 The following is a sequence of amino acids in a protein written using the single-letter code:' IYPVADDRLC. Based on that sequence:

(a) Which amino acid side-chain is acidic?

(b) Write out the sequence using the three-letter code.

(c) Name the amino acids with hydrophobic side-chains.

12.2 Ionic behaviour of amino acids

Chapters 10 and 11 showed how the carboxyl and amino groups behave at different acidities (pH). The pK_a of the α-amino group is between 9.3 and 10.7, while the pK_a of the α-carboxyl group is between 1.8 and 2.5. This means that at physiological pH (about neutral), the α-amino and α-carboxyl groups are both in their ionised (charged) form. In solution, the amino acid glycine will be mainly in the form $H_3{}^+NCH_2COO^-$. The side-chains of acidic and basic amino acids are ionised (bear a charge) at neutral pH. Glycine contains both a positive and a negative charge. Molecules that contain both charges (whether the net charge is zero or not) are called zwitterions. Amino acids in solution at neutral pH are usually zwitterions.

12.3 The peptide bond

Chapter 11 discussed the formation of the peptide bond as the product of the reaction between an amine and a carboxylic acid ester. The direct formation of the peptide link can be carried out artificially using strong dehydrating agents, which remove water. We call the removal of water as part of a chemical reaction a condensation reaction. The formation of a peptide bond by direct condensation is shown below:

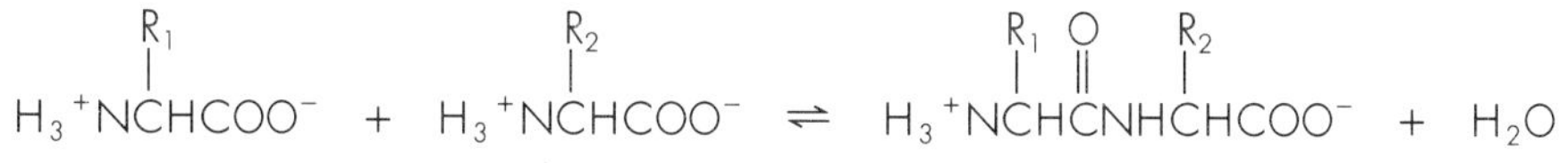

$$\underset{\displaystyle H_3{}^+NCHCOO^-}{\overset{\displaystyle R_1}{|}} \ + \ \underset{\displaystyle H_3{}^+NCHCOO^-}{\overset{\displaystyle R_2}{|}} \ \rightleftharpoons \ \underset{\displaystyle H_3{}^+NCHCNHCHCOO^-}{\overset{\displaystyle R_1 \ \ O \ \ \ R_2}{|\ \ \ ||\ \ \ |}} \ + \ H_2O$$

The product contains two amino acids (side-chains R_1 and R_2) covalently linked together by a peptide bond. Amino acids R_1 and R_2 can form two possible dipeptides, the one shown in the structure above (R_1R_2) and one in which the order of side-chains is reversed (R_2R_1). A **dipeptide** is two amino acids linked together by a peptide bond. More amino acids can be linked together by peptide bonds to form longer peptides and polypeptides. Some of these peptides are named as shown in Table 12.2. The word polypeptide can mean any long peptide chain.

Table 12.2 Naming of peptides according to the number of amino acids in the chain

Number of amino acids in chain	Name of peptide
2	Dipeptide
3	Tripeptide
4	Tetrapeptide
5	Pentapeptide
many	Polypeptide

The formation of a peptide bond means the loss of one carboxyl and one amino group when compared to the corresponding amino acids. Polypeptide chains retain one α-amino and one α-carboxyl but the rest get lost in the formation of the peptide bonds as shown below. We call the amino acid at the end of the polypeptide that retains the α-amino group the **amino terminal** amino acid and the end is the **amino terminus**. The **carboxyl terminus** is at the other end. Numbering of the amino acids in the polypeptide chain always starts with the number 1 at the amino terminus:

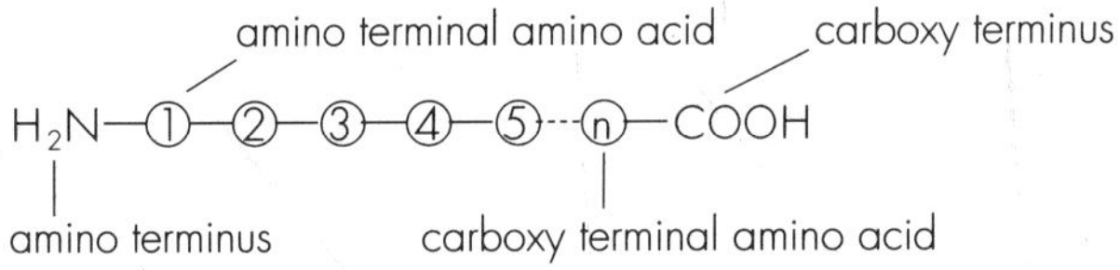

$$H_2N-①-②-③-④-⑤\cdots ⓝ-COOH$$

amino terminal amino acid   carboxy terminus

amino terminus   carboxy terminal amino acid

The numbered circles represent amino acids linked together by peptide bonds.

The role of the α-amino and α-carboxyl groups becomes of minor significance when compared with the side-chains. A knowledge of the properties of the side-chains (although beyond the scope of this book) is essential to understand the function of proteins and polypeptides. The precise order of amino acids is called the amino acid sequence, which is unique to any polypeptide. The sequence of bases in the DNA contained in the genome determines the amino acid sequence. The amino acid sequence determines the function of the polypeptide. We call the amino acid sequence the **primary structure**.

The peptide bond is an example of an amide (discussed in Chapter 11, page 100) and has many of the features of an amide. This includes the **rigid** planar structure of the **amide** bond which results from the partial double bond. The rigid planar structure limits the freedom of movement of a polypeptide chain in water. There is some freedom of movement around some bonds. These are indicated by arrows in the polypeptide structure shown below. This flexibility allows the polypeptide chain to fold up into some stable more compact structures. The flexible and rigid areas of a polypeptide are shown below (the backbone hydrogens have been left out for clarity and 'rigid' areas are surrounded by a box):

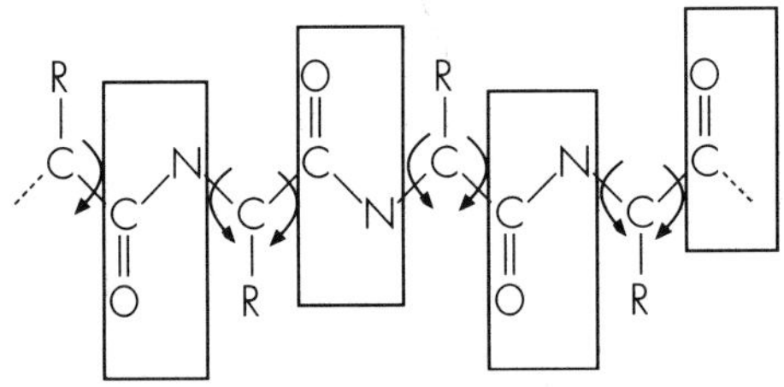

The most common structures found in polypeptides are the extended chain, the α-helix and the β-pleated sheet, although others can exist. Linus Pauling and R.B. Corey first predicted the structure of the α-helix and the β-pleated sheet for which work Pauling was later awarded the Nobel Prize (1954).

Question

Q12.9 The following is a stretch of a polypeptide chain. Copy this onto a piece of paper.

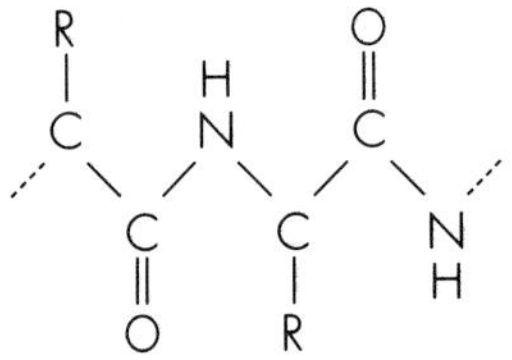

(a) Indicate the part of the structure that is inflexible by placing a box around it (on your piece of paper!).

(b) Show where the molecule can turn to fold into a three-dimensional conformation using curved arrows.

12.4 Polypeptide secondary structure

The α-helix and the β-pleated sheet are examples of the secondary structure of polypeptides.

The α-helix is a right-handed helix (see Figure 12.1) in which hydrogen bonding between the carbonyl oxygen of amino acids 1, 2, 3 etc. and the amide hydrogen of amino acids 4, 5, 6 etc., respectively, stabilises the conformation (see Figure 12.2). Every carbonyl oxygen and amide hydrogen in the helix forms a hydrogen bond. The helix has 3.6 amino acids per turn and 3.6 hydrogen bonds per turn. The hydrogen bonds are aligned in the same direction as the axis of the helix, which gives the helix great stability along its axis. In this structure, the amino acid side-chains point outwards from the helix. Certain amino acids, such as the side-chains of alanine and leucine, stabilise the helix. Glycine destabilises the helix as the small side-chain allows too much flexibility. Neighbouring amino acid side-chains with similar charges will repel each other and destabilise the helical structure. Finally, the rigid structure of proline effectively means that a prolyl residue cannot fit into an α-helix.

Figure 12.1 A right-handed α-helix

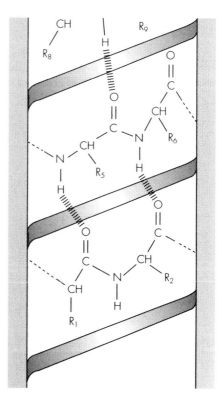

Figure 12.2 Front view of an α-helix showing hydrogen bonds as dashed lines (||||||) between carbonyl oxygens and amide hydrogens

Questions

Q12.10 How many hydrogen bonds are there per turn of an α-helix?

Q12.11 Which amino acid cannot fit into an α-helix?

12.5 The β-pleated sheet

The β-pleated sheet is the other form of stable secondary structure. In this structure, adjacent stretches of polypeptide chain form hydrogen bonds across the stretch. These stretches can be next to each other in the sequence of amino acids or separated by intervening stretches of α-helix etc. Figure 12.2 shows the precise structure of the α-helix. The β-pleated sheet is so called because several strands of a polypeptide chain can form a flat sheet-like structure, while the alignment of chains that allows maximum hydrogen bonding means that the sheet has a pleated effect like a concertina. The direction of the two strands of the polypeptide chain forming the sheet can be the same, in which case the sheet is said to be parallel, or opposite, in which case the sheet is said to be antiparallel. The structures below show both parallel and antiparallel β-pleated sheets (some hydrogen atoms left out for clarity):

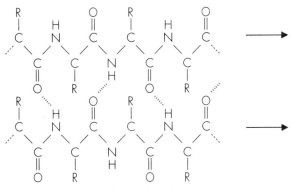

parallel β-pleated sheet

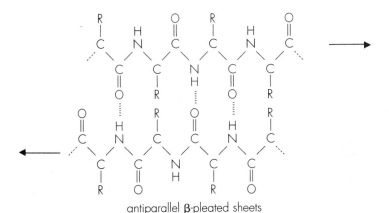

antiparallel β-pleated sheets

Table 12.3 Comparison of the α-helix and the β-pleated sheet

Feature compared	α-helix	β-pleated sheet
Stabilising bonds	Hydrogen bonds	Hydrogen bonds
Direction of hydrogen bonds	Same as direction of axis	At right angles to the direction of axis
Number of strands in structure	One	At least two
Stabilising amino acids	Small hydrophobic	Non-bulky side-chains
Destabilising amino acids	Proline, glycine: adjacent ionised with same charge	Adjacent ionised with same charge

In β-pleated sheets the direction of hydrogen bonding is at right angles to the axis of the amino acid chain, while the side-chains point alternately up and down from the plane of the sheet. The main features of both the α-helix and the β-pleated sheet are summarised in Table 12.3.

Question

Q12.12 Give (a) one similarity and (b) two differences between an α-helix and a β-pleated sheet.

12.6 Tertiary structure

Several of the stretches of amino acids may contain either of the secondary structures we have just discussed, as well as others. A polypeptide may have many helices broken up by extended chains, or pleated sheets. In looking at how the areas of secondary structure relate to each other, a simple method of representing the α-helix and the β-pleated sheet is needed. One of the most common methods is to use a cylinder to show areas of α-helix and flattened ribbons to represent the stretches of β-pleated sheet. You will often see the β-pleated sheet represented by a flattened ribbon with an arrow head that points the ribbon in the amino-to-carboxyl direction. Another method simply represents the entire polypeptide chain as a ribbon. A third method that is becoming popular, shows the α-helix as a folded ribbon and the β-pleated sheet as a flattened ribbon with an arrow head. You will see others in text books. A sample of these methods of showing secondary structure is found in Figures 12.3 and 12.4.

The folding of secondary structure in three dimensions is called the **tertiary structure**. Myoglobin (shown in Figure 12.3 (a)) consists almost entirely of stretches of α-helix broken by areas of extended polypeptide chain.

The major bond that stabilises the secondary structure is hydrogen bonding between amide hydrogens and carbonyl oxygens of the backbone of the polypeptide chain. We will examine the bonds holding tertiary structure together. The bonding that maintains tertiary structure results from interactions between adjacent amino acid side-chains in the folded polypeptide. There are five types of bond that stabilise the tertiary structure. We shall now consider four of them (as the fifth, van der Waals' forces, is beyond the scope of this text).

Covalent bonds

The side-chains of two neighbouring cysteine residues are susceptible to mild oxidation. Cysteine–cysteine oxidation results in the formation of a covalent S–S link between the cysteines, which is known as a cystine bridge. Mild reducing agents such as thiol esters can break the cystine bridge (see Chapter 10, page 88). Cystine bond formation by oxidation of adjacent

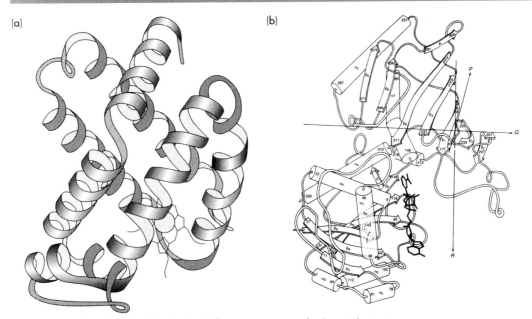

Figure 12.3 Ribbon (a) and ribbon/cylinder (b) representations of polypeptide structure

side-chain residues is shown below. Usually the hydrogen is not lost as H_2 but transferred to another molecule.

$$HC-CH_2SH \ + \ HSCH_2-CH \ \rightleftharpoons \ HCCH_2S-SCH_2CH \ + \ H_2$$

cysteine   cysteine   cystine   hydrogen

Ionic interactions

Ionic attractions between positively (lysine, arginine, histidine) and negatively (aspartate, glutamate) charged amino acid side-chains stabilise tertiary structure. You will find ionic interactions called salt links or salt bridges in textbooks. A representation of a salt bridge is shown below:

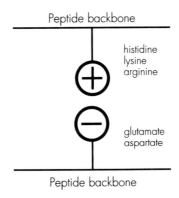

Peptide backbone

histidine
lysine
arginine

glutamate
aspartate

Peptide backbone

Type of structure	Representation		
	Ribbon/cylinder	Tube	Arrowed ribbon/ribbon

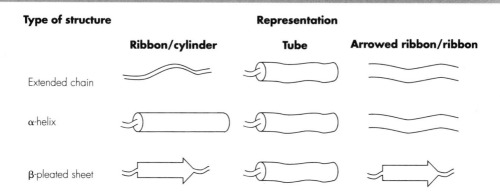

Figure 12.4 Different methods of showing secondary structure in proteins

Hydrogen bonds

Hydrogen bonding stabilises tertiary structure. Several amino acid side-chains are capable of forming hydrogen bonds, including those with hydroxyl, carboxyl and amino groups. This is outlined below:

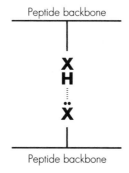

Hydrophobic interactions

Hydrophobic (neutral non-polar) amino acids associate with each other in aqueous solution in order to 'escape' the aqueous medium. In consequence, polypeptide chains often fold so that hydrophobic amino acid side-chains are on the inside (away from water) of the structure, while the surface of the polypeptide often contains polar amino acids. Amino acids involved include tryptophan, phenylalanine, leucine, isoleucine, valine and methionine.

Questions

Q12.13 Which amino acid(s) can participate in covalent bonding in polypeptides?

Q12.14 Name three amino acids that can form ionic bonds with glutamate.

12.7 Quaternary structure

Many proteins consist of more than one polypeptide chain. The way in which the different subunits arrange themselves with respect to each other is called the quaternary structure. Many proteins, such as myoglobin, are one polypeptide chain. In consequence, these proteins do not have quaternary structure. Proteins such as haemoglobin, on the other hand, consist of more than one polypeptide chain. Proteins that contain more than one polypeptide chain are called multisubunit proteins. Each polypeptide in a multisubunit protein may be called a subunit (or monomer if the subunits are identical polypeptides). The forces holding subunits together are the same forces that hold tertiary structure in place. These forces result from interactions between the side-chains of amino acids on different subunits. Haemoglobin has four subunits (two α and two β) and is represented in Figure 12.5.

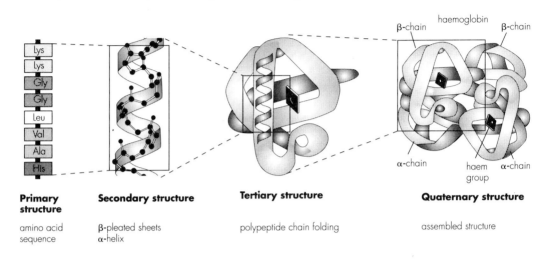

Primary structure	Secondary structure	Tertiary structure	Quaternary structure
amino acid sequence	β-pleated sheets α-helix	polypeptide chain folding	assembled structure

Figure 12.5 The four levels of protein structure

12.8 Functions of proteins

Proteins are so varied in their functions that it is beyond the scope of this book to deal with all of them. With 20 amino acids, even short polypeptides can differ markedly in structure and properties, and so can carry out quite varied functions within a cell. Some proteins, such as elastin and collagen, form long extended threads and have a structural role in the body. Others become enzymes catalysing metabolic processes. Some become molecular transporters such as haemoglobin while others carry messages between cells. The precise function is defined by the sequence of amino acids, which in turn is defined by the sequence of bases that comprise the DNA in the genome.

Summary

Amino acids have structural features in common: these are the α-amino, α-carboxyl and α-carbon. They differ in the composition of the side-chain. Amino acid side-chains can be divided into four groups: acidic, basic, neutral polar, and neutral non-polar. Amino acids are joined together as linear chains in polypeptides and proteins by the peptide bond to form the primary structure. The peptide bond has limited flexibility and can only assume a number of defined shapes. This affects the way the peptide chain can fold. Folding of polypeptides gives two main structures: the α-helix and β-pleated sheet. The force stabilising the secondary structure is almost entirely due to hydrogen bonding. In polypeptides, the secondary structure may be further folded to give the tertiary structure. Tertiary structure is stabilised by ionic bonds, covalent bonds, hydrogen bonds and hydrophobic interactions. Proteins may consist of more than one polypeptide chain; the arrangement of these chains is called the quaternary structure. Proteins have a wide range of functions in the body.

Self-assessment questions

Try these questions to test your understanding of Chapter 12.

Q12.15 This is a sequence of amino acids in a protein written out using the three-letter code:

1 2 3 4 5 6 7 8 9 10 11 12

Thr-Cys-Asp-Tyr-Gly-Ala-Val-Pro-Leu-Lys-Cys-Ser

From this sequence:
(a) Explain the meaning of the numbers 1 and 12.
(b) Write out the sequence using the one-letter code.
(c) Which amino acid(s) will not be part of an α-helix?
(d) Which amino acid side-chains can form covalent bonds with each other?
(e) Give the number of any neutral polar amino acids.
(f) Could this polypeptide fold to allow an ionic bond (salt link) to form? If the answer is yes, between which amino acids will the salt link be formed?

Q12.16 List four types of interaction that stabilise tertiary structure.

Q12.17 What type of interactions can stabilise quaternary structure?

Sugars and Carbohydrates

Introduction

This chapter will cover the structure and cellular function of an important class of biomolecules, the carbohydrates. Sugars and carbohydrates are among the most important biomolecules, with functions as diverse as cell walls, biological energy stores and biological messengers. The structural elements of sugars can be defined, however, by a few simple and logical rules. Complex carbohydrates can be very large polymeric structures, but the bonds holding them together are of only one or two types.

The word carbohydrate implies that the structures are 'hydrates' (water) of carbon, and will have a general formula $(CH_2O)_n$ where n is greater than two.

Objectives

After completing this chapter you should be able to:
- name simple carbohydrates with differing carbon backbones;
- comprehend the principles of isomerism of simple carbohydrates;
- recall that common sugars can form ring structures;
- identify the isomers that result from ring formation;
- represent ring sugars pictorially;
- understand the formation of the glycosidic bond and polymerisation of sugar monomers;
- appreciate the structural and functional features of different sugar polymers.

Questions

If you are familiar with the subjects covered, try answering the questions below. If your answers are correct, you could move onto the next chapter.

Q13.1 Here is a list of types of sugars: aldotetrose, ketotetrose, aldopentose, ketopentose, aldohexose, ketohexose, aldoheptose and ketoheptose. Look at molecules (i) to (v) below:

(i) (ii) (iii) (iv) (v)

(a) Choose the name from the list that best represents the type of sugar shown.
(b) Decide for each sugar if it is the L- or D-isomer.

Q13.2 Four 2-ketopentoses are shown below:

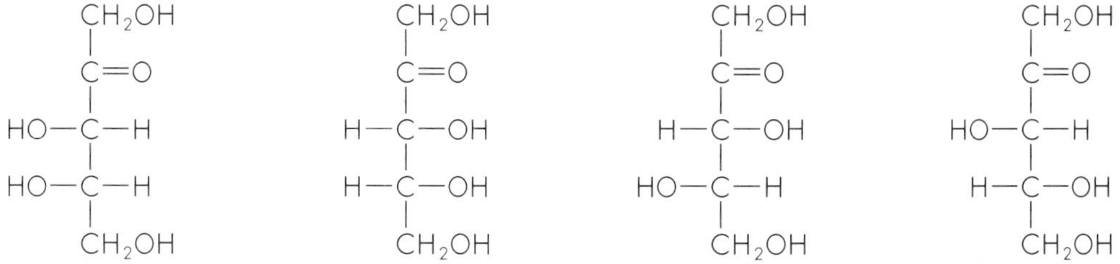

| (i) | (ii) | (iii) | (iv) |

(a) Choose the two L-isomers.
(b) Which sugar is the enantiomer of sugar (iii)?
(c) Give a diastereoisomer of sugar (iii).

Q13.3 Below is a Fischer projection of D-glucose in the straight-chain form.

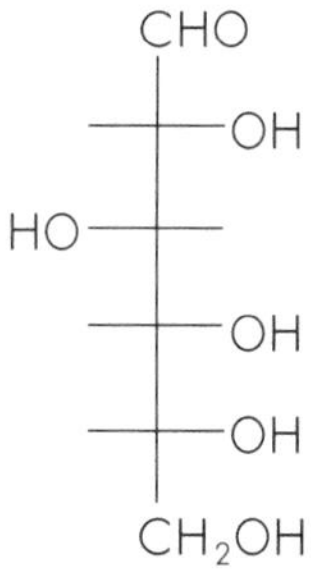

(a) Number the carbons 1 to 6; draw the structure of the α-D-glucopyranose in (b) Fischer and (c) Haworth projections that result from this method for numbering the carbons.

Q13.4 Explain what is meant by a homopolysaccharide.

Q13.5 α-D-Glucopyranose is shown below:

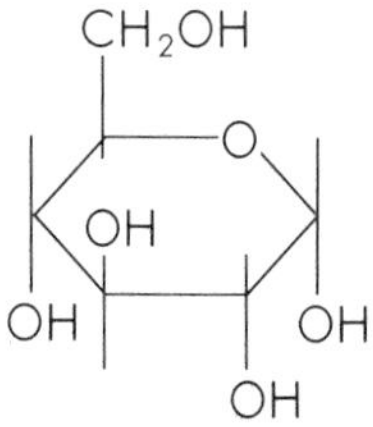

Construct an α(1 → 6) disaccharide of α-D-glucopyranose.

Q13.6 What feature does an β(1 → 4) link give polysaccharides of glucose that makes them good in a structural role?

13.1 Naming simple carbohydrates

Most simple sugars conform to the formula $(CH_2O)_n$ but can differ in the number of carbons in the sugar. The names given to the types of sugar are detailed in Table 13.1, overleaf.

Table 13.1 Naming sugars by length of carbon chain

Number of carbons	Name
3	Triose
4	Tetrose
5	Pentose
6	Hexose
7	Heptose

The simplest carbohydrates, glyceraldehyde and dihydroxyacetone, shown below, contain only three carbon atoms. The two sugars contain different functional groups. These are the aldehyde group (RCHO) and the 'keto' group (R_2CO). Both contain the carbonyl (C=O) group (see Chapter 9, page 73).

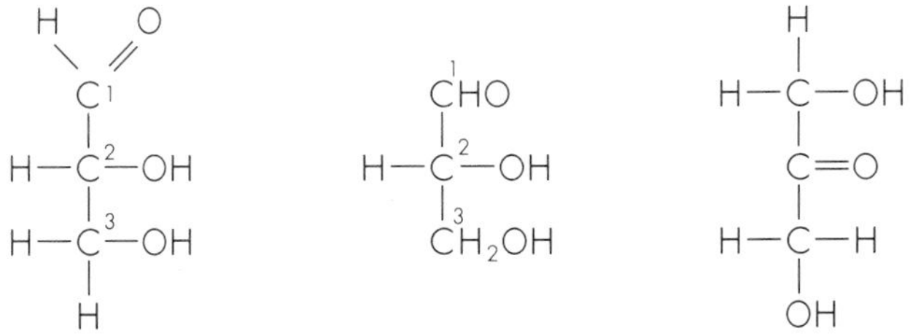

D-glyceraldehyde		dihydroxyacetone
full structure	*abbreviated structure*	*full structure*

The functional groups give rise to two families of sugars. Keto sugars, also known as ketoses, contain a keto group and aldo sugars, which can be called aldoses, contain an aldehyde group in their structure. A five-carbon sugar containing an aldehyde group can be called an aldo-pentose.

Example 13.1
Look at the sugars below and classify them into one of the following types: aldotriose, ketotriose, aldotetrose, ketotetrose, aldopentose, ketopentose, aldohexose, ketohexose, aldo-heptose, ketoheptose.

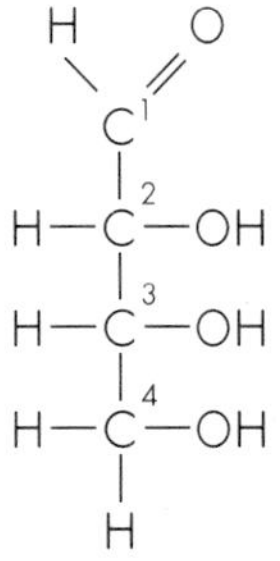

(i) 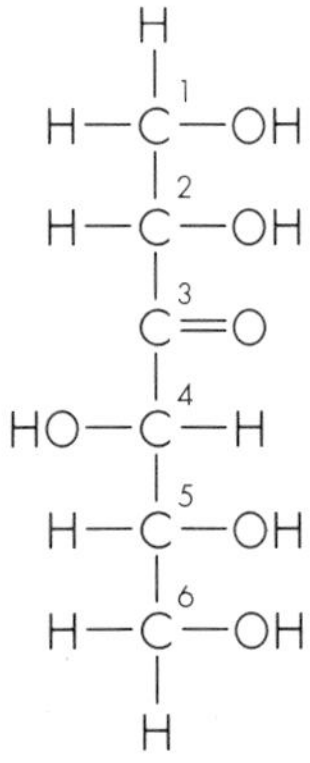   (ii)

Look at structures (i) and (ii). Decide where the carbonyl group (C=O) is. The carbonyl group is shown in bold below. The carbonyl in sugar (i) is at the end of the carbon chain. This makes structure (i) an aldo sugar. The carbonyl sugar in (ii) is not at the end of the carbon chain. This makes structure (ii) a keto sugar.

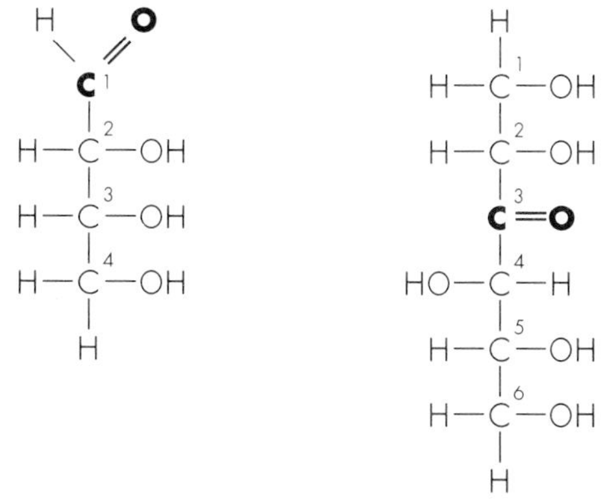

(i)　　　　　(ii)

Count the number of carbons in the chain. Sugar (i) has four carbons in the chain (see above). Table 13.1 gives this as a tetrose. Sugar (ii) has six carbons in the chain. Table 13.1 shows that this is a hexose. Therefore sugar (i) is an aldotetrose and sugar (ii) is a ketohexose.

Question

Q13.7 Using 'aldo' and 'keto' as well as triose, tetrose, pentose, hexose and heptose, classify the following sugars:

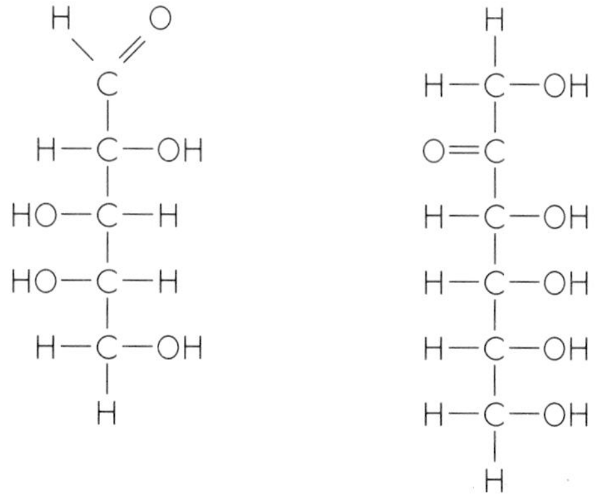

(i)　　　　　(ii)

13.2 Isomerism in sugars

Glyceraldehyde's structure is shown opposite. Let us examine the groups attached to the central 2-carbon more closely. To the left is —H, the right —OH, up is —CHO, and down is —CH$_2$OH. The 2-carbon has four different groups attached. The left and right groups can be changed over to give left —OH and right —H; the resulting molecule is still glyceraldehyde! The two different forms of glyceraldehyde (—OH to the left or —OH to the right) are non-superimposable mirror images. This can be seen more clearly next:

$$\begin{array}{c} CHO \\ | \\ C \\ H \diagup \vdots \diagdown OH \\ CH_2OH \end{array}$$

D-glyceraldehyde

$$\begin{array}{c} CHO \\ | \\ C \\ HO \diagup \vdots \diagdown H \\ CH_2OH \end{array}$$

L-glyceraldehyde

The 2-carbon can be called an asymmetric centre as its presence means that the same molecule can exist in two forms. Any carbon with four different groups attached must be an asymmetric centre. Glyceraldehyde has only one asymmetric centre. Look at the 1-carbon and 3-carbon of glyceraldehyde; they are not asymmetric centres. Dihydroxyacetone has no asymmetric centre.

The method of naming the two different forms of glyceraldehyde depends upon the relative position of the —OH group when the —CHO group is at the top of the molecule and the —CH$_2$OH is at the bottom. With the —OH to the left we call the molecule L-glyceraldehyde; to the right D-glyceraldehyde. Thus the glyceraldehyde structure shown on page 118 should more properly be called D-glyceraldehyde. Both D-glyceraldehyde and L-glyceraldehyde are shown above. The prefixes 'D-' and 'L-' refer to the absolute configuration of the glyceraldehyde molecule. L- and D-glyceraldehyde are examples of molecules called isomers. Isomers are molecules with identical molecular formulae but different structures. The L- and D-isomers of otherwise identical sugars are called **enantiomers**. L-Glyceraldehyde is the enantiomer of D-glyceraldehyde. The R- and S-method of notation is replacing D- and L- respectively, although many biology texts still use D- and L- to prefix stereoisomers.

For the aldotrioses there is only one carbon (C^2) which has four different groups attached. The aldotetroses have two carbons (C^2) and (C^3) with four different groups attached. There are two places where aldotetrose can make isomers, and therefore four isomers of an aldotetrose:

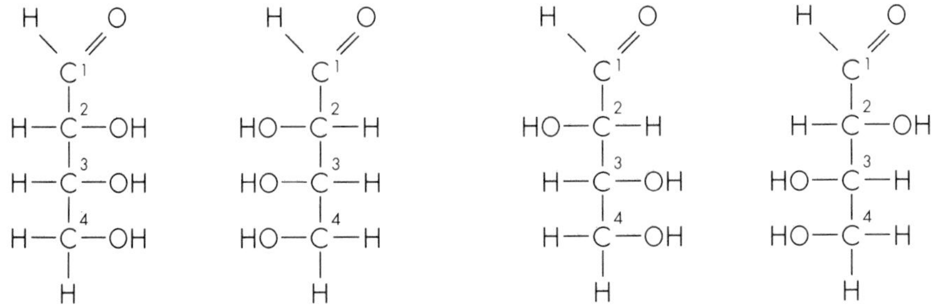

$$\begin{array}{c} H \diagdown \quad O \\ C^1 \\ | \\ H-C^2-OH \\ | \\ H-C^3-OH \\ | \\ H-C^4-OH \\ | \\ H \end{array}$$

D-erythrose

$$\begin{array}{c} H \diagdown \quad O \\ C^1 \\ | \\ HO-C^2-H \\ | \\ HO-C^3-H \\ | \\ HO-C^4-H \\ | \\ H \end{array}$$

L-erythrose

$$\begin{array}{c} H \diagdown \quad O \\ C^1 \\ | \\ HO-C^2-H \\ | \\ H-C^3-OH \\ | \\ H-C^4-OH \\ | \\ H \end{array}$$

D-threose

$$\begin{array}{c} H \diagdown \quad O \\ C^1 \\ | \\ H-C^2-OH \\ | \\ HO-C^3-H \\ | \\ HO-C^4-H \\ | \\ H \end{array}$$

L-threose

Another rule on the naming of L- and D-sugars becomes apparent when considering the position of the hydroxyl group attached to carbon-3 of the aldotetroses. This is the carbon that defines whether or not the aldotetrose is a D- or L-form. It is the furthest asymmetric carbon from the aldehyde group. There are two pairs of enantiomers in aldotetroses. There are also two pairs of isomers of aldotetroses that are not enantiomers. These are called **diastereoisomers**. In the case of aldotetroses, D-erythrose is a diastereoisomer of D-threose and L-threose (but not of L-erythrose). In addition, sugars that are not enantiomers but which only differ at one asymmetric centre are called **epimers**. D-Erythrose is an epimer of D-threose, but not of L-threose. Most important sugars in biology are D-sugars. Most important amino acids are L-amino acids (see page 105) although the occurrence of L-sugars is more common than the occurrence of D-amino acids.

Example 13.2

Below are four aldopentose sugars:

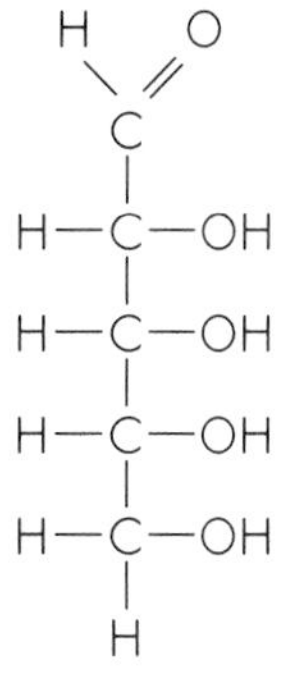

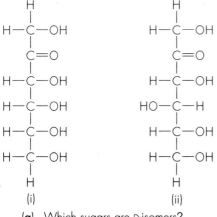

(i) 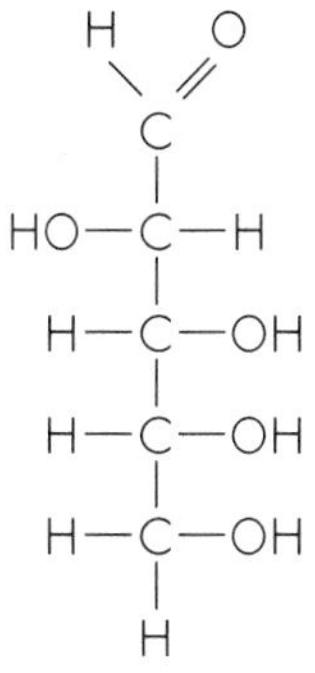 (ii) 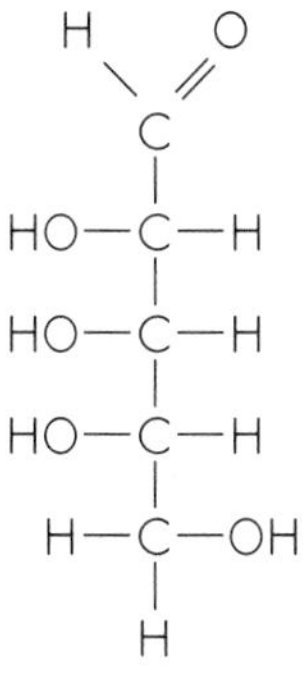 (iii) 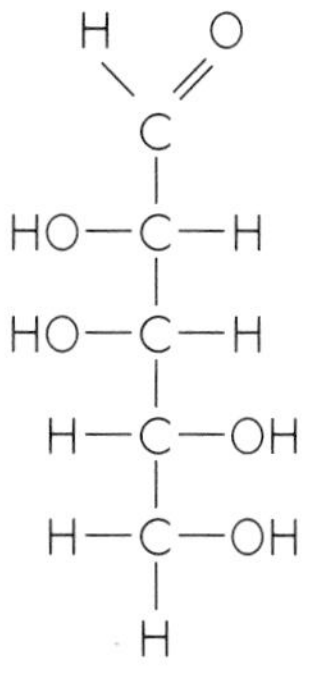 (iv)

(a) Which sugars are D-isomers?
(b) Which sugar is an enantiomer of (i)?
(c) Which sugar(s) is an epimer of (i)?
(d) Which sugar(s) is a diastereoisomer (i)?

(a) (i) First, identify the aldehyde group (—CHO).
 (ii) The four sugars shown above have their aldehydes at the top.
 (iii) Go to the other end of the sugar and count back one carbon. This carbon defines whether the sugar is an L- or D-isomer.
 (iv) Sugars (i), (ii) and (iv) have the hydroxyl group to the right and so are D-isomers.
(b) (i) Enantiomer is another name for mirror image.
 (ii) Sugar (i) has —OH groups on three asymmetric carbons (the middle ones) on the right.
 (iii) Sugar (iii) has the —OH groups on the three asymmetric carbons to the left and is therefore an enantiomer of sugar (i).
(c) (i) Epimers differ in only one asymmetric centre.
 (ii) Only sugar (ii) is an epimer of sugar (i).
(d) (i) Diastereoisomers are isomers that are not enantiomers.
 (ii) Sugar (iii) is an enantiomer of sugar (i). Sugars (ii) and (iv) are diastereoisomers.

Question

Q13.8 Below are four ketohexoses (i)–(iv):

(i) (ii) 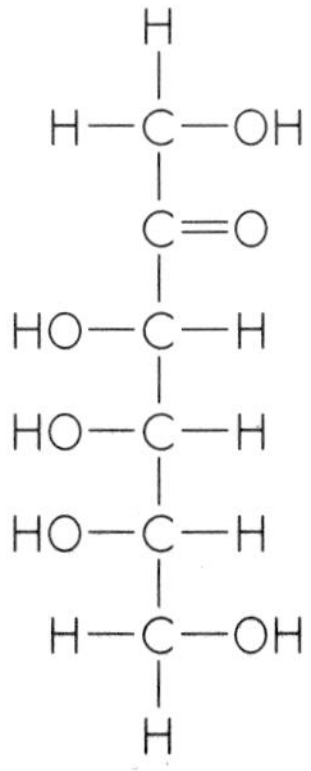 (iii) 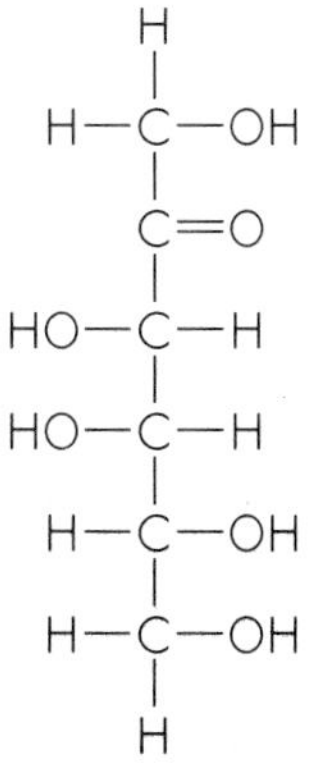 (iv)

(a) Which sugars are D-isomers?
(b) Which sugars are enantiomers?
(c) Which sugar is an epimer of sugar (i)?
(d) Which sugar is a diastereoisomer of sugar (i)?

13.3 Numbering the carbons in sugars

The carbons in aldoses and ketoses are numbered (if the number of the carbon is necessary) in the same way that aldehydes and ketones are numbered. Numbering aldoses is simple. The carbon that has the aldehyde bond is carbon 1 and the carbons are numbered in descending order. In ketoses, the end of the carbon chain nearest the carbonyl group is given the number 1. Sugars often form cyclic structures and the numbering of carbons in the straight-chain form is retained when the sugar forms a ring.

13.4 Formation of ring sugars

The reaction of aldehydes or ketones with hydroxyl groups was discussed in Chapter 9. You may wish to refresh your memory by re-reading Chapter 9. Hydroxyls react with aldehydes and ketones to form hemiacetals and hemiketals respectively.

Aldopentoses and aldohexoses contain both hydroxyl and aldehyde groups. These freely react in solution to form hemiacetals (see below). The hydroxyl forms the hemiacetal link (shown in bold below) and the aldehyde is reduced to a hydroxyl group (shown in bold italics below). Some hydrogens have been left out of the cyclic structure:

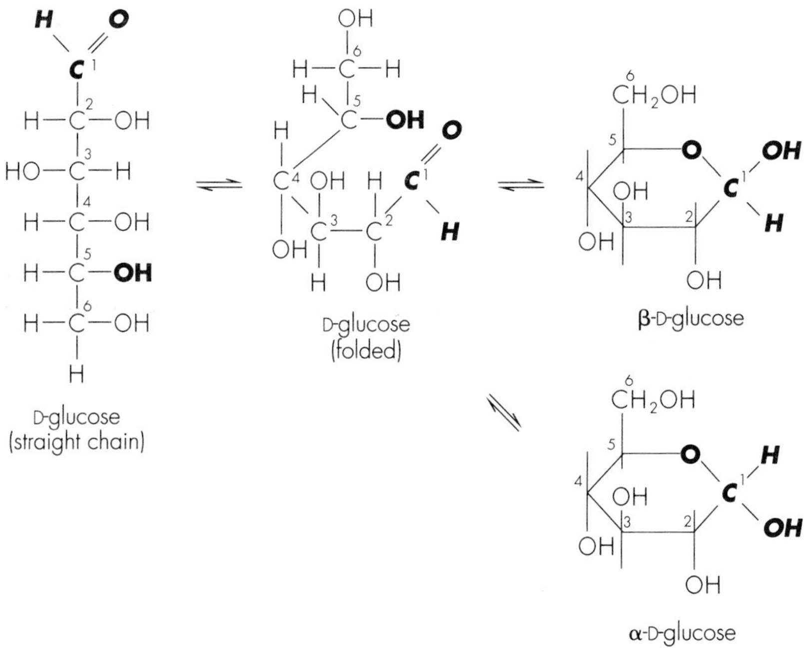

The aldehyde is not an asymmetric centre in the straight-chain form of glucose, but on formation of cyclic glucose the reduced aldehyde (hydroxyl) can be caught in either an up (β) or down (α) position, making a new asymmetric carbon. The α and β forms are called **anomers**. A six-membered ring containing an oxygen is most commonly formed; this is called a **pyran** ring. The resulting structure is D-glucopyranose, either α or β depending on the orientation of the hydroxyl group at carbon-1. The aldehyde can also react with the hydroxyl at position 4 to form a five-membered ring with one oxygen – a furan ring. The resulting sugars are α- or β-D-glucofuranose. The six-membered ring is much more stable and in solution over 90 per cent of the glucose is found as a pyranose and 64 per cent of the pyranose is in the β-form.

Keto sugars such as D-fructose also cyclise and will normally form **furan** rings. The cyclisation of D-fructose is shown below. Again the hydroxyl resulting from ketone reduction can be held in α and β anomers. The resulting sugars are α- or β-D-fructofuranose.

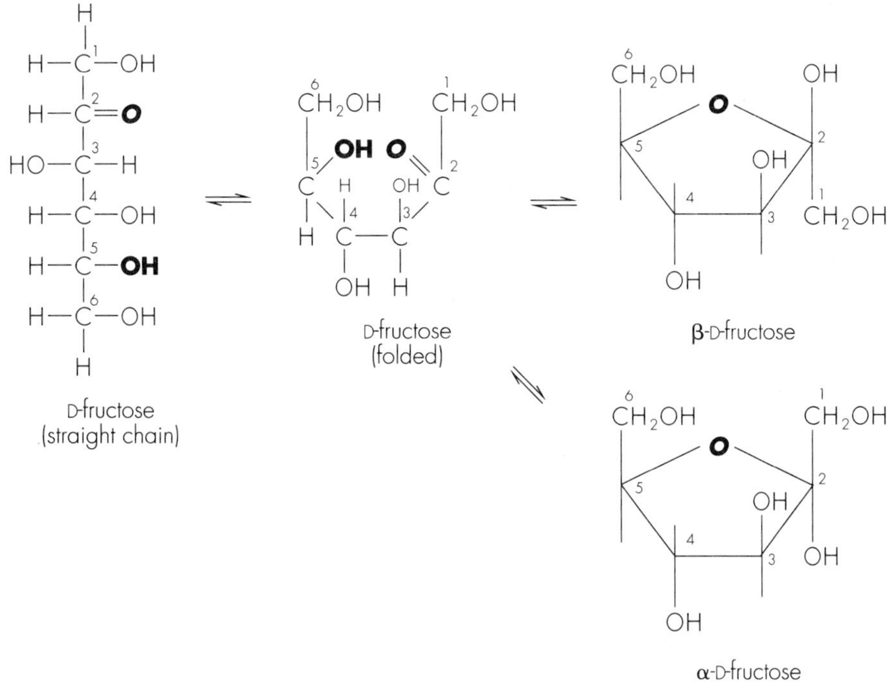

D-fructose
(straight chain)

D-fructose
(folded)

β-D-fructose

α-D-fructose

Five-membered sugars such as D-ribose also tend to form furan rings, and the structure of β-D-ribofuranose shown below can be compared with β-D-fructofuranose shown above. Ribose is an important sugar as it is a constituent of RNA as well as ribonucleotides. The related sugar β-D-deoxyribofuranose is one of the major parts of deoxyribonucleotides, one of the building blocks of DNA. The pentoses β-D-ribofuranose and β-D-2-deoxyribofuranose are shown below:

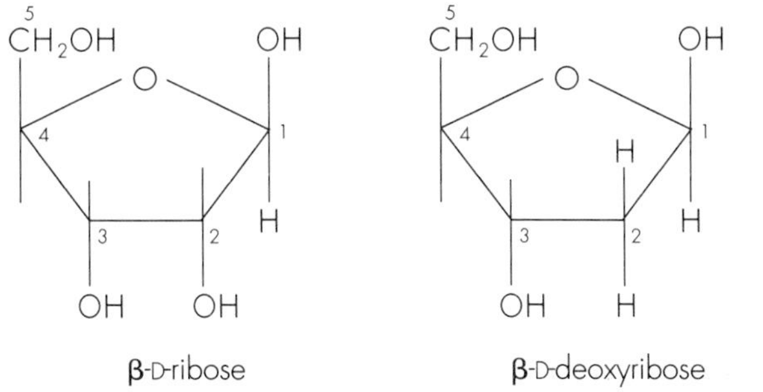

β-D-ribose

β-D-deoxyribose

13.5 Drawing sugars

The chapter, so far, has concentrated on drawing sugars showing all bonds and atoms as lines in two dimensions. Carbon atoms are not arranged like this, but each carbon in a sugar is tetrahedral with respect to neighbouring carbons. Thus D-glyceraldehyde shown overleaf in structure (a) can be more correctly shown as structure (b). The two-dimensional figure is called a Fischer projection. The horizontal lines can be seen as pointing upward, the vertical lines as pointing downward. Fischer projections are written in straight-chain form with the aldehyde or ketone nearest the top. The aldehyde and hydroxyls are often abbreviated as shown in structures (c) and (d). The whole structure can be further abbreviated by removing hydrogens (structure (e)).

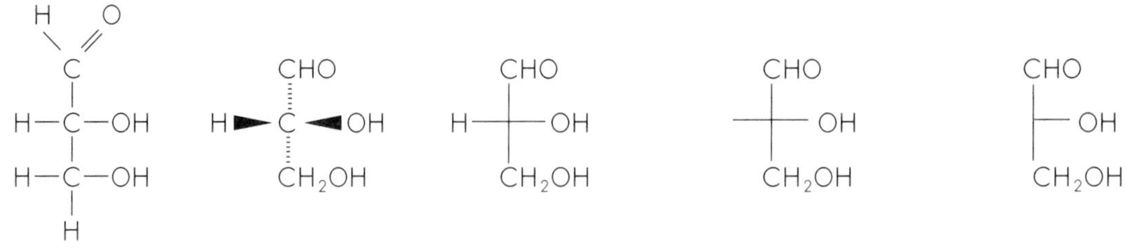

(a) (b) (c) (d) (e)

◀ = bond coming out of paper at 30°, ⋯⋯ = bond going below paper at 30°

The straight-chain structure of D-glucose is shown below in (a) and the abbreviated form in structure (b). Further abbreviation is shown in structure (c). Formation of α-D-glucopyranose is shown in structure (d) as a Fischer projection. The structures (a), (b), (c) and (d) do not show the position of hydroxyl groups relative to the ring clearly and so a Haworth projection (structure (e)) is often preferred in order to represent cyclic sugars. The hydroxyls and hydrogens in the Haworth projection do not point straight up and down but stick out (up and down) from the centre of the ring. The Haworth projection represents the pyranose ring as a flat structure. In fact, the ring is a folded structure.

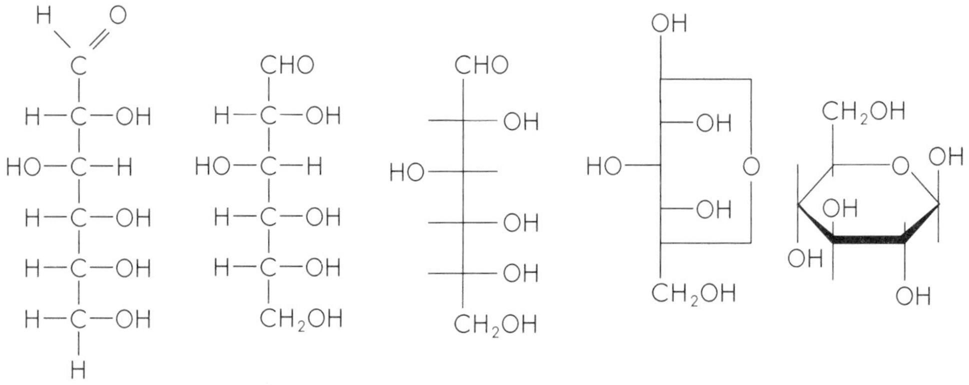

(a) (b) (c) (d) (e)

Note that hydroxyls to the right in Fischer projections appear below the ring in the Haworth projection.

A more correct structure for α-D-glucopyranose with bond angles and ring folding is shown in the chair conformation:

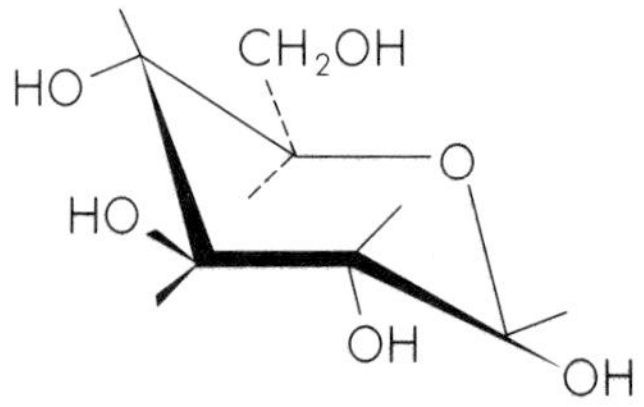

Example 13.3

A Fischer projection of D-mannose in straight-chain format is shown below:

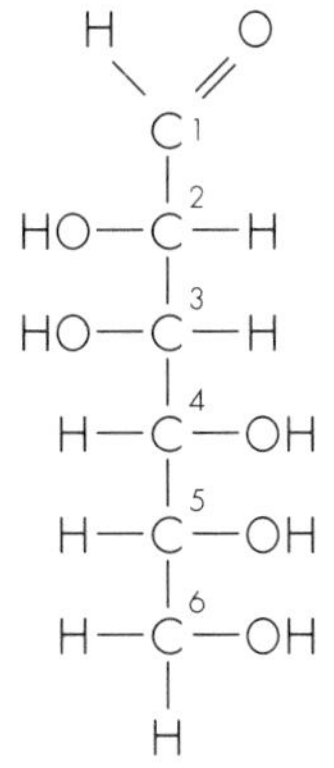

H
O
C1
2
HO—C—H
3
HO—C—H
4
H—C—OH
5
H—C—OH
6
H—C—OH
H

(a) Write out the structure in abbreviated straight-chain conformation.
(b) Which groups will react in the formation of D-mannopyranose?
(c) Draw a Fischer projection of β-D-mannopyranose.
(d) Represent β-D-mannopyranose in a Haworth projection.

(a) The abbreviated format represents carbons as crosses and hydrogens as lines, and reduces the ends to —CHO and —CH_2OH:

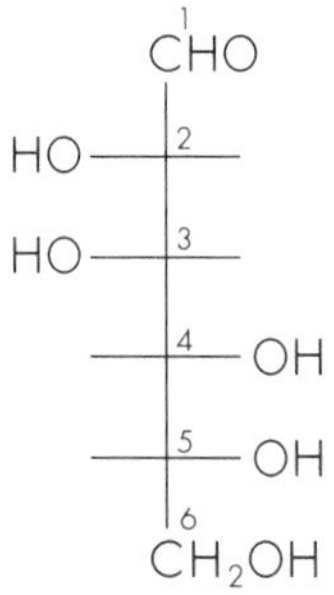

1
CHO
HO
2
HO
3
4
OH
5
OH
6
CH2OH

(b) Mannopyranose contains a pyran ring which is six membered with an oxygen. The reaction is between an aldehyde and a hydroxyl. The aldehyde at carbon-1 will make a pyran ring when it reacts with the hydroxyl at carbon-5.

(c) Fischer projection of β-D-mannopyranose. The hydroxyl on the β-form is on the left (up) in a Fischer projection.

HO
1
HO
2
HO
3
O
4
OH
5
6
CH2OH

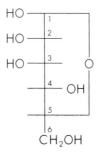

(d) Haworth projection of β-D-mannopyranose. The β-anomer has the hydroxyl pointing up (a useful aide memoire is up-beat to remind you that beta is up).

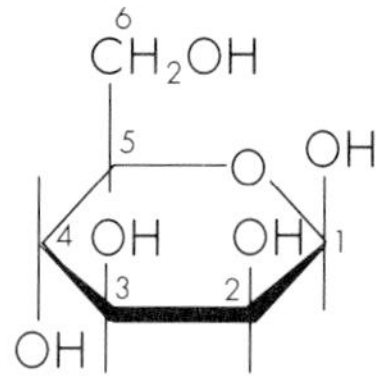

Question

Q13.9 Below is a straight-chain representation of D-galactose.

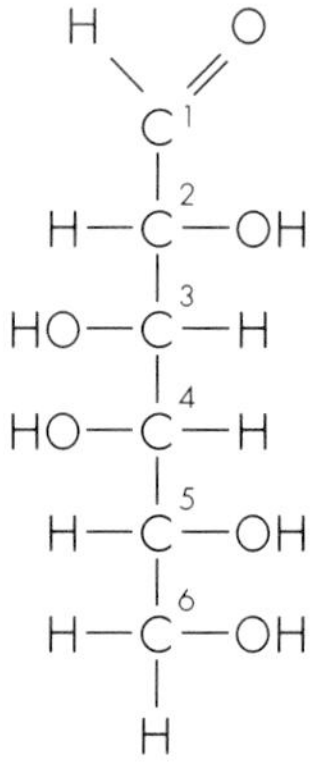

(a) Draw the structure in abbreviated form.
(b) Which groups on which carbons will react to form a furan (five-membered ring, one oxygen)?
(c) Draw α-D-galactofuranose in Haworth projection.

The hydroxyl groups of sugars are chemically reactive. Some important reactions of sugar hydroxyls give rise to covalently modified sugars. These compounds have differing roles in living cells. The formation and use of many of these sugar derivatives are beyond the scope of this chapter, although some indication of biological function is given in Table 13.2 (opposite). The sugar derivatives are found in structures as diverse as chitin (the insect exoskeleton), bacterial cell walls, vitamins and intermediates in the cell's metabolism.

13.6 Polymers of simple sugars

The sugars that we have looked at so far can be used as the building blocks of complex structures in the same way that amino acids form the building blocks of proteins (see Chapter 12). Sugars that are joined together are often referred to by the number of sugar monomers in the chain. The polymer sugar is given the suffix -saccharide. The part at the beginning has a similar prefix to the ones used for proteins. Table 13.3 (page 128) shows this naming procedure.

Table 13.2 Some biologically important sugar derivatives

Type of derivative	Examples of biologically important sugars	Structure	Function
(a) Sugar acids			
—OH → COOH	D-Gluconic acid	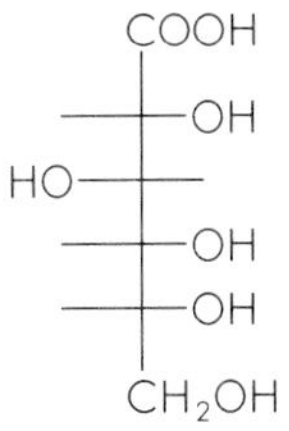 COOH —OH HO— —OH —OH CH_2OH	Carbohydrate metabolism
	D-Glucuronic acid	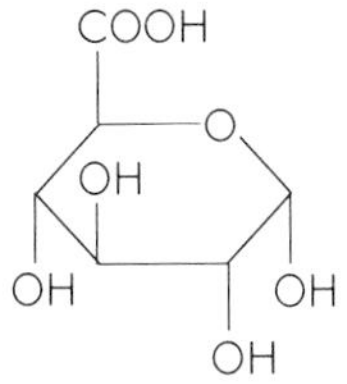 COOH, O, OH, OH, OH, OH	Part of many polysaccharides
	L-Ascorbic acid	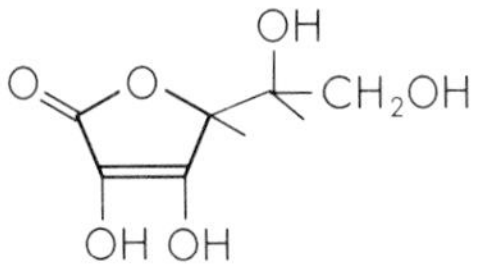 OH, O, O, CH_2OH, OH OH	Vitamin C
(b) Sugar alcohols			
—CHO → CH_2OH C=O → HC—OH	Glycerol Inositol	Structures not shown	Lipid building block; cellular messenger
(c) Sugar phosphates			
—OH → —O—PO_3^{2-}	α-D-Glucose-6-phosphate	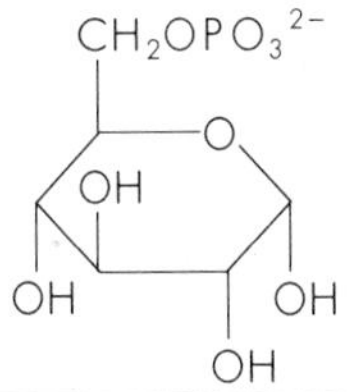 $CH_2OPO_3^{2-}$, O, OH, OH, OH, OH	Glycolysis
(d) Amino sugars			
—OH → —NH_2	α-D-Glucose-2-amine	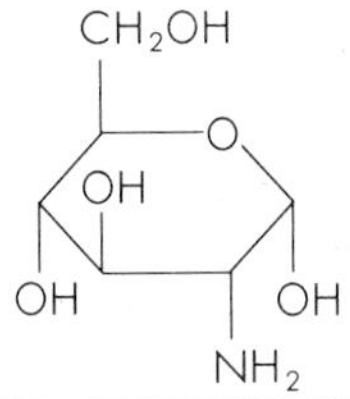 CH_2OH, O, OH, OH, OH, NH_2	Polysaccharides in plant, animal and bacterial cell walls and exoskeletons
(e) Amino sugar derivative			
—NH_2 → —$NHOCCH_3$	α-N-Acetyl-L-glucose-2-amine	Structure not shown	Bacterial cell wall
(f) Complex derivative			
	N-Acetylmuramic acid N-Acetylneuraminic acid	Structures not shown	Complex carbohydrates

Table 13.3 Naming of saccharides according to chain length and comparison with the naming of peptides

Number in chain	Name of saccharide	Name of peptide
2	Disaccharide	Dipeptide
3	Trisaccharide	Tripeptide
4	Tetrasaccharide	Tetrapeptide
5	Pentasaccharide	Pentapeptide
many	Polysaccharide	Polypeptide

Two simple sugars can join together to make a disaccharide. The most common disaccharide is sucrose or table sugar. The formation of sucrose requires a β-D-fructofuranose and an α-D-glucopyranose sugar. The carbon-2 of the fructose is covalently linked by an oxygen bridge to the carbon-1 of the glucose. The linkage is called a **glycosidic bond**. The reaction joins two hydroxyls by removing water and is another example of a condensation reaction:

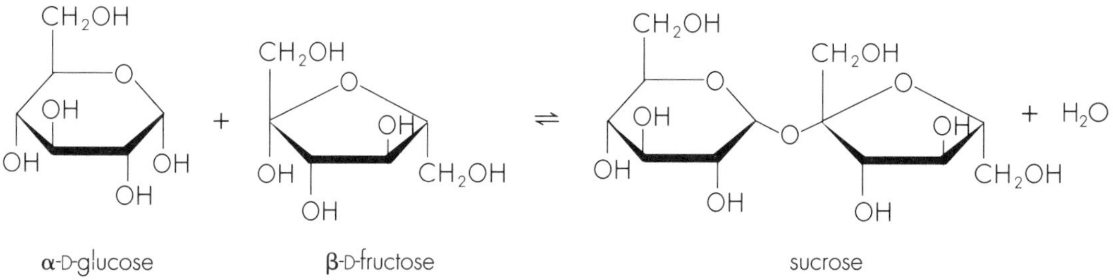

α-D-glucose   β-D-fructose   sucrose

The linkage goes from the carbon-1 of glucose to carbon-2 of fructose. The proper name of the disaccharide is O-α-D-glucopyranosyl-(1 → 2)-β-D-fructofuranoside. The linkage is more often referred to as an α(1 → 2) linkage. This is because the linkage is (1 → 2) and the carbon-1 is the α-anomer of glucose. Two other common linkages are shown below for the α(1 → 4) and β(1 → 4) disaccharides maltose and cellobiose.

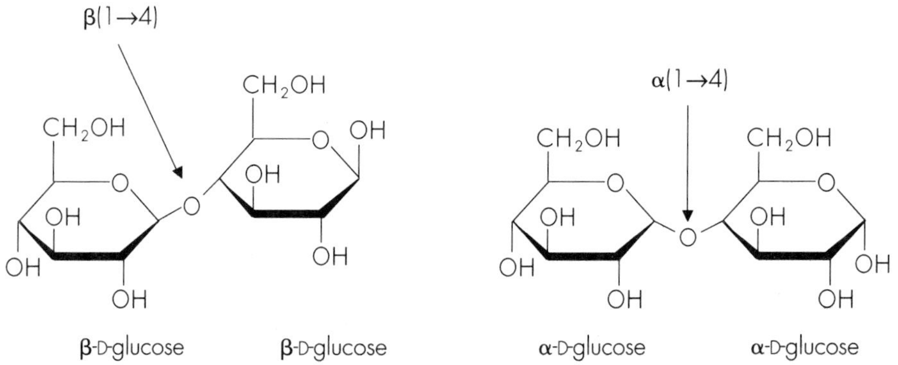

β-D-glucose   β-D-glucose   α-D-glucose   α-D-glucose

The α and β differences may seem trivial, but humans cannot digest cellobiose as they have no enzyme capable of breaking a β(1 → 4) link. Humans do have an enzyme called maltase, however, which cleaves α(1 → 4) disaccharides. This is one of the reasons why humans cannot digest cellulose (as cellobiose comes from cellulose breakdown).

Example 13.4

β-D-Glucose is shown below in Haworth projection. Draw a disaccharide containing a β(1 → 6) linkage.

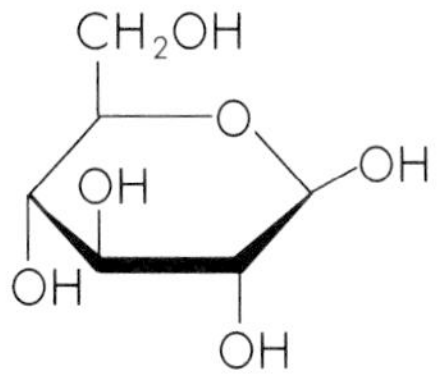

CH$_2$OH

OH

OH

OH

OH

β-D-glucose

First, put two β-D-glucose molecules side by side:

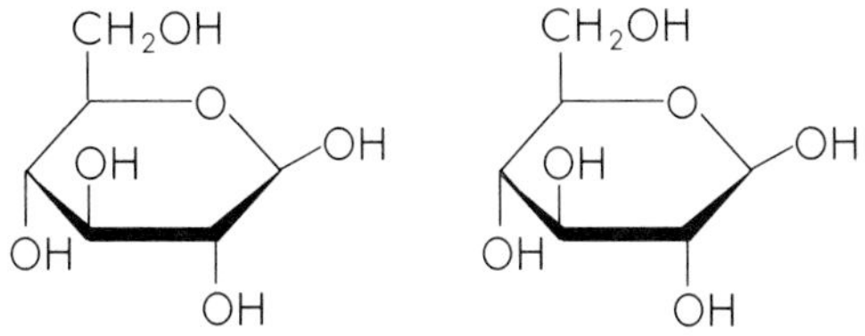

CH$_2$OH

OH

OH

OH

OH

β-D-glucose

CH$_2$OH

OH

OH

OH

OH

β-D-glucose

Number the carbons on them 1 to 6:

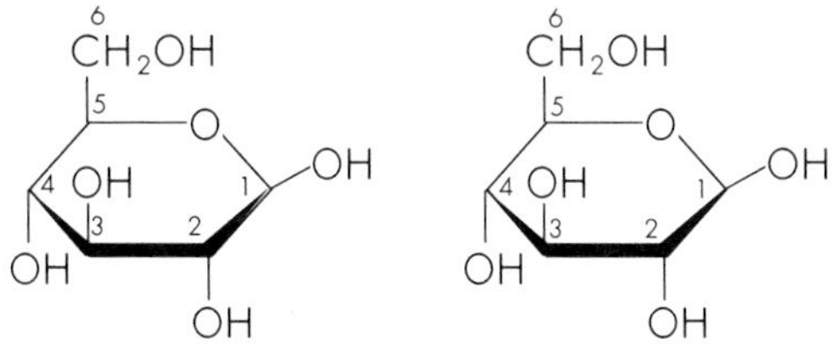

6
CH$_2$OH
5
4 OH
3   2   1
OH   OH
OH

β-D-glucose

6
CH$_2$OH
5
4 OH
3   2   1
OH   OH
OH

β-D-glucose

Join the carbon at position 1 to position 6 on the adjacent glucose molecule removing water and leaving carbon-1 in the β position. The bond is shown below:

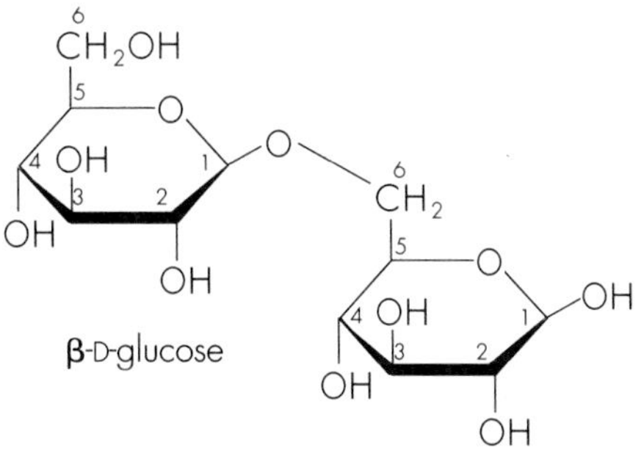

6
CH$_2$OH
5
4 OH
3   2   1
OH
OH
OH

β-D-glucose

O
6
CH$_2$
5
4 OH   1   OH
3   2
OH
OH

β-D-glucose

Question

Q13.10 Draw an α(1 → 6) link between two α-D-glucopyranose molecules (see page 128 to get the structure of α-D-glucopyranose).

13.7 Functions of carbohydrates

Polysaccharides may contain just one type of sugar (homopolysaccharide) or may be complex mixtures of sugars (heteropolysaccharide). We will consider just two. Glycogen is the first; it serves as a **storage** polysaccharide in animals. Starch is the equivalent polysaccharide in plants. Glycogen acts as a glucose store until it is needed to obtain energy. It consists of short chains of α-D-glucopyranose linked together as α(1 → 4) bridges. When linked in α(1 → 4) linkages, glucopyranose polymers form a helix. The centre of the helix binds iodine, changing its colour from yellow to blue. This forms the basis of the iodine test for starch. The structure of the helix is not stable (Figure 13.1). This allows enzymes to attack the α(1 → 4) linkages when the cells need glucose, while retaining a compact osmotically inactive store of glucose. The chains of α(1 → 4) glucoses in glycogen are branched with α(1 → 6) bridges to other chains of α(1 → 4) polyglycosides. In glycogen, branching occurs at every 8 to 12 sugars; in starch branching occurs every 10 to 20 sugars.

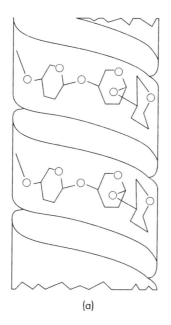

(a)   (b)

Figure 13.1 Structure of glycogen: (a) the amylose helix (a β-7.0 helix); (b) glycogen structure (dots represent glucose monomers). The chains are all α(1 → 4) glycosidic bonds whereas the branches are all α(1 → 6) glycosidic bonds

Cellulose is one of the main **structural** polysaccharides. It is found throughout the plant kingdom. Like glycogen, it is a polymer of D-glucose, but unlike glycogen the glycosidic bonds are β(1 → 4) links. This small difference means that cellulose exists in extended chains. The β(1 → 4) link allows hydrogen bonding to take place between neighbouring glucose monomers in the chain. Two H-bonds are formed parallel to the chain for each glycosidic link. These are between the ring oxygen and hydroxyl hydrogen of C^3 and between the hydroxyl oxygen of C^6 with hydroxyl hydrogen of C^2. In addition, when chains are aligned, intrachain hydrogen bonds hold the chains together. These hydrogen bonds give cellulose its great strength. In the cellulose structure shown below, the sugar structures have been abbreviated to show hydrogen bonding. The arrows show the directions of the chains.

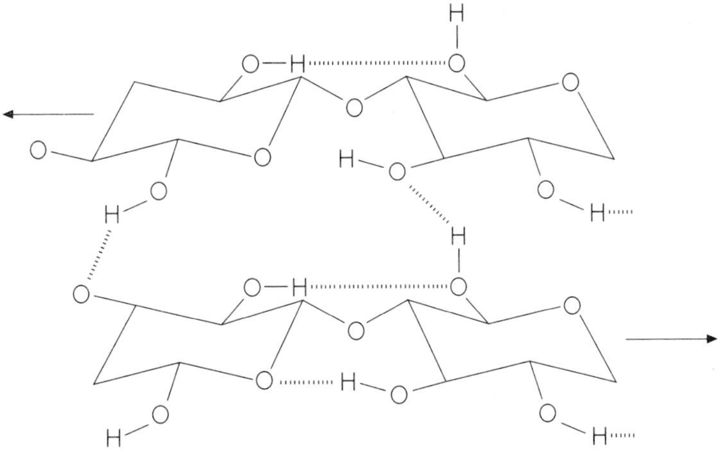

Summary

Simple sugars are named according to the number of carbons as trioses (3), tetroses (4), pentoses (5), hexoses (6) and heptoses (7). They can be further classified into aldoses, containing aldehyde groups, and ketoses, containing ketone groups. Aldotriose sugars can also differ between L- and D-isomers according to the relative position around an asymmetric carbon. Longer sugars have more asymmetric carbons and therefore have more isomers. The isomers can be classified into types such as diastereoisomer, epimer and enantiomer. Longer sugars can form ring structures as carbonyl groups can react with hydroxyl groups. The formation of ring sugars leads to further asymmetry forming α- and β-anomers. A variety of styles exists for drawing sugars; the most common are the Fischer and Haworth projections. The hydroxyl groups can also react with other compounds to form biologically important sugar derivatives. Sugars can be joined together by the glycosidic bond and are then called saccharides. The biological role of saccharides depends on their structure. The α(1 → 4)-linked sugars give typical storage polysaccharides, such as amylose, whereas the β(1 → 4) linkage gives structural polysaccharides.

Self-assessment questions

Try these questions to test your understanding.

Q13.11 Look at sugars (i)–(v) and decide:
- (a) whether the sugar is an aldose or ketose;
- (b) which of the sugars (i)–(v) are D-sugars;
- (c) which two sugars are enantiomers;
- (d) which two sugars are epimers.

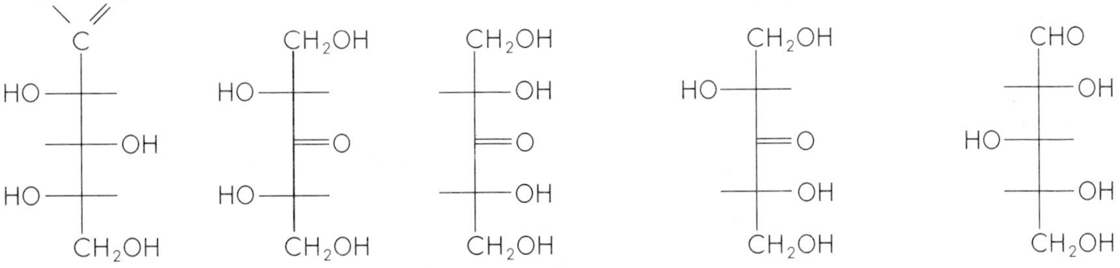

Q13.12 Below is a picture of α-D-fructofuranose.
　　(a) Number the carbons.
　　(b) Draw β-D-fructofuranose.

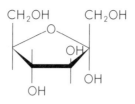

α-D-fructofuranose

Q13.13 Explain what is meant by a heterotrisaccharide.

Q13.14 Construct a β(1 → 4) glycosidic link between two β-D-galactopyranoses (structure shown below).

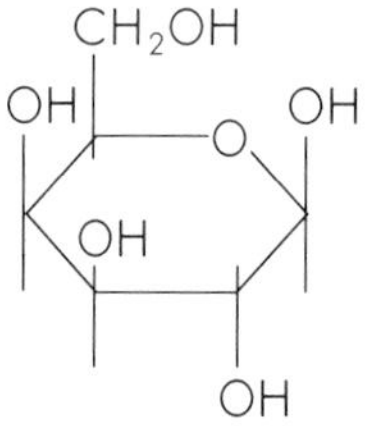

β-D-galactopyranose

Q13.15 Give two features of glycogen that make it a useful storage polysaccharide.

Fats, Oils and Lipids

Introduction

The past two chapters have covered the structure and function of two major classes of biomolecules, proteins and carbohydrates. A third major class of biomolecules are fats, oils and related compounds. Fats and oils provide much of the energy requirements of the body, and are one of the three major sources of metabolic energy in animals. The phospholipids are related structurally to fats and have a major role in structural biology. They form part of many different membranes in the cell, and act as another class of cellular messengers. This chapter deals with the formation, structure, physical properties and biological functions of fats, oils and lipids.

Objectives

After reading this chapter, you should understand:
- the role of glycerol in fat, oil and lipid structure;
- the formation and structure of glycerides, monoglycerides, diglycerides and triglycerides;
- the formation of phosphoglycerides;
- the formation of common phospholipids;
- the solubility of fats, oil, phosphoglycerides and phospholipids;
- the amphiphilic nature of phospholipids;
- stable conformations such as bilayer and micelle.

Questions

If you find the topics outlined familiar, try these questions. If your answers are correct, you could proceed to Chapter 15.

Q14.1 Give the name of the product of esterification of a fatty acid by glycerol.

Q14.2 What is meant by a monounsaturated fatty acid?

Q14.3 In what way does a fat differ from an oil?

Q14.4 Draw in block diagram form a phosphatidic acid.

Q14.5 Define what is meant by an amphiphilic molecule.

Q14.6 Draw a block diagram to represent a phosphatidylserine.

Q14.7 Explain why a 'bilayer' is a stable arrangement for phospholipids in water.

14.1 The building blocks of fats

Fats and oils, like the other biomolecules discussed, are made by joining together simple molecules with covalent bonds. Fats and oils are built by joining together two types of molecules, glycerol and long-chain unbranched carboxylic acids (fatty acids is another term for long-chain carboxylic acids). Glycerol (propan-1,2,3-triol) is a compound that contains three hydroxyl groups. Each of the —OH groups can react with a fatty acid to form an ester bond (see

Chapter 10, page 87, to review ester-bond formation). The reaction of glycerol with one fatty acid is shown below (the fatty acid component is shown in bold). The product is called a **monoacylglycerol**. The name monoacylglycerol can be broken down; mono means one, acyl refers to the fatty acid ester, and glycerol the molecule to which the fatty acid is bonded.

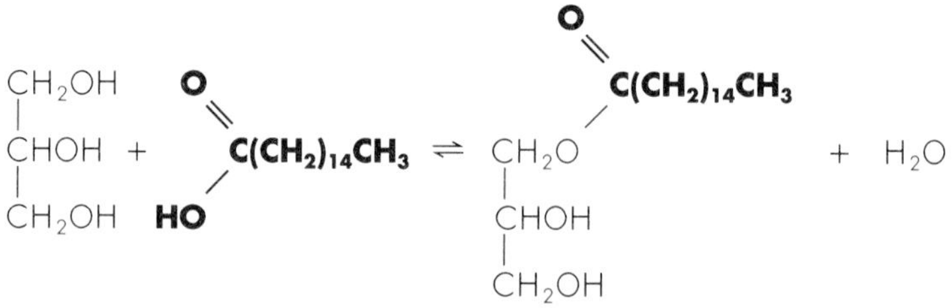
CH2OH
CHOH +
CH2OH
O
C(CH2)14CH3
HO
O
C(CH2)14CH3
CH2O
CHOH
CH2OH
+ H2O

glycerol fatty acid monoacylglycerol

Monoacylglycerols have only one of the glycerol hydroxyl groups esterified. The other two hydroxyl groups can be esterified in the same way. Esterification of two hydroxyls yields a **diacylglycerol**; esterification of three groups yields a **triacylglycerol**. A block diagram of a diacylglycerol and a triacylglycerol is shown below (the fatty acid components are shown in bold):

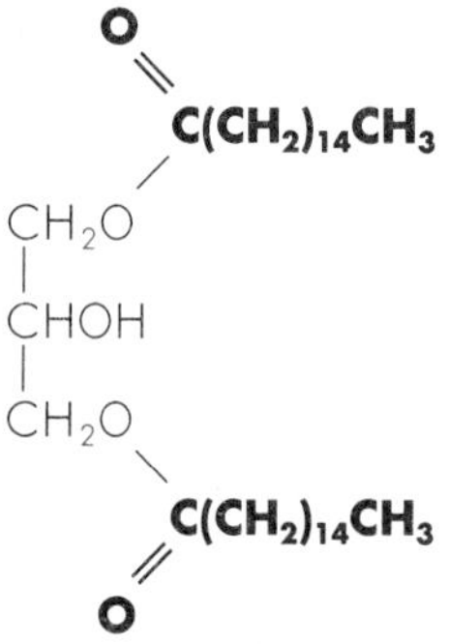
O
C(CH2)14CH3
CH2O
CHOH
CH2O
C(CH2)14CH3
O

structural diagram

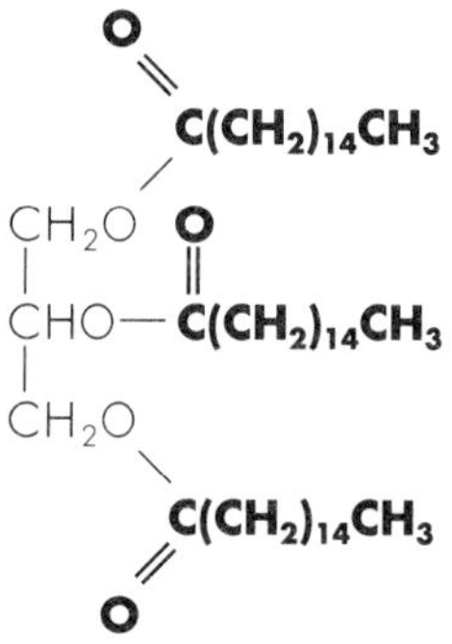
O
C(CH2)14CH3
CH2O O
CHO— C(CH2)14CH3
CH2O
C(CH2)14CH3
O

structural diagram

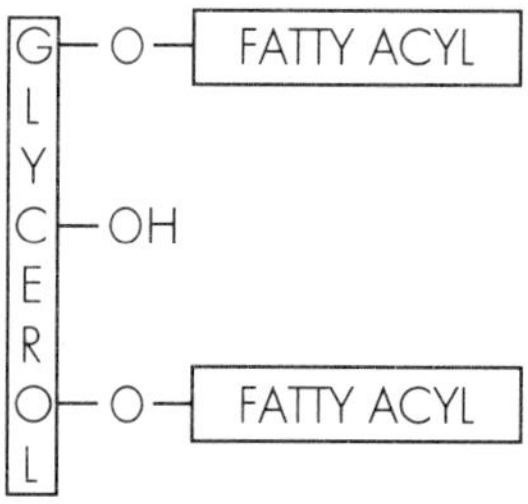
GLYCEROL
O
FATTY ACYL
OH
O
FATTY ACYL

block diagram

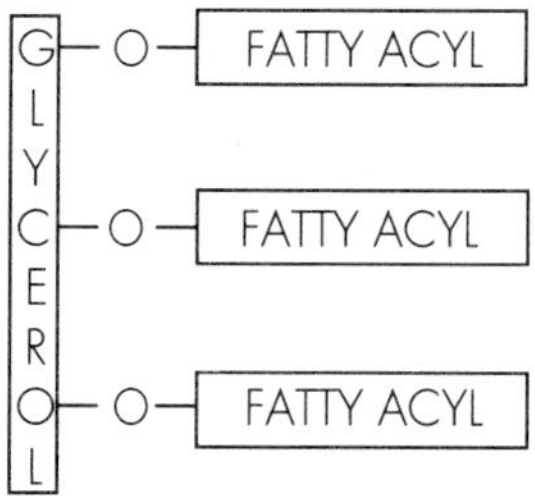
GLYCEROL
O
FATTY ACYL
O
FATTY ACYL
O
FATTY ACYL

block diagram

diacylglycerol triacylglycerol

Monoacylglycerols, diacylglycerols and triacylglycerols are collectively known as the acylglycerols or glycerides. There are many different forms of glycerides as the fatty acyl part can vary. The two main variations are the number of carbons in the fatty acyl group (the chain length) and the number of double bonds (the degree of unsaturation). The chain length of most fatty acids derived from common oils and fats is between 12 and 20 carbons atoms long, depending on the source of the oil. Animal fats and oils contain a high percentage of fatty acids with no double bonds (saturated fats), while many vegetable oils have one double bond (monounsaturated fats) and some have two or more double bonds (polyunsaturated fats). An indication of different degrees of saturation is shown below.

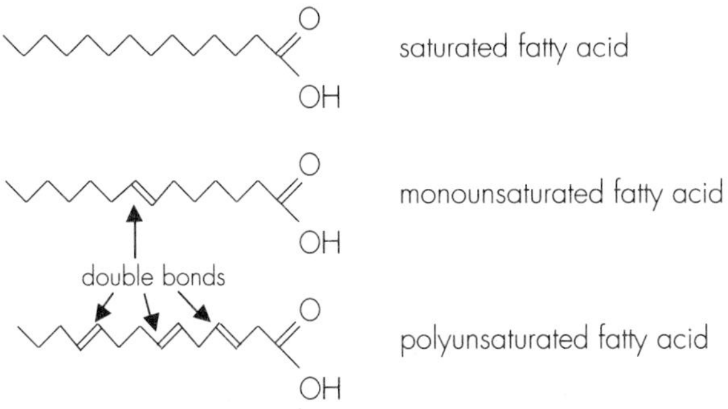

All natural oils and fats are complex mixtures of different diacylglycerols and triacylglycerols. Fats and oils are insoluble in water, but soluble in less-polar solvents such as ethanol. Oils are liquid at room temperatures whereas fats are solid. One major factor in determining whether a triacylglycerol is a fat or an oil is the degree of unsaturation. Oils tend to contain more unsaturated fatty acyl groups. Chemical conversion of unsaturated triacylglycerols into saturated triacylglycerols, a process called hydrogenation, is widely used in the food industry to partially or completely saturate some of the fats. Fats are easier to store and handle than oils (think of margarine!).

14.2 Phosphoglycerides and phospholipids

Molecules of phosphoglycerides have a glycerol ester-linked to two fatty acids and to one phosphoric acid. The structure of a phosphoglyceride, phosphatidic acid, is shown below.

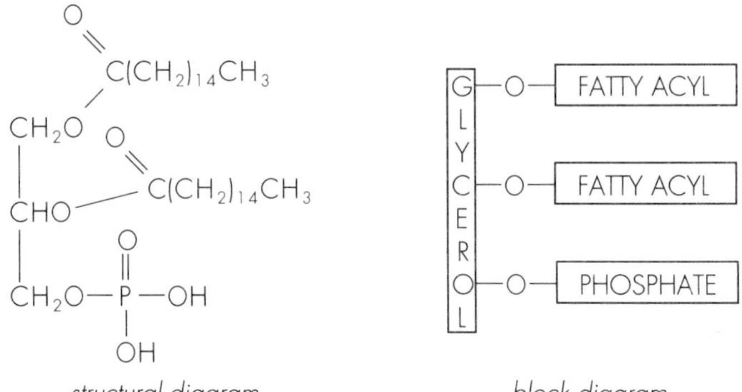

structural diagram   block diagram

The addition of the phosphate group introduces a major structural change to the glyceride. The phosphate group likes the company of water and will readily mix in water (hydrophilic), while the fatty acyl groups do not 'like' water and try to arrange themselves away from water. 'Liking' water is also called hydrophilic, while 'hating' water is called hydrophobic. A molecule that contains both hydrophobic and hydrophilic parts is called amphiphilic. A phosphoglyceride is an amphiphilic molecule. The amphiphilic nature of phosphatidic acid is given in Figure 14.1, overleaf.

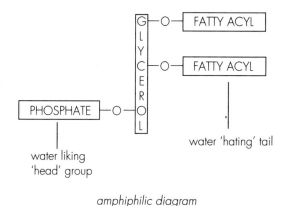

amphiphilic diagram
phosphatidic acid

Figure 14.1 Block diagram of phosphatidic acid to show the amphiphilic nature of the compound

Phosphatidic acid is so called because the phosphate group is acidic. This phosphate group can react with an alcohol to make a phosphate ester. The resulting molecule is called a **phospholipid**:

phosphatidic
acid

+ **HOR**
alcohol

phospholipid + H_2O

Several alcohols are often found esterified to phosphate in phospholipids. These include choline, ethanolamine and serine (see below). Phospholipids derived from these alcohols are called phosphatidylcholine, phosphatidylethanolamine and phosphatidylserine.

$HOCH_2CH_2N^+(CH_3)_3$
choline

$HOCH_2CH_2NH_3^+$
ethanolamine

$HOCH_2\overset{\overset{\displaystyle NH_3^+}{|}}{C}HCOO^-$
serine

Example 14.1
Draw the structure of a phosphatidylcholine.
Draw out a phosphatidic acid. Draw out choline. Identify the choline hydroxyl. Join up the choline to the phosphate removing one hydrogen from the choline and an —OH group from the phosphate. This is shown in block diagram and then by using structures (see below for structural formulae with the choline hydroxyl shown in bold):

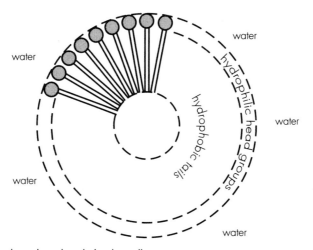

phosphatidic acid   +   choline   ⟶   phosphatidylcholine   +   water

Question

Q14.8 Draw out the structure of a phosphatidylethanolamine.

14.3 Solubility of phospholipids

The amphiphilic nature of phospholipids has been discussed. Phospholipids are only sparingly soluble in water, but are quite soluble in organic solvents such as ethanol or chloroform : methanol mixtures. Phospholipids dissolved in organic solvents can be mixed with water to create an opaque 'suspension' called a colloid. This opaque suspension is the basis of the ethanol emulsion test for fats. In water, the phospholipid will form structures where the hydrophobic ends (or tails) are not exposed to water. The simplest structure is a sphere (ball) in which the hydrophobic tails point inwards, while the hydrophilic heads point outwards facing the water. This arrangement of phospholipids is called a micelle, and is shown in Figure 14.2.

Figure 14.2 Cross-section through a phospholipid micelle

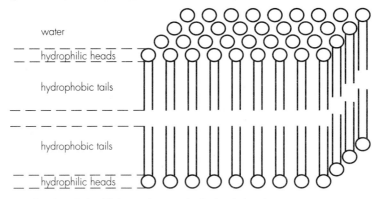

Figure 14.3 Main features of a phospholipid bilayer showing the hydrophobic core

Another stable structure formed by phospholipids is a 'bilayer'. The bilayer consists of a thin film of phospholipids, two lipid molecules thick. The head groups are arranged at the surface of the film, while the tails point inwards towards the middle of the film. This arrangement is shown in Figure 14.3. This structure is extremely important in biology as the bilayer is the basic structure of all biological membranes.

The bilayer forms a barrier that does not allow many molecules to cross except for gases and small hydrophobic molecules. This means that cells and organelles within cells can control their internal environment. The membranes in cells allow certain important molecules to cross them. This is done by incorporating proteins into the bilayer to form 'holes' that are specific for certain molecules. A detailed description of movement across biological membranes is beyond the scope of this text.

Apart from phospholipids and proteins, the other major constituent of cell membranes is cholesterol. Cholesterol contains four rings joined together (structure shown in Chapter 9, page 77). Cholesterol is a rigid planar molecule that is hydrophobic and prefers to be in the hydrophobic interior of the lipid bilayer.

14.4 Fats, oils and lipids as energy stores

Fats and oils are used almost universally as stores of energy. Indeed our common sources of stored fats and oils are vegetable seeds. One of the reasons why fats and oils are such good energy stores is the relatively low number of oxygen atoms in their structure. Oxidation of fatty acids gives a greater yield of energy than oxidation of proteins or carbohydrates. The complete oxidation of fatty acids gives an amount of energy comparable to that given from the burning of fossil fuels. If lipids are compared with sugars, we can see that lipids have relatively few oxygens as part of their structure (Table 14.1). The energy yield per carbon is about two-fold greater for fats than sugars.

As discussed earlier, fats and oils are insoluble in water and are held in cells as fat droplets (Figure 14.4). Movement of fats around the body is carried out by creating micelle-like structures that are water soluble.

Table 14.1 Comparison of oxygen contents of a fatty acid (n-hexadecanoic acid) and a sugar (glucose)

Molecule	Formula	C/O	H/O
n-Hexadecanoic acid	$C_{16}H_{32}O_2$	8	16
Glucose	$C_6H_{12}O_6$	1	2

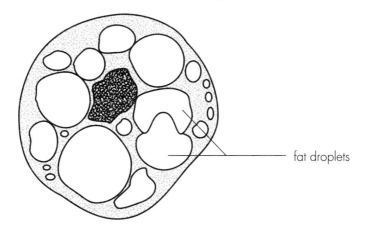

fat droplets

Figure 14.4 Drawing of a fat cell showing fat droplets

Summary

Fats, oils and lipids are all esters of glycerol with fatty acids. Glycerol can be esterified by one, two or three fatty acids to yield monoacylglycerols, diacylglycerols and triacylglycerols. The properties of fats and oils are determined by two factors: the length of the acyl groups and the degree of saturation of the fatty acids. Oils are liquids at room temperature, while fats are solids. Phospholipids are all based upon the structure of phosphatidic acids, the phosphate ester of diacylglycerols. The phosphate group of phosphatidic acid can be further esterified with an alcohol to yield the common phospholipids. Phospholipids are amphiphilic molecules which are arranged in water so that their hydrophobic tails are held out of contact with water. There are two common structures that allow this: micelles and bilayers. The phospholipid bilayer is the basic structure of all biological membranes.

Self-assessment questions

Q14.9 Name the type of bond that links fatty acids to glycerol in triacylglycerols.

Q14.10 Give one structural difference between an oil and a fat.

Q14.11 What is meant by hydrogenation of fats?

Q14.12 Which parts of phosphoglycerides are hydrophobic and which are hydrophilic?

Q14.13 Give a block-diagram representation of a phosphatidylethanolamine.

Q14.14 Which molecules can freely cross a phospholipid bilayer?

Nucleotides, DNA and RNA

Introduction

Humans are an extremely complicated mixture of chemicals that constantly change from day-to-day. We inherit all of our physical features from our parents. The information for these features, such as eye and hair colour, is passed down to us as messages stored in our genes. This genetic information is stored in about 100 000 genes made up of a few simple molecules polymerised together in a linear sequence. This sequence is unique to any individual and, like the letters of a language, it communicates to an organism the sequence of amino acids needed for the production of many thousands of protein molecules. The monomer unit of the sequence is called a nucleotide, which when polymerised forms DNA. Genes are polymers of nucleotides and the sequence of these polymers carries the genetic information. The elucidation of how these messages are stored and transmitted is one of the major achievements in understanding biology. It has laid the foundations of much improved methods to counter diseases and improve crop yields.

Objectives

After studying this chapter you will be able to:
- recall the structure of nucleosides, nucleotides and nucleic acids;
- use standard abbreviations for nucleosides, nucleotides and nucleic acids;
- understand the formation and properties of nucleic acids;
- appreciate the concept of complementary base pairs and the structure of DNA;
- be aware of the processes of replication and transcription;
- know of other functions of nucleotides.

Questions

Now try these questions to test your familiarity with this topic. Your answers will help you decide if you need to review the chapter.

Q15.1 The sequence of nucleotides in DNA is a code for the synthesis of which group of molecules?

Q15.2 What are the 'units' of a nucleoside?

Q15.3 (a) Give the standard abbreviation for deoxycytosine-5'-diphosphate.
(b) Draw the structure of this molecule.

Q15.4 What type of group links nucleotides in nucleic acids?

Q15.5 This diagram shows an abbreviated method of writing nucleic acid structure.

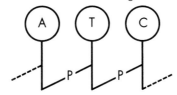

(a) What molecule is represented by the vertical lines?
(b) Which molecule is represented by P?

Q15.6 Give the complementary DNA sequence to the one listed: A C C C G T A G.

Q15.7 How many bases in DNA are needed to code for a single amino acid?

Q15.8 Which molecule is responsible for carrying the DNA message to the site of protein synthesis?

Q15.9 Name the energy carrier in cells.

15.1 Nucleotides

A nucleotide is a molecule that consists of three units: a base, a sugar, and some phosphate groups:

The most variable part of a nucleotide is the base. There are two types of amine bases, purines and pyrimidines (see Chapter 11, pages 96, 97). There are two common purine bases, adenine and guanine, and three common pyrimidine bases, uracil, cytosine and thymine. The purine and pyrimidine bases depicted below show where the base is covalently bound to carbon-1 (C^1) of the sugar unit in a nucleotide (the nitrogen to which the ring is attached is shown in bold).

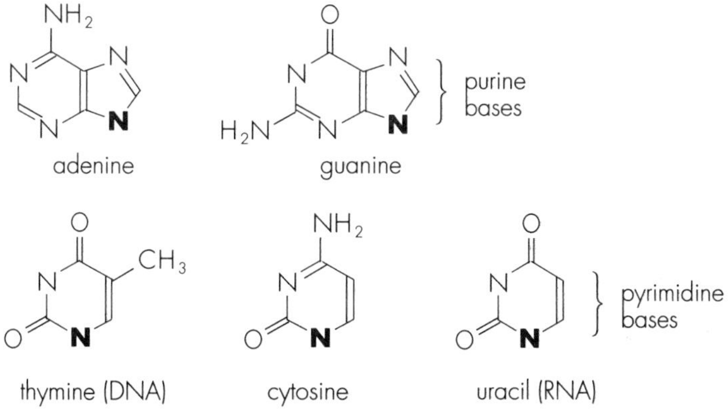

adenine   guanine   } purine bases

thymine (DNA)   cytosine   uracil (RNA)   } pyrimidine bases

The N is covalently bound directly to the C^1 of one of two types of sugar, ribose or 2'-deoxyribose (see Chapter 13, page 123). When a base is joined to a sugar, the resulting compound is called a nucleoside. The structure of the nucleoside, adenosine, is shown below. When the hydroxyl attached to C^2 (which is boxed in the diagram) is replaced by a hydrogen, the nucleoside formed is 2'-deoxyadenosine.

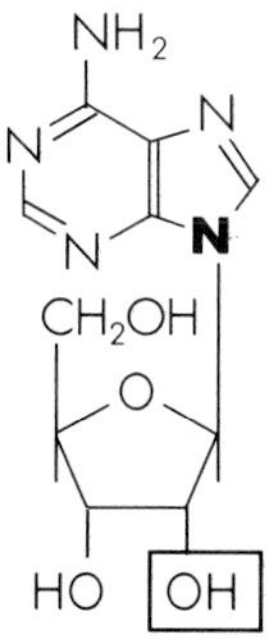

adenosine

Table 15.1 Names of common nucleosides and nucleotides

Base	Nucleoside	Nucleotide		
	BASE—SUGAR	BASE—SUGAR—P_i	BASE—SUGAR—P_i—P_i	BASE—SUGAR—P_i—P_i—P_i
Adenine	Deoxyadenosine Adenosine	Deoxyadenosine-5'-phosphate Adenosine-5'-phosphate	Deoxyadenosine-5'-diphosphate Adenosine-5'-diphosphate	Deoxyadenosine-5'-triphosphate Adenosine-5'-triphosphate
Guanine	Deoxyguanosine Guanosine	Deoxyguanosine-5'-phosphate Guanosine-5'-phosphate	Deoxyguanosine-5'-diphosphate Guanosine-5'-diphosphate	Deoxyguanosine-5'-triphosphate Guanosine-5'-triphosphate
Cytosine	Deoxycytosine Cytosine	Deoxycytosine-5'-phosphate Cytosine-5'-phosphate	Deoxycytosine-5'-diphosphate Cytosine-5'-diphosphate	Deoxycytosine-5'-triphosphate Cytosine-5'-triphosphate
Thymine	Deoxythymidine Thymidine	Deoxythymidine-5'-phosphate Thymidine-5'-phosphate	Deoxythymidine-5'-diphosphate Thymidine-5'-diphosphate	Deoxythymidine-5'-triphosphate Thymidine-5'-triphosphate
Uracil	Uridine	Uridine-5'-phosphate	Uridine-5'-diphosphate	Uridine-5'-triphosphate

A nucleotide is formed when the 5' carbon of that sugar is esterified by phosphoric acid, diphosphoric acid, or triphosphoric acid. The nucleotide is one of nucleoside monophosphate, nucleoside diphosphate, or nucleoside triphosphate, depending on which acid reacted to form the ester. The structures of adenosine-5'-monophosphate, adenosine-5'-diphosphate, and adenosine-5'-triphosphate are shown below. The relationship between the names of the base, nucleoside and nucleotide is shown in Table 15.1.

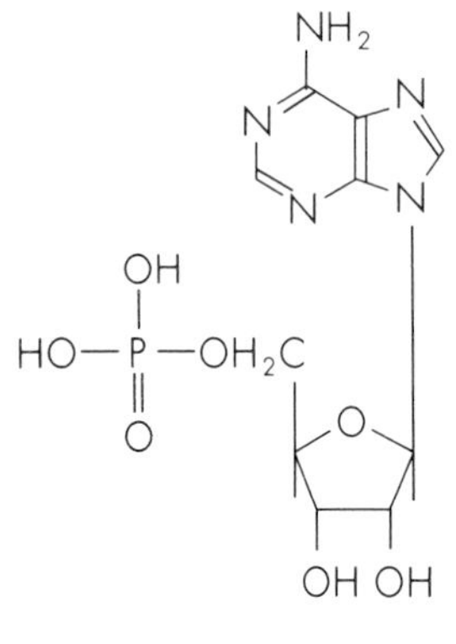

adenosine-5'-monophosphate 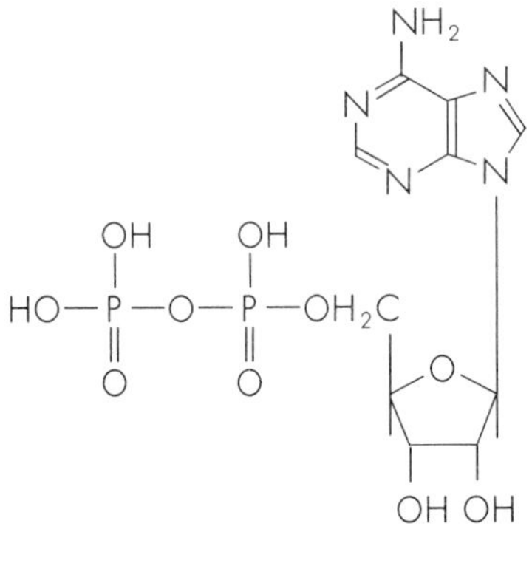   adenosine-5'-diphosphate 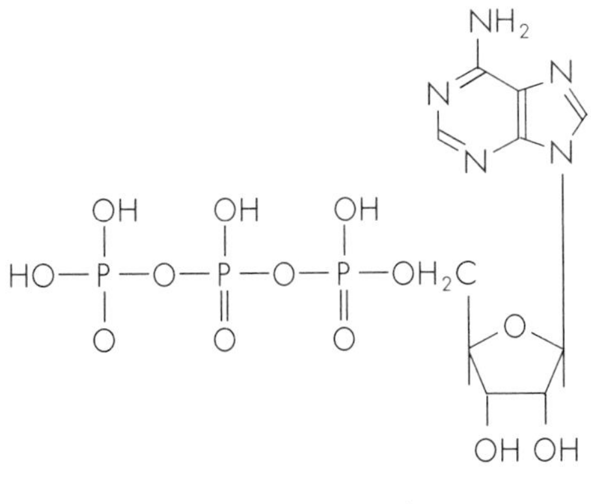   adenosine-5'-triphosphate

Table 15.1 gives the full names of all common nucleotides and nucleosides. The regular use of these names is unwieldy and therefore a series of abbreviations of the terms are used (Table 15.2).

Example 15.1
(a) Draw the full structure of 2-deoxyguanosine-5'-diphosphate.
(b) Write out the name using the standard abbreviation.

(a) Draw a block diagram of 2'-deoxyguanosine-5'-diphosphate and then write names into the diagram:

Table 15.2 Standard abbreviations for parts of nucleotides

Part	Abbreviation
deoxy	d
adenine or adenosine	A
guanine or guanosine	G
cytosine	C
thymine or thymidine	T
uracil or uridine	U
-5'-phosphate	MP
-5'-diphosphate	DP
-5'-triphosphate	TP
nucleoside (meaning any)	N

Copy out the structures of guanine (see page 141) and deoxyribose (see page 123):

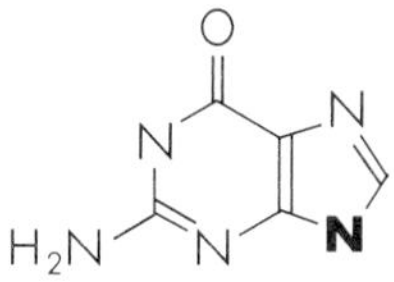

guanine 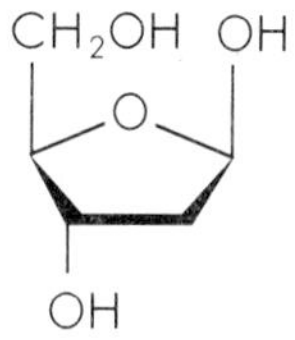   2'-deoxyribose

Join C^1 of deoxyribose to N (drawn in bold) of guanine, removing the —OH group.

2'-deoxyguanosine

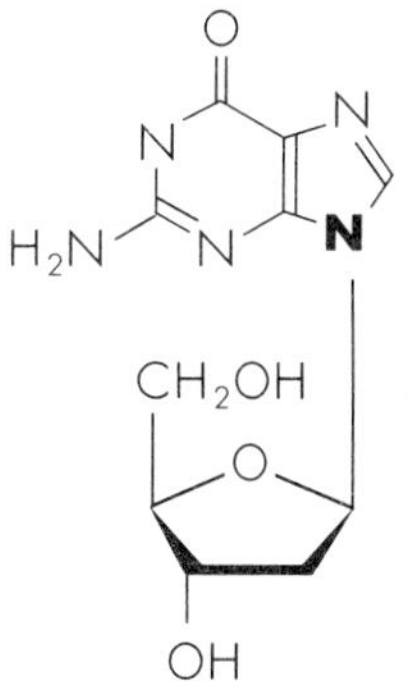

Add a diphosphate group to 5'—OH, removing H.

2'-deoxyguanosine-5'-diphosphate

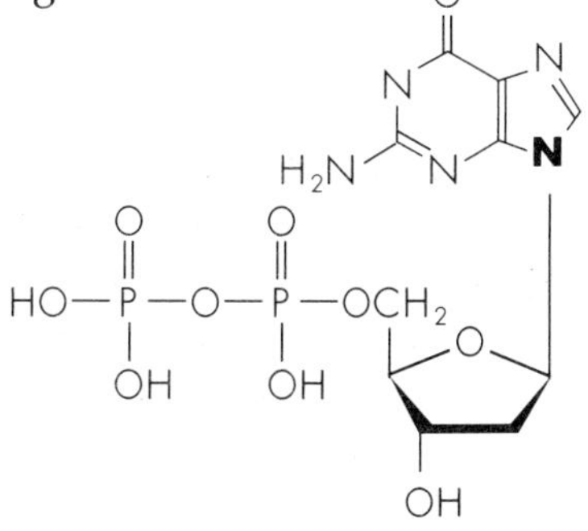

(b) 2-deoxyguanosine-5'-diphosphate.

    (i)   Break the word into parts.
    (ii) Substitute letters for parts.
    (iii) Join the letters together:.
    (i)   2-deoxy   ... guanosine   ... -5'-diphosphate
    (ii)   d   G   DP
    (iii) dGDP

Question

Q15.10 (a) Give the standard abbreviation for these nucleotides:
        (i) thymidine-5'-phosphate;
        (ii) deoxycytosine-5'-triphosphate;
        (iii) deoxyadenosine-5'-triphosphate;
        (iv) adenosine-5'-triphosphate.
    (b) Draw the full structure of guanosine-5'-triphosphate.

15.2 Formation of nucleic acids

Molecules such as deoxyribonucleic acid (abbreviated DNA) and ribonucleic acid (abbreviated RNA) are polymers of nucleotides. The nucleotide monomers are bridged by a covalent bond between the phosphate of one sugar (attached to C^5) and the hydroxyl attached to C^3 of the next sugar:

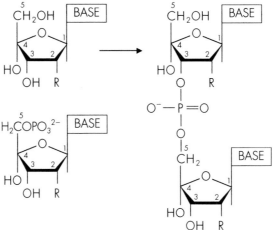

R = –H in DNA and –OH in RNA
The 'bases' are shown in block format.

The phosphate has formed phosphate ester bonds with two hydroxyls (C^5 from one sugar and C^3 from the other) and the linkage is often called a **phosphodiester bridge**. The enzymes that catalyse this reaction use nucleoside triphosphates. When many nucleotides are joined together by phosphodiester bridges, a structure is formed in which there is a backbone of ... sugar-phosphate-sugar-phosphate ... links, with the different bases joined to the sugar residues:

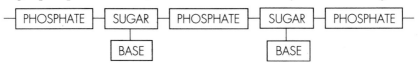

An alternative schematic drawing in which phosphate groups are given the symbol P, sugars denoted by a vertical line (|) and bases represented by the single letter code (A, T, C, G) is shown below. Carbons are represented as C^1 (at the top of the line) to C^5 (at the bottom). The base is given a single-letter code. By convention, nucleotides are always numbered in the 5' → 3' direction, from left to right.

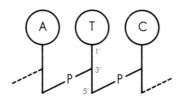

Although this abbreviated format is a greatly simplified diagram, many DNA molecules are millions of nucleotides long and to write out even the simple structure shown above would take a lot of time. The only difference between this polynucleotide and any other is the order of bases. Most representations of DNA or RNA simply have the sequence of bases written out using a single letter code to represent the sequence of bases (in the 5' → 3' direction). Short polymers of nucleotides, less than 50 nucleotides long, are sometimes called oligonucleotides; longer strands are called either polynucleotides, DNA or RNA (DNA or RNA depends on the sugar).

15.3 Properties of nucleic acids

The phosphate groups still retain some of their acidic polar properties even after the formation of phosphodiester bonds. Sugars are polar structures. The bases are weak and at pH 7.0 are relatively non-polar structures in solution. DNA and RNA will seek shapes that keep the polar backbone facing outwards towards the water. Although the bases are amines, their pK_a values are relatively low and at pH 7.0 are uncharged (see Section 11.3, page 99). In polynucleotides, the bases are more stable if they are 'stacked' like plates on a shelf, because of hydrophobic interactions.

Bases also have an affinity with each other due to the ability of the bases to form hydrogen bonds. The 'best' fit of hydrogen bonding was found to be between the bases **adenine–thymine** and **guanine–cytosine**, which are found in DNA (see below). Uracil, which replaces thymine in RNA, does not form base pairs very well with adenine. The finding of these optimal base pairings was part of the information that helped James Watson and Francis Crick work out the structure of DNA.

15.4 Structure of DNA

The sequence of bases in DNA is now known to contain all the cell's genetic information. The rationale for assuming that DNA was the store of genetic information was worked out in the 1930s and 1940s and is not discussed here. Some of the more important structural details, which are largely unaltered from the model first proposed by Watson and Crick, will be summarised. The understanding that in the best fit A pairs with T and C with G suggested a structure for DNA where hydrogen bonding between these two complementary bases was possible. X-ray studies of DNA crystals gave further clues as to the structure:

  (i)   the DNA existed as two strands side by side;
  (ii) the DNA was organised as a helix;
  (iii) two lengths of 'repeating' structures at 0.34 nm and 3.4 nm were suggested.

Previous studies by Chargaff had indicated that the A:T and C:G ratios in DNA were close to 1 for all DNA sources. This, coupled with the base-pairing, led Watson and Crick to suggest two complementary helical strands with A–T and C–G pairs (Figure 15.1). Figure 15.1 shows the nature of the double helix starting with a single right-handed helix (Figure 15.1(a)), then a double antiparallel helix (Figure 15.1(b)), a double helix showing the position of bases and direction of hydrogen bonding (Figure 15.1(c)) and finally a schematic drawing of the actual structure in Figure 15.1(d). If you look at the sugar residues in Figure 15.1(d), the antiparallel nature of the chains is shown: on the left-hand side the oxygen of the ribose is upwards; on the right-hand chain the oxygen points downwards. Another important feature is the matching of the complementary base pairs A–T and C–G.

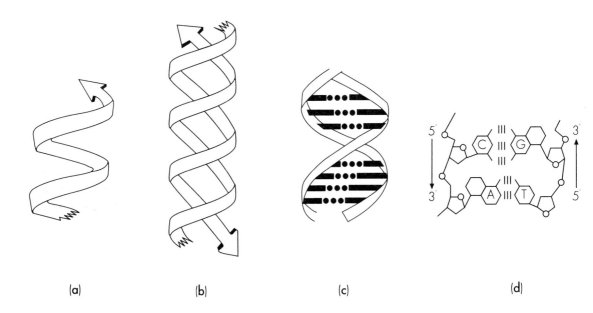

(a)   (b)   (c)   (d)

Figure 15.1 The DNA double helix. (a) A single right-handed helix; (b) a twin or double helix; (c) a section of double helical DNA. The bases are shown as blocks pointing towards the centre with hydrogen bonds shown as a series of dots (••••); (d) the double helix stretched out to show complementary base pairing and antiparallel nature

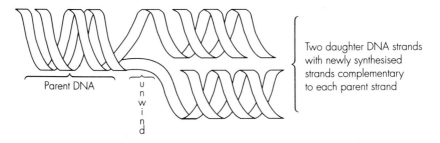

Figure 15.2 Unwinding and synthesis of DNA in replication

Replication of DNA during cell division was suggested by this model to occur by separation of the two complementary strands and synthesis of new strands that are complementary to each of the old strands (Figure 15.2).

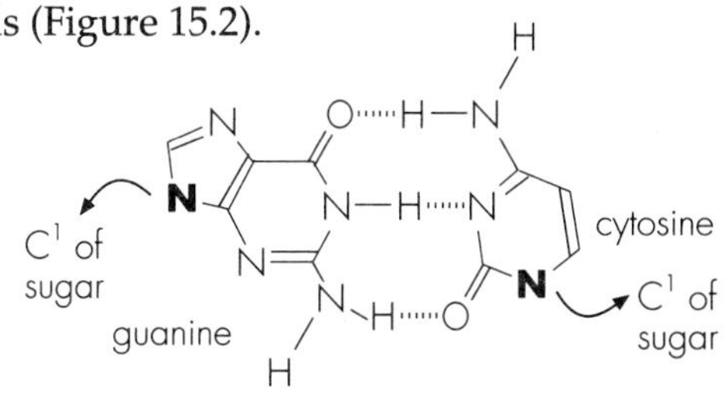

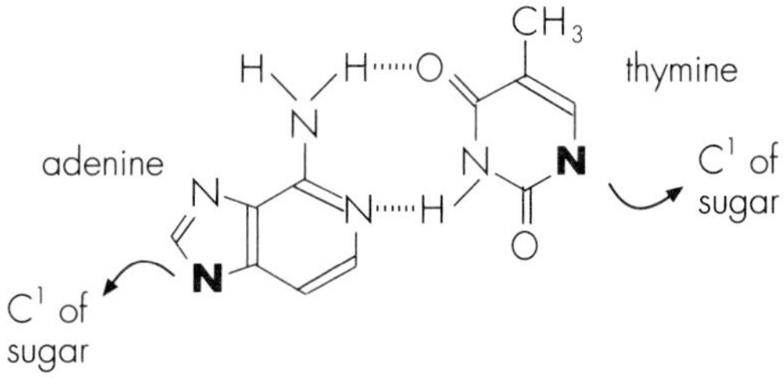

15.5 The genetic code

The elucidation of the genetic code and transfer of the information contained in the code to the cell will be covered in most biology texts. A brief résumé is given here. DNA can make copies of itself during replication and both daughter strands have a newly synthesised base sequence that is **complementary** to the parent:

```
                                    Daughter   ATCGCGAT
                                               TAGCGCTA
                      ATCGCGAT
              Parent  TAGCGCTA

                                               ATCGCGAT
                                    Daughter   TAGCGCTA
```

Both daughter strands are identical to the parent. The 'message' stored in the sequence of bases has been preserved. The message has been retained by the synthesis of two complementary new strands (shown in bold above), each newly synthesised strand being complementary to one of the parent strands. Each parent strand is retained in one of the daughters.

Example 15.2

(a) Using single-letter codes, draw a complementary strand to this DNA sequence: CCGATGCCATG (I);

(b) In replication of this strand of DNA, what is the sequence of the newly synthesised daughter strands?

(a) For each G, the complementary base is C
C, the complementary base is G
T, the complementary base is A
A, the complementary base is T.
Therefore the complementary strand is GGCTACGGTAC (II).

(b) Daughter strand complementary to (I) is (II); daughter strand complementary to (II) is (I).

Question

Q15.11 This is a sequence of DNA: 5' A G C C G A G G G T A T A 3'.

    (a) Write out the sequence of the complementary strand using the single-letter code.

    (b) Write out the sequence of the newly synthesised daughter strands.

    (c) What is meant by 5' and 3'?

Most of the activities in the cell are carried out by proteins and since proteins are made up of polypeptides it is logical to assume that the sequence of bases in DNA codes for the sequence of amino acids in a polypeptide. There are 20 common amino acids and only four nucleotides. A single base cannot code for all amino acids, a pair of bases could only code for 16 (4^2), so three bases (a triplet) must be the minimum number required to code for 20 amino acids. This has indeed been found to be the case. Three bases could code for up to 64 different messages (4^3). It was found that some amino acids are coded for by more than one triplet. The exact nature of the code is shown in Table 15.3.

Table 15.3 The genetic code. The left-hand column is for the first base (as read) of the triplet code, the right-hand column is for the last base, the centre columns are for the middle base. Stop indicates that the polypeptide chain has been completed and that polypeptide synthesis should stop

5'-OH terminal base	The middle base				3'-OH terminal base
	U	C	A	G	
U	Phe	Ser	Tyr	Cys	U
	Phe	Ser	Tyr	Cys	C
	Leu	Ser	Stop	Stop	A
	Leu	Ser	Stop	Trp	G
C	Leu	Pro	His	Arg	U
	Leu	Pro	His	Arg	C
	Leu	Pro	Gln	Arg	A
	Leu	Pro	Gln	Arg	G
A	Ile	Thr	Asn	Ser	U
	Ile	Thr	Asn	Ser	C
	Ile	Thr	Lys	Arg	A
	Met	Thr	Lys	Arg	G
G	Val	Ala	Asp	Gly	U
	Val	Ala	Asp	Gly	C
	Val	Ala	Glu	Gly	A
	Val	Ala	Glu	Gly	G

For the code on DNA to be turned into the protein product, the DNA sequence first has to be copied onto RNA. Copying of a message is normally called **transcription**. The RNA contains a message complementary to the DNA. The RNA made in transcription is called **messenger RNA** (mRNA) as it carries the sequence of bases (the message) from the DNA to the site of protein synthesis, the ribosomes.

The mRNA message is turned into protein. One can easily see how mutations can arise if bases are not added correctly. In the disease sickle cell anaemia, a single base substitution in the sequence of DNA that codes for the protein haemoglobin is changed, so that a valine is incorporated into the protein instead of glutamic acid. This causes the haemoglobin molecules to become 'sticky' and to stick together in long chains. This causes the red blood cells to 'sickle' or change shape. This shape change makes the cells break easily, causing people with the complaint many problems as less oxygen is transported around the body.

15.6   Other uses of nucleotides

There are three other major functions of nucleotides in cells: chemical energy carriers; cofactors and coenzymes; and cellular messengers. The role of chemical **energy carrier** in cells is normally carried out by adenosine-5'-triphosphate (ATP). ATP has a triphosphate group attached to C^5 of the ribose. The splitting of the end phosphate to make ADP and inorganic phosphate (P_i) is an energy yielding reaction:

adenosine-5'-triphosphate + water $\longrightarrow$ adenosine-5'-diphosphate + phosphate + energy

ATP   + H_2O $\longrightarrow$ ADP   + P_i + energy

At pH 7.0 the reaction yields about 30 kJ mol^{-1} of energy. Many unfavourable reactions that occur in cells, such as muscle movement and sugar movements, are driven by being linked to the energy from ATP hydrolysis.

Many **coenzymes** are nucleotide-containing molecules. These include NAD$^+$ (nicotinamide adenine dinucleotide), FAD (flavin adenine dinucleotide) and coenzyme A.

The transmission of the signal given by a **hormone** to the cell is often carried out in the cell by special nucleotides. The most important of these messengers are adenosine 3',5'-cyclic monophosphate and guanosine 3',5'-cyclic monophosphate. The phosphate in these molecules is esterified at both the 3'-hydroxyl and the 5'-hydroxyl of the same sugar. The concentrations of both these compounds often change when hormones bring about changes in cells.

Summary

All of the information about living organisms is stored in genes. Genes are made up of the molecule DNA. DNA is a polymer of four nucleotides. Nucleotides have three basic units: a base, a sugar and a phosphate ester. There are four common bases in DNA: adenine, guanine, cytosine and thymine. In a nucleotide, the base is bound to C^1 of ribose in RNA or 2'-deoxyribose in DNA, while the phosphate group is bound to C^5 of the sugar. The full names of nucleotides are abbreviated using a standard code. Nucleic acids are polymers of nucleotides where the phosphate group forms the bridge between adjacent nucleotides by being esterified at the 5'- and 3'-hydroxyls of different nucleotides to form a phosphodiester bond. The structure of nucleic acids can then be written out simply by reference to the sequence of bases. The direction of writing is 5' → 3'. The DNA will fold in water into a favourable conformation. This will involve hydrogen-bonding between base pairs. Best-fit hydrogen bonds are between adenine–thymine and guanine–cytosine. In cells, DNA exists as a double helix of complementary strands with base pairs hydrogen-bonded in the centre. Replication of DNA occurs by the helix unwinding and complementary strands being manufactured. The sequence of DNA codes for proteins, three bases on a DNA strand corresponding to one amino acid. Nucleotides have other functions as energy stores, coenzymes and cellular messengers.

Self-assessment questions

Q15.12 Where is the message concerning the sequence of amino acids in a protein stored?

Q15.13 Define the basic groups of a nucleotide.

Q15.14 (a) Draw the structure of uridine-5'-diphosphate.
(b) Give the standard abbreviation for this molecule.

Q15.15 The phosphodiester link in nucleic acids links which two hydroxyl groups of different sugars?

Q15.16 This diagram shows a shorthand form of writing the nucleic acid structure:

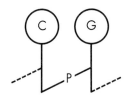

    (a) What is represented by the C?

    (b) Why does the line containing the P have a diagonal slope upwards from left to right?

Q15.17 Give two reasons for assuming that A–T and C–G are the complementary bases in DNA.

Q15.18 Name the process of copying the DNA message onto mRNA.

Q15.19 Give two functions of nucleotides.

Part 3

Important Physical Concepts

Rate, Energy and Enzymes in Metabolism

Introduction

The living cell contains a complex mixture of substances. Many reactions are going on, often quite rapidly. Enzymes promote these reactions, ensuring that they proceed fast enough for the cell metabolism to be maintained effectively. Separate reactions remain independent because of the specific nature of enzyme catalysts. Energy has to be supplied to the cell to drive these processes. This may be in the form of light for plant cells or as nutrients for animals cells.

Objectives

When you have studied this chapter you should be able to:

- recall the factors that affect the rate of a reaction;
- understand the terms rate, rate constant and order of reaction;
- write a rate equation;
- appreciate the special nature of enzymes as catalysts;
- use the concept of activation energy to explain the role of enzymes in promoting reactions;
- use the concept of initial rate to explain the saturation of an enzyme by the substrate;
- explain the mechanism of enzyme reactions in terms of an enzyme–substrate complex;
- understand how the Michaelis constant is derived and how it can be applied;
- describe the concept of enzyme inhibition;
- explain the importance of enzyme inhibition in metabolism;
- appreciate the significance of energy in biochemical processes;
- explain the concept of energy transduction;
- understand the link between bond energies and endergonic or exergonic reactions;
- give examples of endergonic and exergonic reactions;
- describe the role in metabolism of coupling endergonic and exergonic reactions;
- appreciate the fundamental role of adenosine triphosphate in the energetics of metabolism.

Questions

Try the following questions to test your knowledge of reaction rate and enzymes as catalysts. If your answers are correct, you could proceed to Chapter 17.

Q16.1 In cell respiration, fumarate combines with water in the presence of fumarase to form malate.
- (a) Write the rate equation for this process.
- (b) Explain the significance of each of the terms used.

Q16.2 List three distinctive characteristics of enzyme catalysts.

Q16.3 The phosphorylation of glucose is catalysed by glucokinase with the formation of glucose 6-phosphate. At high concentrations of glucose the enzyme becomes saturated with the substrate.
- (a) Explain the meaning of the term 'saturated' in this context.
- (b) What is the order of reaction under conditions of saturation?

Q16.4 What is meant by the term enzyme inhibition?

Q16.5 What is an exergonic reaction?

Q16.6 Draw an energy-level diagram to show that the hydrolysis of adenosine triphosphate to adenosine diphosphate is an exergonic process.

Q16.7 What is meant by the term 'coupled reaction'?

16.1   Rate of reaction

Section 3.4 (page 23) showed that the rate (speed) of a biochemical reaction depends on a number of factors. Concentration of substrates (reactants), temperature, pH or acidity, and the presence of a catalyst all affect the rate of reaction. When the conditions used for a particular reaction are held constant, the rate remains the same. This idea can be expressed by the relationship:

$$\text{rate of reaction} = \text{constant} \times \text{concentration of substrate}$$

In terms of symbols:

$$\text{rate} = k[S]$$

'Rate' means the speed at which the substrate, S, is used up as the time from the start of the reaction increases. The square brackets around the symbol for substrate denotes concentration of substrate. Concentration is expressed in moles per cubic decimetre (mol dm^{-3}). When more than one substrate takes part in the reaction, the concentration of each is included in the equation. The constant k has a fixed value for a specific reaction. It is called the rate constant. The above equation is called the rate equation.

In some biological reactions, such as those catalysed by enzymes, the reaction rate does not depend on substrate concentration at high substrate concentrations. This can be explained in terms of an idea called 'order of reaction' and by considering the enzyme–substrate interaction (see below). The order of reaction is the power to which the concentration of the substrate is raised in the rate equation. Where rate does not depend on substrate concentration, the order of reaction is zero. This is written in the rate equation as follows:

$$\text{rate} = k[S]^0$$

Any number or the concentration of substrate raised to the power 0 is equal to one. Thus the equation becomes:

$$\text{rate} = k \times 1$$

This is written:

$$\text{rate} = k$$

In many other reactions the order is 1 for each of the substrates. This may be written:

$$\text{rate} = k[S]^1$$

It is usual to leave out the '1'.

Example 16.1
In cell respiration, glucose reacts with adenosine triphosphate, ATP, to form glucose-6-phosphate and adenosine diphosphate, ADP. Write the rate equation for the process.

The rate depends on the concentrations of the two substrates, glucose and ATP. So the equation is:

$$\text{rate} = k[\text{glucose}][\text{ATP}]$$

Question

Q16.8 Dihydroxyacetone phosphate is converted into glyceraldehyde-3-phosphate by the enzyme triose phosphate isomerase in glycolysis.
(a) Give a rate equation for this reaction.
(b) How would the rate equation change if the order of reaction was 0?

16.2 Enzymes as catalysts

A catalyst speeds up the rate of reaction but is unchanged at the end of the reaction. Enzymes are the catalysts found in biological systems. They are proteins and are by no means ordinary catalysts. Enzymes are highly efficient, thus the hydration of carbon dioxide to carbonic acid proceeds 10^7 times faster in the presence of the enzyme carbonic anhydrase:

$$\text{carbon dioxide + water} \xrightarrow{\text{carbonic anhydrase}} \text{carbonic acid}$$

Enzymes are extremely specific; they react only with one type of substrate. Only a single type of reaction takes place. The enzyme trypsin will break only the peptide bonds on the carboxyl side of lysine and arginine residues.

Enzymes are sensitive to the conditions around them. They are most effective at a specific pH value and their activity declines as the pH value moves further away from the optimum value. Like other proteins, enzymes are denatured by heat and by large changes in pH. Catalytic activity is lost on denaturation.

An energy barrier has to be overcome for a reaction to take place. This is called the activation energy. Enzymes speed up the rate of a reaction by lowering the activation energy. Thus the enzyme succinate dehydrogenase lowers the activation energy for the conversion of succinate into fumarate. This is shown in the reaction profile given in Figure 16.1.

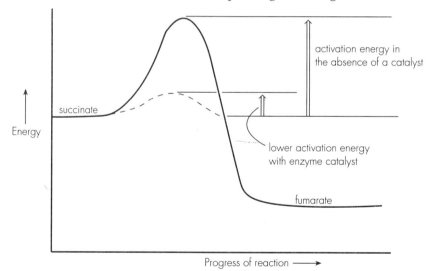

Figure 16.1 Activation energy in the presence or absence of an enzyme catalyst

The enzyme catalase speeds up the decomposition of hydrogen peroxide to water and oxygen.

$$\text{hydrogen peroxide} \xrightarrow{\text{catalase}} \text{water + oxygen}$$

$$2H_2O_2 \xrightarrow{\text{catalase}} 2H_2O + O_2$$

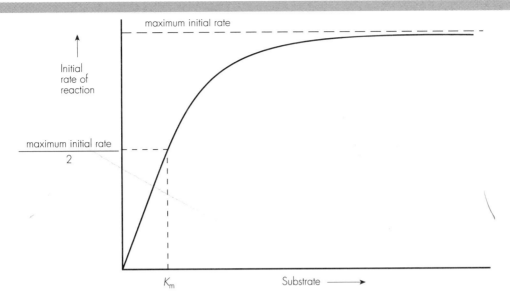

Figure 16.2 Variation of initial rate with substrate concentration

The progress of the reaction can be followed by measuring the rate of evolution of oxygen. When the initial rate (the rate at the start of the reaction) is measured for different concentrations of hydrogen peroxide, it varies as shown in Figure 16.2. The initial rate increases steadily with an increase in the concentration of hydrogen peroxide at the start of the reaction. The rate of reaction is first order. At higher concentrations of hydrogen peroxide, the rate gradually levels off until eventually the rate remains constant. At this stage the reaction is said to be 'saturated' with substrate. The rate of reaction has zero order.

Question

Q16.9 (a) What is the activation energy for a biochemical process?
  (b) How is it changed by an enzyme catalyst?

The order can be explained by considering the detailed interaction between substrate and enzyme molecules. Michaelis and Menten first suggested these ideas. The enzyme E is considered to combine reversibly (see Section 3.5, page 24) with the substrate S to form an enzyme–substrate complex, ES:

$$\text{enzyme} + \text{substrate} \rightleftharpoons \text{enzyme–substrate complex}$$
$$\text{E} + \text{S} \rightleftharpoons \text{ES}$$

The complex then breaks down to give the product P and releases the enzyme:

$$\text{enzyme–substrate complex} \rightleftharpoons \text{product} + \text{enzyme}$$
$$\text{ES} \rightleftharpoons \text{P} + \text{E}$$

At low substrate concentrations, many enzyme molecules are available to react with the substrate. Free enzyme molecules are always present. The initial rate of reaction is low; the reaction is first order. At higher substrate concentrations, most enzyme molecules are involved in forming the ES complex. The initial rate is high. At very high concentrations of substrate, all the enzyme molecules are used but many substrate molecules remain in excess. The initial rate is high with a zero order of reaction. The enzyme is saturated with substrate. This is shown in Figure 16.3, overleaf.

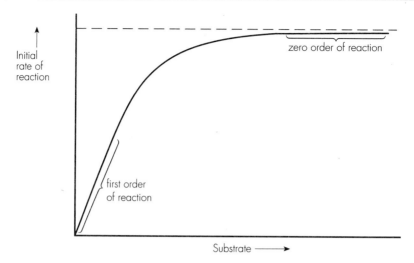

Figure 16.3 Change in order of reaction with substrate concentration for an enzyme-catalysed reaction

Useful information on the enzyme catalase can be obtained from the curve in Figure 16.2. The maximum initial rate can be measured. If this figure is divided by two, the corresponding value of the substrate concentration can be found from the curve (see Figure 16.2). The value obtained is the Michaelis constant, K_m, which is used in the assay of enzyme activity in tissues. Within the cell, substrate concentrations are often low and so the K_m value indicates how effective the enzyme will be at a given concentration. An enzyme with a low K_m will work at maximum rate at a low substrate concentration.

K_m has the units of moles per cubic decimetre and values in the range 10^{-1}–10^{-5} mol dm^{-3} of the substrate.

Question

Q16.10 Briefly explain the mechanism of enzyme reactions on the basis of enzyme–substrate interactions.

Enzyme inhibition

The effectiveness of enzymes as catalysts may be affected by the presence of various substances. Some of these enhance the activity of the enzyme, while others interfere with and slow down the reaction of the substrate. A competitive inhibitor, a substance that is very close to the substrate in its composition and structure, slows down the reaction. The enzyme succinate dehydrogenase catalyses the oxidation of succinate to fumarate:

succinate $\xrightarrow{\text{succinate dehydrogenase}}$ fumarate $+$ hydrogen

This process is inhibited by malonate, which is similar to succinate. Malonate forms an enzyme–substrate complex in the same way as succinate, but malonate cannot undergo oxidation in the same way as succinate. It remains bound to the enzyme preventing the succinate from linking with it:

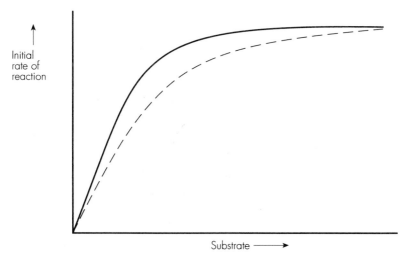

When the initial rate of reaction is plotted against substrate concentration for a fixed concentration of inhibitor, the inhibition steadily decreases as the substrate concentration increases (Figure 16.4).

The substrate and the inhibitor bind to the enzyme molecule at a specific site, the active site. The nature of the active site is critical in determining enzyme–substrate interactions. A discussion of the active site is beyond the scope of this book, but the idea of inhibition is important in metabolism. The presence of an inhibitor can be used to control an enzyme-catalysed reaction, or sequence of reactions, in the cell. The product of a reaction sequence can act as an inhibitor for an earlier stage in the sequence. This prevents formation of an undesirable excess of the final product. The term feedback control or negative feedback is used to describe this situation, where a product acts as an inhibitor for its formation.

Figure 16.4 Variation of initial rate with substrate concentration in the presence of a competitive inhibitor. ——, no inhibitor present; – – –, competitive inhibitor present

Question

Q16.11 Explain the mechanism by which an inhibitor affects the rate of an enzyme-catalysed reaction.

16.3 Exergonic and endergonic reactions

When a biochemical reaction takes place, energy is involved. The oxidation of glucose to carbon dioxide and water releases energy. This energy is used by the organism to bring about physical or chemical changes, such as muscle contraction or the synthesis of glycogen. Energy available for release in a biochemical reaction is potential energy, which is released as heat, mechanical energy or in other forms. This interconversion of energy is called transduction. The unit bringing about the interconversion is known as a transducer. Cell mitochondria act as transducers to convert chemical energy into heat energy and other forms of chemical energy. Since animals and plants are continually using energy for their metabolic processes, it needs to be replaced at intervals.

Animals obtain energy by taking in food, which contains potential energy. Green plants take in light energy from the sun and use it to synthesise nutrients. Ultimately, almost all life forms depend on the energy of the sun and the role green plants play in trapping it. Let us consider how energy is captured and transferred. The process of photosynthesis uses light energy to rearrange the chemical bonds in carbon dioxide and water to form new bonds in glucose and other carbohydrates (see Chapter 18). Energy has to be taken in by the plant to break chemical bonds and energy is released when the new bonds are formed. If the energy required to break the bonds in carbon dioxide and water is measured and compared with the energy released when the new bonds are formed, we find that more energy is required than is released (Figure 16.5). A reaction, such as photosynthesis, that requires energy is called an endergonic reaction.

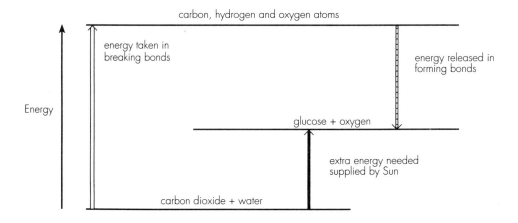

Figure 16.5 Photosynthesis as an endergonic reaction

Question

Q16.12 Explain what is meant by the statement: 'Photosynthesis is an endergonic reaction'.

When animals use carbohydrates in respiration to give carbon dioxide and water, the energy released is greater than the energy required. This is an exergonic reaction (Figure 16.6). The energy released is available for use by the organism. It may be used immediately or may be stored in a readily available form such as ATP. Energy is required to phosphorylate ADP to form ATP. This energy is easily used by the cell. ATP is involved in many specific aspects of

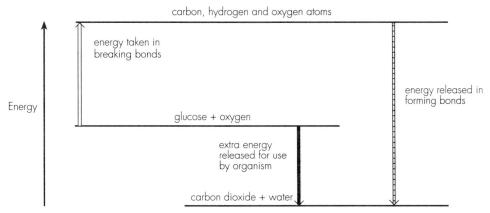

Figure 16.6 Respiration as an exergonic reaction

cell metabolism, including transport across cell membranes, building up of protein, fat and carbohydrate macromolecules, and muscle contraction. ATP releases its energy to the cell when it takes up water and is converted into adenosine diphosphate (ADP) and an inorganic phosphate group. This is an exergonic reaction.

$$\text{adenosine triphosphate} + \text{water} \longrightarrow \text{adenosine diphosphate} + \text{phosphate}$$
$$\text{ATP} + H_2O \longrightarrow \text{ADP} + P_i$$

The energy changes involved can be shown on an energy level diagram (Figure 16.7).

Question

Q16.13 Draw an energy-level diagram to show that the conversion of glyceric acid diphosphate into glyceric acid 3-phosphate is an exergonic reaction.

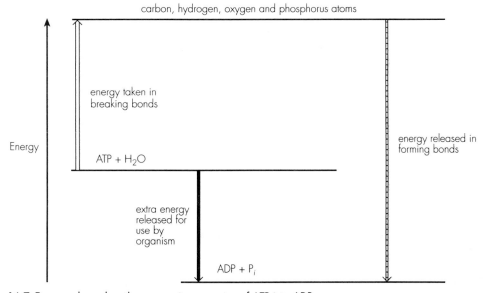

Figure 16.7 Energy released on the exergonic conversion of ATP into ADP

The exergonic conversion of ATP into ADP liberates energy of about 30 kJ mol^{-1}, i.e. 30 kilo joules for each mole of ATP broken down. The reaction can be coupled to an endergonic process that is useful to the cell and that requires less than 30 kJ mol^{-1}. The conversion of glucose into polysaccharides takes place by a reaction between the growing polysaccharide chain and glucose phosphate formed in an endergonic process from glucose and inorganic phosphate:

$$\text{glucose} + \text{phosphate} \longrightarrow \text{glucose phosphate}$$

The conversion requires energy of about 16 kJ mol^{-1} to be supplied. However, it can be coupled to the ATP–ADP reaction to give a process that is exergonic overall:

$$\text{ATP} + \text{glucose} \longrightarrow \text{ADP} + \text{glucose phosphate}$$

The coupling of exergonic and endergonic reactions is a most important mechanism in cell metabolism. Some examples are shown in Figure 16.8.

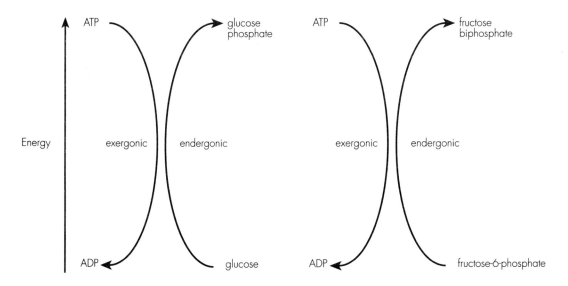

Figure 16.8 Coupling of exergonic and endergonic reactions in metabolic processes

ATP is a convenient store of energy, but it has to be formed from ADP and inorganic phosphate in an endergonic reaction. The energy needed is obtained from photosynthesis in plants (see Chapter 18) and from respiration in animals (see Chapter 17). The energy diagram (Figure 16.9) shows that extra energy is needed to convert ADP into ATP. The coupling of ATP formation to photosynthesis and to respiration is outlined in Figure 16.10. The overall coupled process is exergonic in each case.

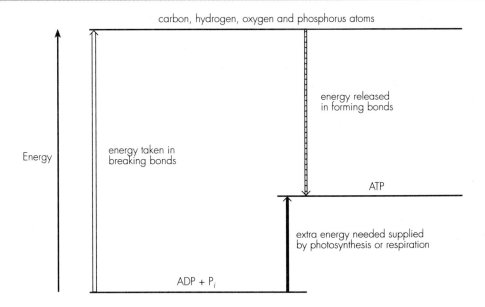

Figure 16.9 Synthesis of ATP from ADP. The extra energy required for this endergonic reaction is provided by photosynthesis or respiration

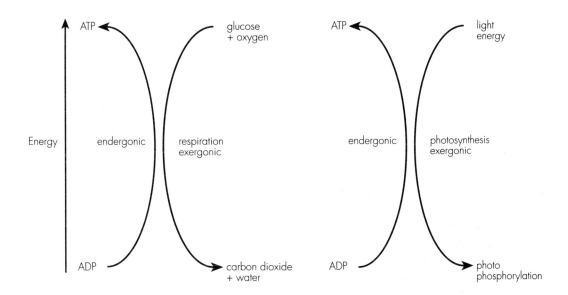

Figure 16.10 Coupling of ATP synthesis to respiration and photosynthesis

Summary

The rate of a biochemical reaction is affected by changes in the concentration of substrates, the temperature, the pH and by the presence or absence of a catalyst. The rate of reaction may be defined by a rate equation. Enzyme catalysts show high specificity, high efficiency and pH sensitivity. They promote reactions within the cell and help reduce the energy barrier to the reaction. Enzymes are often active under conditions in which the substrate is in large excess. The mechanism of enzyme reactions may be understood in terms of enzyme–substrate interactions. The reactions are inhibited by various substances and sometimes by the product of reaction. This leads to feedback control of the process. Energy is changed from one form to another in the living cell, which requires a constant supply of energy to be available. Exergonic reactions, which give out energy, are used to drive metabolic processes. These usually involve endergonic reactions, which take in energy. ATP undergoes an exergonic change when it forms ADP. This reaction is often coupled to an endergonic process.

Self-assessment questions

Try the following questions on rate, enzymes and energy.

Q16.14 Glucose combines with fructose to form sucrose with the elimination of water.
  (a) Write a word equation to represent this reaction.
  (b) Give a rate equation for the process.

Q16.15 What is meant by the term 'order of reaction'?

Q16.16 Enzymes are highly specific, highly efficient catalysts. Why are these factors important in cell metabolism?

Q16.17 Draw an energy profile for the conversion of ATP into ADP and P_i to show how the activation energy varies with presence or absence of the enzyme ATPase.

Q16.18 (a) Use a sketch graph to illustrate how the initial rate of an enzyme-catalysed reaction varies with concentration of substrate.
  (b) Show how the graph can be used to determine the Michaelis constant for the reaction.

Q16.19 The phosphorylation of glucose to glucose-6-phosphate in the presence of hexokinase is inhibited by the product.
  (a) What do you understand by the term 'inhibited' in this context?
  (b) How does this reaction illustrate the concept of feedback control (negative feedback)?

Q16.20 Biochemical reactions may be described in energy terms as either exergonic or endergonic. What is the difference between these two types of reaction?

Q16.21 Write a word equation to indicate how ATP releases energy in cell metabolism.

Q16.22 Sketch an energy diagram to show the coupling of ATP synthesis from ADP with cell respiration. Label the exergonic and endergonic parts of the process.

Reduction and Oxidation

Introduction

Most organisms need the energy derived from oxidation to carry out their daily functions, and use reduction processes to manufacture biomolecules. These types of reactions are very important to the cell. You will have been introduced to reduction and oxidation in Chapter 6 (page 41). Some of the fundamental principles outlined there will be reinforced in this chapter.

Objectives

When you have completed this chapter you will be able to:
- give alternative definitions for oxidation and reduction;
- understand the concept of linking oxidation and reduction;
- appreciate the concept of electron donors, carriers and acceptors;
- recall the major cellular electron carriers;
- explain energy yielding electron transfer as exemplified by mitochondrial electron transport chains.

Questions

If these objectives seem familiar, test your knowledge by answering the following questions.

Q17.1 Explain whether the following alterations to a molecule's structure are oxidations or reductions:
  (a) removing electrons;
  (b) removing hydrogens;
  (c) removing oxygen.

Q17.2 The following is a redox reaction:

$$\text{acetaldehyde} + NADH + H^+ \rightleftharpoons \text{ethanol} + NAD^+$$

  (a) Which of the reactants becomes reduced?
  (b) Which of the reactants becomes oxidised?
  (c) Which compound is the reductant?
  (d) Which compound is an electron acceptor?
  (e) Write out the half reactions for acetaldehyde and NADH.

Q17.3 Use Table 17.1 to decide whether the following reactions will proceed in the forward (left to right) or backward direction:
  (a) $$\text{acetaldehyde} + NADH + H^+ \rightleftharpoons \text{ethanol} + NAD^+$$
  (b) $$\text{ubiquinone}_{(ox)} + \text{cytochrome } c_{(red)} \rightleftharpoons \text{ubiquinone}_{(red)} + \text{cytochrome } c_{(ox)}$$

Q17.4 Name one product produced by mitochondria as a result of 'downhill' electron transport.

Q17.5 Give the names of two commonly occurring quinones and state their location in the cell.

17.1 Oxidation and reduction reactions

The overall reactions for many of the processes found in biology involve the reduction or oxidation of compounds. For example, the complete oxidation of glucose sugar is:

$$\text{glucose} + \text{oxygen} \longrightarrow \text{carbon dioxide} + \text{water}$$
$$C_6H_{12}O_6 + 6O_2 \longrightarrow 6CO_2 + 6H_2O$$

In this reaction, the sugar has been broken down and oxygen has been added to both the carbon and hydrogen atoms. The carbon dioxide formed has a maximum number of oxygens bound to it and is said to be completely oxidised. Likewise, in a water molecule, each hydrogen atom is bonded to oxygen and is said to be completely oxidised. Conversely, in the sugar, some of the carbons and hydrogens are bound to each other. The glucose is said to be 'reduced' when compared with carbon dioxide. Reduction can be seen as adding hydrogen atoms, or removing oxygen atoms; oxidation is the opposite, removing hydrogen or adding oxygen atoms.

When hydrogen atoms are added to a molecule, covalent bonds are formed. Covalent bonds are electron-sharing bonds. Electrons are also added.

Reduction is one of three processes: adding hydrogen
                                                adding electrons
                                                removing oxygen.

Oxidation is the opposite: removing hydrogen
                                                  adding oxygen
                                                removing electrons.

The oxygen involved in the complete oxidation of sugar ends up as part of carbon dioxide or water. The oxygen has been reduced. This is an important feature of all oxidation and reduction reactions, in that both oxidation and reduction must occur during the course of the reaction. The reaction between any two molecules A and B involving an oxidation and reduction can be written:

$$A_{oxidised} + B_{reduced} \rightleftharpoons A_{reduced} + B_{oxidised}$$

The word oxidised is abbreviated to ox and reduced to red. Reactions involving reduction and oxidation are often called redox reactions. The redox reaction between A and B shown above can be rewritten:

$$A_{ox} + B_{red} \rightleftharpoons A_{red} + B_{ox}$$

In this reaction, A has been reduced by B and B has been oxidised by A. B is called a reducing agent or reductant and A is called an oxidising agent or oxidant.

Example 17.1

Look at the following redox reactions. Decide for each which is the oxidant and which is the reductant:

(a) $HOOC-CH_2-CH_2-COOH$ + FAD $\longrightarrow$ $HOOC-CH=CH-COOH$ + $FADH_2$
                succinate   + FAD $\longrightarrow$ fumarate   + $FADH_2$

(b) $6CO_2 + 6H_2O \xrightarrow[\text{energy}]{\text{light}}$ glucose + $6O_2$

(c) Zn (metal) + Cu^{2+}(ion in solution) $\rightarrow Zn^{2+}$ + Cu (precipitate)

Method

The reaction in redox reaction (a) shows FAD $\rightarrow$ FADH$_2$. The FAD has had $2H^+$ and $2e^-$ added to its structure. It has become reduced. The succinate has had $2e^-$ and $2H^+$ removed. It has become oxidised. Succinate is the reductant and FAD is the oxidant.

The reaction (b) shows $6CO_2 \rightarrow C_6H_{12}O_6$. The carbon dioxide has been reduced ($+H$ and $-O$) so the carbon dioxide is the oxidant. Water has been oxidised to oxygen ($-H$ and $+O$) so water is the reductant.

In redox reaction (c), the Zn has lost two electrons to the copper. The reaction for zinc should be $Zn \rightarrow Zn^{2+} + 2e^-$. Zinc has been oxidised. Zinc is the reductant. The opposite is true for copper $Cu^{2+} + 2e^- \rightarrow Cu$. Copper has gained two electrons and has been reduced. Copper is the oxidant.

Question

Q17.6 Look at the following redox reactions. For each decide which is the oxidant and which is the reductant:

(a) $Fe^{2+} + Cu^{2+} \rightarrow Fe^{3+} + Cu^+$

(b) pyruvate + NADH + H$^+$ $\longrightarrow$ lactate + NAD$^+$

$$\begin{array}{ccc} COO^- & & COO^- \\ | & & | \\ C=O & \longrightarrow & H-C-OH \\ | & & | \\ CH_3 & & CH_3 \end{array}$$

(c) glucose + O_2 → gluconolactone + H_2O_2

17.2   Redox half reactions

In Example 17.1, the answer was made simple by considering the fate of each reactant separately. Thus in reaction (a) the fate of FAD and succinate were considered separately for the reaction between succinate and FAD. Each redox reaction can be split into two **half reactions**. The two half reactions for Example 17.1 (a) are shown below:

$$FAD + 2H^+ + 2e^- \longrightarrow FADH_2$$
$$succinate \longrightarrow fumarate + 2H^+ + 2e^-$$

If the two left-hand half reactions are added together, the left-hand half of the reaction shown in Example 17.1 is formed if the H$^+$s and e$^-$s that appear on both sides of the equation for the reaction are cancelled out. The same will happen if we add the two right-hand half reactions together. An important feature that is emerging is the importance of electron transfer in redox reactions. In Example 17.1 (a) succinate gives two protons and two electrons to FAD. In this reaction succinate is an electron donor and FAD is an electron acceptor. In the cell, the FAD carries its electrons to the mitochondrial electron-transport chain where it then acts as an electron donor (to ubiquinone and eventually to oxygen). Molecules such as FAD, which act as intermediates in overall processes, are also called electron carriers. As with many other reactions, redox half reactions have a general formula. This is

$$OX + ne^- \rightarrow RED$$

Example 17.2
Write down the half reactions for the following overall reactions:
(a) $Zn + Cu^{2+} \rightarrow Zn^{2+} + Cu$;
(b) $Fe^{2+} + Cu^{2+} \rightarrow Fe^{3+} + Cu^+$.
Half reactions are:
(a) $Zn \rightarrow Zn^{2+} + 2e^-$ and $Cu^{2+} + 2e^- \rightarrow Cu$;
(b) $Fe^{2+} \rightarrow Fe^{3+} + e^-$ and $Cu^{2+} + e^- \rightarrow Cu^+$.

Question

Q17.7 Break the following reactions down into half reactions:

(a)   cytochrome $b(Fe^{2+})$ + cytochrome $c(Fe^{3+})$ $\rightleftharpoons$ cytochrome $b(Fe^{3+})$ + cytochrome $c(Fe^{2+})$

(b)   pyruvate + NADH + H$^+$ $\rightleftharpoons$ lactate + NAD$^+$

17.3 Standard reduction potentials

To find out in which direction redox reactions will proceed, the abilities of different redox half reactions to act as electron donors or acceptors are compared. To do this, all half reactions must be compared in the same direction, i.e. ox + ne^- → red. A scale known as the **standard reduction potential** (standard electrode potential) scale is used to compare half reactions. A list of some biochemical redox half reactions with standard reduction potentials is shown in Table 17.1. The standard reduction potential is given the symbol E'_0.

The units of redox potential are **volts** (V). The more negative E'_0 will normally act as the electron donor, the more positive as the electron acceptor (given equal concentrations of oxidised and reduced forms).

Example 17.3

Use Table 17.1 to predict the direction of electron transfer between the following half reactions:
(a) $NAD^+/NADH + H^+$ and pyruvate/lactate;
(b) ubiquinone (oxidised)/ubiquinone (reduced) and $\frac{1}{2}O_2/H_2O$.

For the half reactions in (a): the $NAD^+/NADH$ standard reduction potential (E'_0) = -0.32 V; and the pyruvate/lactate standard reduction potential (E'_0) = -0.19 V.
Electrons will flow from negative to positive (or less negative), that is from -0.32 V to -0.19 V, or from NADH to pyruvate:

$$H^+ + NADH \longrightarrow NAD^+ + 2H^+ + 2e^- \quad \text{(NADH gives electrons).}$$
$$\text{pyruvate} + 2H^+ + 2e^- \longrightarrow \text{lactate} \quad \text{(lactate accepts electrons)}$$

Table 17.1 Standard redox potentials of some half reactions

Oxidant	Reductant	Number of electrons (n)	E'_0 (V)
Succinate + CO_2	α-Ketoglutarate	2	−0.67
Acetate	Acetaldehyde	2	−0.60
Ferredoxin (oxidised)	Ferredoxin (reduced)	1	−0.43
2 H^+	H_2	2	−0.42
NAD^+	$NADH + H^+$	2	−0.32
$NADP^+$	$NADPH + H^+$	2	−0.32
Lipoate (oxidised)	Lipoate (reduced)	2	−0.29
Glutathione (oxidised)	Glutathione (reduced)	2	−0.23
Acetaldehyde	Ethanol	2	−0.20
Pyruvate	Lactate	2	−0.19
Fumarate	Succinate	2	0.03
Cytochrome b_1 (+3)	Cytochrome b_1 (+2)	1	0.07
Dehydroascorbate	Ascorbate	2	0.08
Ubiquinone (oxidised)	Ubiquinone (reduced)	2	0.10
Cytochrome c (+3)	Cytochrome c (+2)	1	0.22
Fe (+3)	Fe (+2)	1	0.77
$\frac{1}{2}O_2/H_2O$	H_2O	2	0.82

E'_0 is the standard oxidation–reduction potential (pH 7, 25 °C) and n is the number of electrons transferred. E'_0 refers to the partial reaction written as: oxidant + ne^- → reductant

where concentration of oxidant is the same as reductant.

Add the two half reactions:

$$\text{pyruvate} + \text{NADH} + \text{H}^+ \rightarrow \text{lactate} + \text{NAD}^+$$

(Note that 2H^+ and 2e^- appear on both sides of the added equation and have been cancelled out.)

For (b) $E'_0 = 0.10$ V for ubiquinone/ubiquinone (reduced); and $E'_0 = 0.82$ V for $\frac{1}{2}\text{O}_2/\text{H}_2\text{O}$. Electrons flow from ubiquinone to oxygen:

$$\text{ubiquinone (reduced)} \rightarrow \text{ubiquinone (oxidised)} + 2\text{H}^+ + 2\text{e}^-$$
$$\tfrac{1}{2}\text{O}_2 + 2\text{H}^+ + 2\text{e}^- \rightarrow \text{H}_2\text{O}$$

Add the two half reactions:

$$\tfrac{1}{2}\text{O}_2 + \text{ubiquinone (reduced)} \rightarrow \text{ubiquinone (oxidised)} + \text{H}_2\text{O}$$

(Protons and electrons have been cancelled out.)

Question

Q17.8 Use Table 17.1 to calculate direction of electron flow for the following redox couples:

    (a) cytochrome c $(+3)$/cytochrome c $(+2)$ and ferredoxin $(+3)$/ferredoxin $(+2)$

    (b) cytochrome b_1 $(+3)$/cytochrome b_1 $(+2)$ and cytochrome c $(+3)$/cytochrome c $(+2)$

17.4 Electron flow and energy

We have now seen that given E'_0 values we can calculate which direction electrons wish to flow. If electrons want to flow in the direction shown, then the reaction is energetically favourable and will want to proceed in the direction written. In Example 17.2 (b), electrons will want to flow from ubiquinone to oxygen. The flow of electrons can be considered as running down an energy 'hill' (Figure 17.1).

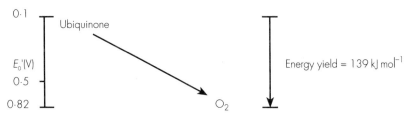

Figure 17.1 The 'downhill' flow of electrons from ubiquinine to oxygen is shown as from $0.1 \text{ V} \rightarrow 0.82 \text{ V}$. This corresponds to a large free energy change

The 'downhill' path of electrons can give a large free energy of around -140 kJ mol^{-1}. This 'downhill' electron flow is used by many cells to drive energetically unfavourable reactions ('uphill'!). The mitochondrial inner membrane contains many electron transport carriers arranged in a chain. The electrons flow 'downhill' through the chain. At various points the energetically 'downhill' flow of electrons is 'linked' (coupled) to the 'uphill' reaction of ADP phosphorylation. A similar series of electron-transport chains in the thylakoid membranes of chloroplasts results in both ADP phosphorylation and 'reducing power' in the form of NADPH (see Chapter 18). The mitochondrial electron-transport chain is shown in Figure 17.2, overleaf, emphasising the points at which ATP synthesis (ADP phosphorylation) takes place.

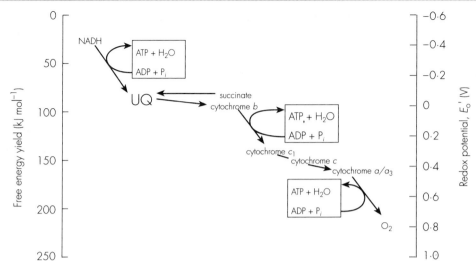

<u>Figure 17.2</u> The electron-transport chain in mitochondria. Note the direction of energetic flow is downhill with three 'steps' large enough to be coupled to ADP phosphorylation

17.5 The major cellular electron carriers

There are several types of electron carriers in living cells. Only the most important will be reviewed here.

Nicotinamide-linked carriers

These are nicotinamide mononucleotide (NMN), nicotinamide adenine dinucleotide (NAD^+ and NADH), and nicotinamide adenine dinucleotide phosphate ($NADP^+$ and NADPH). The nicotinamide changes its structure on reduction to incorporate two electrons and one proton. A typical reaction is shown below for NAD^+; $NADP^+$ and NMN have similar reduction reactions (see Chapter 11, page 97).

$$NAD^+ + 2e^- + H^+ \rightleftharpoons NADH$$

Flavin-linked carriers

These are flavin mononucleotide (FMN) and flavin adenine dinucleotide (FAD or $FADH_2$). The flavin changes its structure on reduction to incorporate two protons and two electrons, shown below for FAD (see also Chapter 11, page 97).

$$FAD + 2H^+ + 2e^- \rightleftharpoons FADH_2$$

Quinones

Two quinones, ubiquinone (also called coenzyme Q) and plastoquinone, are found in mitochondria and chloroplasts, respectively. They are often abbreviated to UQ (or CoQ) for ubiquinone and PQ for plastoquinone. Their structure contains a hydrophobic tail, which acts to anchor the quinone in the membrane, and a quinone head group, which carries two protons and two electrons when reduced. The reduction of UQ is shown below:

$$UQ + 2H^+ + 2e^- \rightleftharpoons UQH_2$$
$$\text{ubiquinone} \rightleftharpoons \text{ubiquinol}$$
$$\text{(reduced ubiquinone)}$$

Cytochromes

These cytochromes are proteins with a covalently bound haem group (similar to the haem in haemoglobin). The haem contains an iron ion in the centre. The iron ion (Fe^{3+}) can undergo a one-electron reduction to give a reduced haem (Fe^{2+}). Several cytochromes are found in mitochondria and chloroplasts, and are distinguished from each other by colour. Reduction of cytochrome c is shown below:

$$\text{Cytochrome } c(Fe^{3+}) + e^- \rightleftharpoons \text{cytochrome } c(Fe^{2+})$$

Metal ions

Many transition metal ions are important in electron movements in cells. Of these iron (Fe^{3+}) and copper (Cu^{2+}) are important. The iron is often held as a complex with sulphur in iron–sulphur proteins (abbreviated FeS or ISP). Both iron and copper undergo one-electron reductions to yield Fe^{2+} and Cu^+, as shown below for iron:

$$Fe^{3+} + e^- \rightleftharpoons Fe^{2+}$$

Summary

Reduction and oxidation are important processes in living cells. Reduction can be viewed as gaining electrons, gaining hydrogen, or losing oxygen; oxidation is the converse. In biological reactions, reduction of one molecule occurs simultaneously with oxidation of another; such reactions are called redox reactions. The molecule that acts to reduce another is called a reductant, and becomes oxidised; oxidisers are called oxidants and become reduced. Some molecules in the cell act as electron carriers. They act as electron acceptors when being reduced and electron donors when being oxidised. In a redox reaction, the fate of one molecule can be separated out to give a redox half reaction. The ability of a half reaction to accept or donate electrons can be defined by the standard reduction potential (E'_0). Electrons will pass from more negative E'_0 to more positive E'_0. Passage of electrons from negative to positive is energetically favourable and can be linked to ADP phosphorylation or manufacture of reducing power. There are five main types of electron carriers in cells: flavins, nicotinamides, quinones, cytochromes and metals.

Self-assessment questions

Q17.9 A molecule is altered by having hydrogens added to its structure. Has this molecule been oxidised or reduced?

Q17.10 Look at the following redox reaction:

$$\text{cytochrome } a(Fe^{3+}) + \text{cytochrome } c(Fe^{2+}) \rightleftharpoons \text{cytochrome } a(Fe^{2+}) + \text{cytochrome } c(Fe^{3+})$$

    (a) Which cytochrome becomes reduced?
    (b) Which cytochrome becomes oxidised?
    (c) Which compounds are the oxidant and reductant?
    (d) Write out the half reactions for cytochrome a and cytochrome c.
    (e) Which reactant is the electron acceptor and which is the electron donor?

Q17.11 Decide whether the following reactions will proceed in the forward (left to right) or backward directions given the (E'_0) values in Table 17.1.

    (a) acetate + NADH + H^+ $\rightleftharpoons$ acetaldehyde + NAD^+
    (b) fumarate + NADPH + H^+ $\rightleftharpoons$ succinate + $NADP^+$

Q17.12 Name two products produced by 'downhill' electron transport in chloroplasts.

Q17.13 Name two cellular electron carriers that are bound to nucleotides.

Molecules and Light

Introduction

The absorption of light by the pigment of leaves and the use of the energy contained in the light to synthesise complex biomolecules is one of the fundamental parts of biological study. The process can be divided into two stages: the light and the dark reactions. The dark reactions involve the alteration of biomolecules to make sugar and more complex molecules. The light reactions are concerned with making the 'energy' required to turn carbon dioxide into sugars. The light reactions involve the conversion of the energy contained in light into the stable energy stores ATP and NADPH.

That light is a form of energy is without question. The power of laser light sources and the use of photocells to make electricity are good examples of the work that can be obtained from light. This chapter will cover some of the elementary scientific ideas that help us to understand this complex area of biology.

Objectives

After studying this chapter you will be able to:
- understand the dual nature of light energy;
- explain the nature of absorption of light energy by specific molecules;
- be aware of the fate of absorbed light energy;
- understand how the measurement of light absorption relates to concentration;
- discuss the importance of light absorption in biological processes.

Questions

If you are familiar with this subject, try the questions below to test your knowledge. If your answers are correct, you could proceed to Chapter 19.

Q18.1 Name the symbol for the wavelength.

Q18.2 The frequencies of two light sources are $5 \times 10^{-16} \, s^{-1}$ and $10 \times 10^{-16} \, s^{-1}$. Which light source has the higher energy?

Q18.3 The absorbance spectrum of NADH is shown in Figure 18.1. Give the λ_{max} for NADH in this wavelength range.

Q18.4 Why is a λ_{max} normally chosen to measure the concentration of a molecule?

Q18.5 The ϵ (molar absorption coefficient) of the haem in cytochrome c is $29\,100 \, mol^{-1} \, dm^3 \, cm^{-1}$ at 551 nm. A solution of cytochrome c extracted from liver cells has an absorbance of 0.582 units at 551 nm in a light path of 1 cm. What is the concentration of haem in the liver cell extract?

Q18.6 Give two possible fates for the absorbed light energy in a molecule.

Q18.7 State the two main products resulting from the light reactions of photosynthesis.

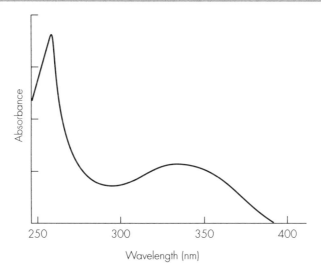

Figure 18.1 The absorbance spectrum of NADH

18.1 The electromagnetic spectrum

Light energy is part of the electromagnetic spectrum and is the part visible to the human eye. The electromagnetic spectrum includes a wide range of energy transmissions ('radiation') including gamma rays, X-rays, ultraviolet, infrared and radio waves. The only difference between these types of radiation is the wavelength.

The wavelength

The wavelength is one of the ways in which light can be described. Light can be viewed as travelling in waves that look like a sine wave (Figure 18.2). The distance between successive peaks is called the wavelength, which is given the symbol λ. Radio waves have very long wavelengths (~200 m), while gamma rays have extremely short wavelengths (~10^{-13} m).

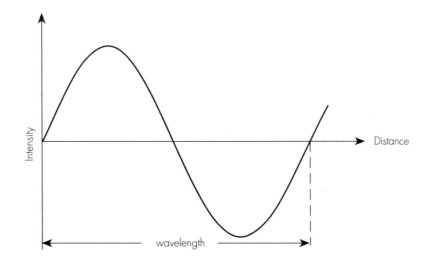

Figure 18.2 Electromagnetic radiation (such as light) can be described by a wave with wavelength λ

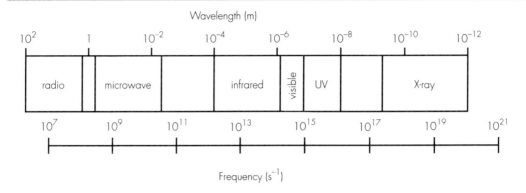

Figure 18.3 The relationship between frequency, type of radiation, and wavelength

Visible light has wavelengths somewhere in between these two values (3.8×10^{-7} m to 7.8×10^{-7} m). All electromagnetic radiation travels at near enough the same speed. This is the speed of light (symbol c) which has the value 3×10^8 m s^{-1}. The number of waves that can fit into one second can be calculated by dividing the speed (c) by the wavelength (λ). This is called the frequency and has the symbol v. The units of frequency are Hertz (Hz, often expressed as s^{-1}). Radio channels are usually referred to by their frequency, and sometimes by their wavelength. The relationship between electromagnetic radiation, frequency and wavelength is shown in Figure 18.3.

Question

Q18.8 Calculate the wavelength range of visible light in nanometres.

The quantum nature of light
Light cannot be fully described by simply thinking of it as a wave. In order to explain the properties of light better, light can also be thought of as a stream of small packets of energy (Figure 18.4). Each packet of energy is called a quantum or **photon**. The energy contained in a photon is defined by the frequency of the light source. The higher the frequency, the higher the energy.

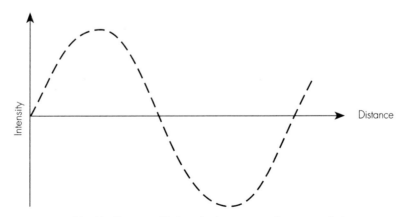

Figure 18.4 A representation of the 'dual' nature of light as both a wave and a stream of photons

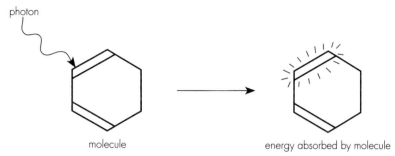

photon

molecule   energy absorbed by molecule

Figure 18.5 Absorption of light energy by a chemical bond

18.2 Light absorption

The absorption of ultraviolet and visible light is related to the electronic structure of individual molecules. The photon absorbed by the molecule must result in a change in the electron's energy level. The electron must be capable of absorbing exactly a photon of energy (Figure 18.5). Biomolecules have widely differing electronic structures and so absorb light at different wavelengths in the ultraviolet and visible region. Each molecule has a characteristic absorption pattern when the wavelength is changed. The variation of light absorption as the wavelength changes is called a **spectrum**. The spectrum of chlorophyll *a* is shown in Figure 18.6, which also shows how the colours of white light are distributed between 400 and 700 nm, the visible range of light.

Chlorophyll absorbs green light poorly (i.e. lets green light pass through) and appears green when in solution. Chlorophyll absorbs light strongly in the red part of the spectrum, due to the arrangement of electrons in the chlorophyll molecule. Only one part of the chlorophyll struc-

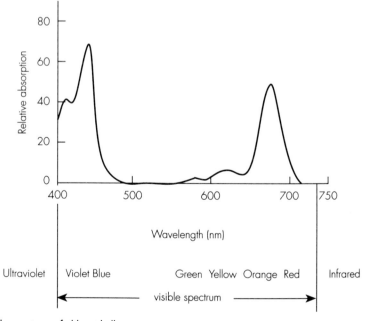

Figure 18.6 The visible spectrum of chlorophyll *a*

ture, the **chromophore**, gives rise to the red absorption peak. The chlorophyll spectrum also has peaks of absorbance in the visible spectrum at about 620 nm, 580 nm, 440 nm and 420 nm. The peak of absorbance is called a wavelength maximum with the symbol λ_{max}. Thus chlorophyll has λ_{max} values at 420 nm, 440 nm, 580 nm, 620 nm and 670 nm.

Question

Q18.9 Why do solutions of chlorophyll appear green?

18.3 Measuring concentrations using colours

Universal indicators can be used to measure the pH of a solution; other biological tests use chemical reactions between biomolecules and other reagents to generate coloured compounds. For example, in the Biuret test for protein, the reagent contains a blue alkaline solution of copper sulphate. When mixed with protein the copper binds to the nitrogen in the peptide bond and changes colour to purple.

The amount of light absorbed by the copper–protein complex is proportional to the concentration of protein in the solution, when measured at a λ_{max}, the most sensitive wavelength at which to measure the concentration. The relationship between absorbance and concentration is given by the Beer–Lambert Law. This is:

$$A = \epsilon c \ell$$

A is the absorbance, c is the concentration, ℓ is the distance that the light has to travel through the solution and ϵ is the absorbance of a one molar solution of the compound (it is a constant for any molecule at a given wavelength). ϵ is also called the molar absorptivity or molar extinction coefficient. The relationship is shown in the graph in Figure 18.7.

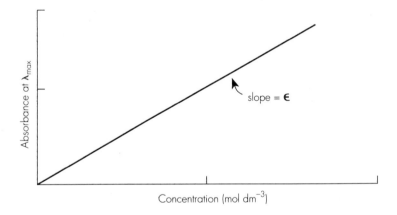

Figure 18.7 The linear relationship between absorbance and concentration expressed by the Beer–Lambert law

In most experiments, the path length is kept to 1 cm, which makes calculations involving the Beer–Lambert Law easy to perform. The instrument used to measure light absorbance is called a spectrophotometer. The use of colour intensity measurements to estimate concentration (spectrophotometry) is one of the most important tools available to the modern biologist. Not only can absolute concentrations be measured for most compounds but often changes in concentrations can be measured. In most living cells the biomolecules are constantly changing and spectrophotometry is one of the ways in which the changes can be measured.

Example 18.1

NADH has an ϵ of $6220 \, mol^{-1} dm^3 \, cm^{-1}$ at 340 nm. A solution of NADH is made to give an absorbance of 0.622 at 340 nm in a 1 cm path length. Calculate the concentration of the NADH solution.

The Beer–Lambert Law is $A = \epsilon c \ell$.

Divide both sides by $\epsilon \times \ell$ to give $A/\epsilon\ell = c$. Now substitute values of A, ϵ and ℓ into the equation to give c:

$$\text{unknown concentration} = \frac{0.622}{6220 \times 1} = 10^{-4} \, mol \, dm^{-3}$$

Question

Q18.10 Calculate the absorbance at 340 nm given by a $2.5 \times 10^{-4} \, mol \, dm^{-3}$ solution of NADH in a 1 cm path length.

18.4 The fate of absorbed light

Energy from light can be absorbed by the electrons in molecules. The electrons that absorb this energy lose stability, and this could result in a chemical reaction in which the structure of the molecule is altered. This property is used in many photographic processes, where light falling on the photographic film causes molecules on the film to change their structure and a picture is formed.

The energy trapped by absorption of light may be passed to a similar molecule by a process known as **resonance energy transfer**. It may be lost as increased movement (bond vibration) resulting in heat generation, or it may be emitted as light of a higher wavelength (fluorescence). The fate of absorbed light is summarised in Figure 18.8.

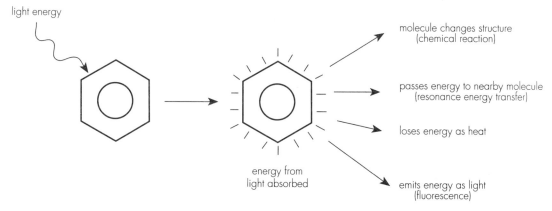

Figure 18.8 The possible fates of absorbed light energy

Light absorption in photosynthesis

Two biological structures make use of light absorption. These are the tissues concerned with 'light' such as the retina of the eye and the chloroplasts of the plant cell. We shall look at the chloroplast.

In photosynthesis, light is trapped by pigments in leaves. Light trapping takes place in the thylakoid membranes of chloroplasts. The trapped light causes a chemical reaction in a part of the thylakoid membrane called a **photosystem**. The part of the photosystem where the chemical reaction takes place is called the **reaction centre**. Plants have two photosystems, I and II.

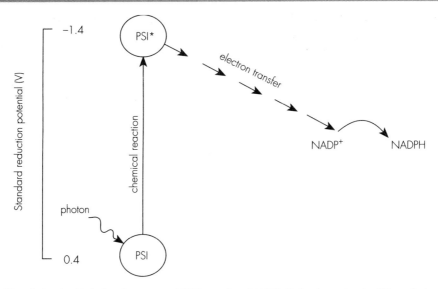

Figure 18.9 Use of absorbed light by photosystem I (PSI) to reduce NADP$^+$. Light absorption by PSI results in a chemical reaction that changes the E'_0 of the reaction centre from +0.4 V to −1.4 V

The chemical reaction in photosystem I (PSI) generates enough energy to drive the reduction of NADP$^+$ (E'_0 for NADP$^+$/NADPH is −0.32 V). The reduction potential of photosystem I changes from +0.4 V to −1.4 V, which gives enough reducing power to drive NADP$^+$ reduction (Figure 18.9). Photosystem II (PSII) catalyses a similar chemical reaction. Light energy causes the photosystem to change its E'_0 from +1.0 V to −0.7 V. The 'downhill' flow of electrons from PSII is linked (indirectly) to ADP phosphorylation (Figure 18.10). The light-absorbing pigment in the reaction centre of PSII has a λ_{max} at 680 nm and so photosystem II is also called P680. A similar name of P700 is used for PSI.

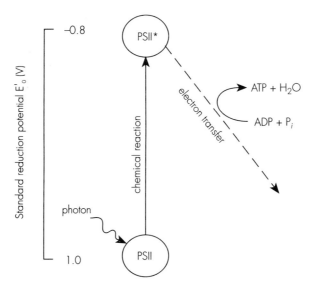

Figure 18.10 Absorption of light by photosystem II. The light absorption results in a chemical reaction where E'_0 changes from +0.1 V to −0.8 V. The energy from this change in E'_0 results in ATP synthesis

Light will only cause a chemical reaction if it strikes P700 or P680 directly. Also the λ_{max} of the reaction centre means that only a limited range of visible wavelengths could be used by the plant for photosynthesis. Plants can, however, successfully use a wide range of visible light to carry out photosynthesis. The two problems are overcome by each reaction centre having a 'network' of light-trapping pigments, known as accessory pigments. These pigments have two properties. Firstly, they can 'trap' light away from the reaction centre. Secondly, there are several different pigments that absorb light over most of the visible spectrum. This allows the trapping of light of most other visible wavelengths.

Light trapped by these pigments is passed to the reaction centre from molecule to molecule by resonance energy transfer. This passing of energy from pigment to pigment to the reaction centre is shown in Figure 18.11.

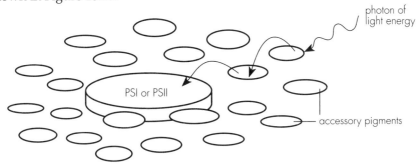

Figure 18.11 Transfer of light from accessory pigments to a reaction centre by resonance energy transfer

Summary

Light is used as an energy source in photosynthesis and vision. Light radiation is the visible part of the electromagnetic spectrum, which is differentiated from other parts of the spectrum by wavelength. Wavelength (symbol λ) results from viewing light transmission as a wave, although light can also be seen as being quanta, known as photons. The energy in photons is related to the wavelength of the light. Light absorption is related to the electronic structure of molecules; molecules with different structures absorb light at different parts of the spectrum. Molecules have peaks of absorbance, known as λ_{max}, at set wavelengths. The absorbance of light at a λ_{max} is linearly related to concentration in solution of any set molecule by the Beer–Lambert Law. Absorbed light energy can be lost from a molecule by chemical reaction, energy transfer, heat or light. Photosynthesis is catalysed by light-driven chemical reactions in chloroplasts.

Self-assessment questions

Now try these questions to test your understanding of this chapter.

Q18.11 Figure 18.12 shows a sine wave. Copy this picture on a piece of paper and mark a wavelength.

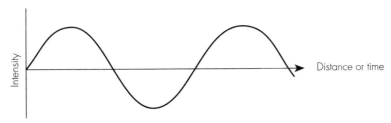

Figure 18.12 A sine wave over distance or time

Q18.12 What is the unit of wavelength?

Q18.13 Which part of a molecule's structure gives rise to absorbance peaks in the visible spectrum?

Q18.14 Vitamin B_{12} has a ϵ of 8630 mol^{-1} cm^{-1} at 550 nm. A solution was needed for a class practical with an absorbance of 1.0 in a 1 cm light path. What concentration should this solution be?

Q18.15 What is the technical term for the process by which absorbed light energy may be passed from molecule to a very close similar molecule?

Q18.16 How does light absorption by photosystem I give rise to reduced NADP$^+$?

Radioactivity in Biology

Introduction

Radioactivity is widely used in biology, so a brief discussion of the principles and applications of its use is important. Most radioactive isotopes of elements behave, metabolically, exactly the same as their non-radioactive forms. The detection and analysis of radioactivity is fairly straight-forward and the applications can range from studies of metabolism to estimation of the concentrations of hormones in serum. 'Ionising' radiation is potentially hazardous and so many of the uses of radioactivity are being replaced by other means, but the subject is still of sufficient importance to be covered here.

Objectives

After working through this chapter you should be able to:
- understand the structure of the nucleus of an atom, particularly in relation to isotopes;
- understand the common radioactive emissions;
- be aware of the different forms of detection of radioactivity;
- understand the uses of radioactivity in biology;
- be alert to the potential dangers of ionising radiation.

Questions

If this subject is familiar to you, try these questions to test your understanding and whether you need to read this chapter.

Q19.1 Oxygen, atomic number eight, has an unstable isotope with mass number 18. Write out this isotope using the $_N^M A$ and $^M A$ formulae.

Q19.2 Which isotope is formed by the decay of $_1^3 H$ by β-emission?

Q19.3 What is meant by the term d.p.m.?

Q19.4 Describe briefly the principle of chromatography.

19.1 Isotopes

Chapter 2 discussed the composition of the nucleus of the atom with respect to relative atomic mass, neutrons and protons. The nucleus was described as consisting of a number of protons (positively charged particles, atomic mass 1) and a number of neutrons (neutral particles, atomic mass 1). The nucleus is surrounded by a 'cloud' of electrons. The number of protons in the nucleus defines the element and is also known as the atomic number. Thus carbon has six protons in the nucleus and has the atomic number 6, while oxygen has eight protons in the nucleus and has atomic number 8. The number of neutrons in the nucleus can vary. The most common arrangement for carbon is to have six protons and six neutrons, giving a relative atomic mass of 12 and an atomic number 6. Some carbon atoms contain seven neutrons (atomic mass 13) or eight neutrons (atomic mass 14). This is usually written as $_N^M A$, where M = mass number, N = atomic number and A = chemical symbol. Thus the different 'forms' of the carbon nucleus could be written as $^{12}_{6}$C, $^{13}_{6}$C and $^{14}_{6}$C. The different forms of the carbon nucleus are described as isotopes. Since the atomic number is constant for any atom, it is often left out when referring to isotopes. This abbreviated formula is ^{M}A, thus $^{12}_{6}$C is often abbreviated to ^{12}C. The isotopes ^{12}C and ^{13}C are very stable, but ^{14}C is unstable. This instability results from an imbalance of protons and neutrons in the nucleus. The nucleus of ^{14}C breaks down as it is unstable. When the ^{14}C nucleus breaks down radioactivity is emitted. The unstable carbon isotope is said to decay. There are several types of 'radioactive' emission; these depend on the way in which unstable isotopes break up.

Example 19.1
An isotope of phosphorus (N = 15) has the mass number 32. Write this **(a)** using the $^{M}_{N}$A formula and **(b)** also abbreviate this further to ^{M}A.

(a) The atomic number is 15; thus N = 15, mass number is 32, so M = 32, chemical symbol for phosphorus is P. Thus the isotope could be written $^{32}_{15}$P, which can be further abbreviated to **(b)** ^{32}P.

Question

Q19.5 Sodium has the atomic number 11. At least two isotopes of sodium exist which have mass numbers 22 and 23. Write out these isotopes using the $^{M}_{N}$A formula and abbreviated formula (^{M}A).

19.2   Radioactive emissions

There are three common emissions from an unstable nucleus, called alpha (α), beta (β) and gamma (γ) after the order in which they were discovered.

α-Particles are emitted mainly by heavy isotopes of elements with a large mass, such as uranium (^{238}U). These α-particles contain two neutrons and two protons (a helium nucleus). Isotopes emitting α-particles become another element. Uranium^{238} emits an α-particle to become thorium-234. The α-particle is large with high energy and so readily collides with any matter. On collision, the α-particle is converted into a helium atom (by gaining electrons). No isotopes that emit α-particles are of biological importance as their atoms are not used by living organisms.

β-Particles are really electrons. These are emitted from nuclei such as ^{14}C and ^{32}P. The emitted electron is the result of neutron breakdown. This can be summarised as:

$$\text{neutron} \longrightarrow \text{proton} + \text{electron}$$

Atoms emitting β-particles change into new elements. Thus: $^{14}_{6}$C $\rightarrow$ $^{14}_{7}$N + β-particle. Note that the atomic number rises by one while mass remains constant. The 'high energy' electrons interact much less with other matter and so penetrate further.

Gamma radiation is not an atomic particle but is a high energy form of electromagnetic radiation. The energy is greater than X-rays and penetrates further as it interacts less with matter.

Example 19.2
$^{32}_{15}$P undergoes decay by emitting β-particles. What isotope is formed?

In β-emission, the atomic number rises by one, the mass remains the same. Thus $^{32}_{15}$P decays to $^{32}_{16}$S.

Question

Q19.6 Which isotope is formed by the β-emitting decay of $^{35}_{16}$S? You may need to refer to the periodic table, page 207.

19.3   Detecting radioactivity

The usual method of detecting radioactivity is to 'measure' the emissions caused by radioactive disintegration. The simplest method of detecting radioactivity is by using a photographic film. When a photographic film is placed next to the source of radiation, the film is blackened. This method is useful in detecting X-rays, as well as being used in a process called autoradiography. Two other methods of detection are common. One relies on the ability of emissions to generate an electric current in some specialised electrical circuits. This is the method used by Geiger-Muller tubes to indicate radioactivity. Commonly Geiger-Muller tubes can convert the 'current' to a number of atomic disintegrations per minute (d.p.m.) to a 'click' sound. The sound intensity given by the rate of clicks is proportional to the disintegration rate.

The other method is to use molecules that absorb the energy from radioactive emissions by giving off a photon of light. The number of photons emitted is related to the disintegration rate. The process of capturing the radioactive emissions and measuring light emissions is known as scintillation counting. Each light emission is called a scintillation and molecules that undergo scintillation are called scintillants or 'fluors'. Different unstable isotopes decay at different rates. The time taken for half of the amount of an isotope to decay is called the half-life. The decay of ^{14}C is such that half of the ^{14}C will decay every 5760 years. This is a slow rate of decay. Other isotopes, such as ^3H and ^{32}P, decay more quickly with half-lives of 12 years and 14 days, respectively. If there are an equal number of ^{32}P and ^{14}C nuclei, then the ^{32}P emits radiation at a much faster rate.

Question

Q19.7 Name two methods used to measure radioactivity.

19.4   Uses of radiation

Radiation occurs naturally as many elements contain some radioactive isotopes. This radiation is called 'background' radiation. To make use of radiation, we need to enrich molecules with a particular isotope. This is usually achieved by generating a particular isotope. This is done by bombarding elements with neutrons or electrons to form a radioactive isotope and then using the purified isotope in a chemical synthesis to make a specific molecule. In this way you can make an amino acid in which all of the carbons are ^{14}C, for example.

In order to see what happens to that amino acid when mixed with a cell, the amino acid must be separated from anything it may have changed to. Suppose that the ^{14}C amino acid could be incorporated into a protein or degraded to give CO_2, the possible paths of ^{14}C can be depicted as shown in Figure 19.1, overleaf. By separating the cell from the medium around it and estimating the ^{14}C in either the cell or the medium, the speed at which the amino acid enters the cell can be calculated. The amount of amino acid ending up as protein can be measured by breaking open the cell and precipitating the proteins in weak acid. The amount of the amino acid used in respiration can be calculated by collecting the carbon dioxide given off. This crude experiment can be refined by using chromatography to separate out the intermediates in the pathway.

Chromatography usually uses a series of immobile beads through which the mixture to be separated flows when it is dissolved in a suitable solvent. Different chemicals have different degrees of stickiness (affinity) to the beads and will move at different speeds through the beads, eventually becoming separated from one another (Figure 19.2, overleaf). The affinity of the chemicals for the beads is related to their chemical structure. In this way, different chemicals can be separated and identified.

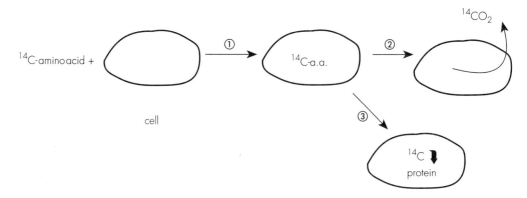

Figure 19.1 Possible fate of ^{14}C amino acid when incubated with whole liver cells. Step ① shows the ^{14}C amino acid entering the cell (a.a = amino acid). In step ② the ^{14}C produces a gas as the amino acid is used in respiration. In step ③ the amino acid is made into protein

Sometimes the chromatography can be performed on sheets of paper or beads coated on the surface of a plastic sheet (thin-layer chromatography). The presence of radioactivity can then be detected by placing an X-ray film next to the sheet (autoradiography). Where the radioactivity is located dark spots will appear on the film. This method is used to locate the first organic compounds made by photosynthesis after carbon fixation. Plants were given $^{14}CO_2$. After two seconds, photosynthesis was stopped, the sugars were extracted and separated by thin layer chromatography, then autoradiographed. After very short times, the radioactivity was almost all found in a spot identified as phosphoglyceric acid. At later times, the radioactivity was found in hexose sugars as well as amino acids.

Example 19.4
The autoradiography technique used in the photosynthesis experiment was applied to extracts of the cytosol of the cells that were given ^{14}C-D-glucose. What spot would you expect **(a)** after two seconds and **(b)** after 60 seconds (the cell cytosol is capable of carrying out glycolysis, but not the TCA cycle).
   Glycolysis is the breakdown of sugar to give pyruvate.
(a) After two seconds most of the ^{14}C will be still as glucose.
(b) After 60 seconds most of the ^{14}C will be found as pyruvate, the end product of glycolysis.

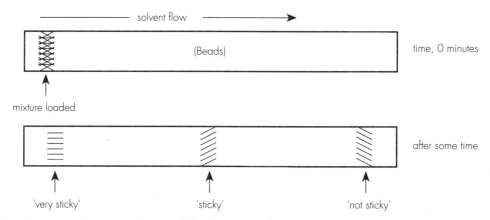

Figure 19.2 Separation of a mixture of chemicals by chromatography

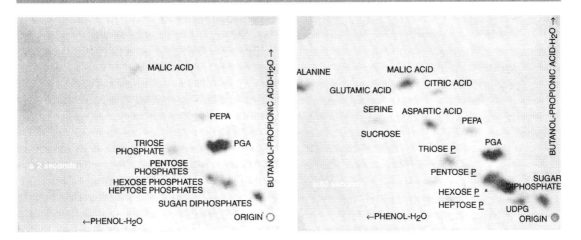

Figure 19.3 Autoradiograms showing the products of photosynthesis by plants. Plants were incubated in $^{14}CO_2$ and stopped (a) after two seconds (b) after 60 seconds in the light. The position of spots corresponding to the known movement of carbohydrates allowed the identification of radioactively labelled organic molecules. These must have resulted from carbon fixation of $^{14}CO_2$ (PGA = phosphoglyceric acid)

Question

Q19.8 How could the autoradiography experiment in Example 19.4 be adapted to show the steps between glucose and pyruvate?

19.5 Harmful effects of radiation

The absorption of ionising radiation by the human body is potentially harmful. When α, β or γ radiation interacts with molecules in the cells of our body chemical reactions take place. If enough chemical reactions take place (a high dose) toxic compounds that can kill the cell are formed. This can be used to kill cancer cells in the treatment of certain cancers; it is called radiotherapy and is particularly useful in combatting leukemias. At lower doses, the DNA can be altered so that the cell mutates. Nothing can be done to remove 'background' radiation, but people can be protected from other forms when working with other radioactive emitters. α-Particles are absorbed by any thin film and β-particles by a perspex screen. The γ-radiation is the most difficult to protect against and requires lead bricks or similar dense substances to provide protection. X-rays are similar to γ-radiation and so protective clothing is worn by radiographers when taking X-rays of patients. The time of exposure to radioactivity is also limited, which decreases the chances of any harmful effects by allowing damaged cells a chance to effect their own repairs.

Summary

Ionising radiation is caused by the breakdown of unstable nuclei. Three different types of breakdown can occur, giving rise to α, β and γ radiations. α-Particles are helium nuclei, β-particles are usually electrons and γ radiation is a form of ray, like a high-energy X-ray. Particles can be detected by systems that create an electric current as a result of ionising radiation (used in Geiger-Muller tubes), by chemicals that emit light after absorbing radiation (scintillation counting) and by 'fogging' of X-ray films (radiography). Radioactive compounds are used to follow pathways of metabolism in cells, but need a system such as chromatography to separate different molecules. Ionising radiation can be harmful if large enough doses are absorbed.

Self-assessment questions

Q19.9 Using the $_N^MA$ and ^MA formula write out the formula of sulphur (mass number is 35, atomic number 16).

Q19.10 The isotope of potassium with molecular mass number 40 and atomic number 19 is unstable, emitting β-particles. Write out the reaction for the breakdown of ^{40}K by β-emission.

Q19.11 On what principle does the process of autoradiography rely?

Q19.12 The complete oxidation of glucose can be summarised as:

$$C_6H_{12}O_6 + 6H_2O \rightarrow 6CO_2 + 6H_2O$$

Given $^{14}C_6H_{12}O_6$ describe how you could measure the rate of respiration.

Answers to questions

Chapter 1
1.1 O, P, K, Fe.

1.2 1 mole of sulphur = 32 g
Mass of 0.2 mole sulphur = $32 \times 0.2 = 6.4$ g

1.3 (a) Methane is (i); (b) carbon dioxide is (iv);
(c) ammonia is (iii).

1.4 H_2O, $CaCO_3$, HCl, Na_2SO_4.

1.5 Ca, Cl, Mg.

1.6 Carbon, nitrogen, sodium, sulphur.

1.7 Mass of 0.8 mole of
sodium = $23 \times 0.8 = 18.4$ g
Mass of 0.6 mole of
potassium = $39 \times 0.6 = 23.4$ g
Thus 0.6 mole of potassium has the larger mass.

1.8 1 mole of carbon = 12 g

Moles in 3.6 g of carbon = $\dfrac{3.6}{12} = 0.3$ mole

1.9 CaO, $FeCl_3$, P_2O_5, $Ca(OH)_2$, Na_2CO_3.

Chapter 2
2.1 Nitrogen 2.5; sodium 2.8.1.

2.2 See Figure 2.16.

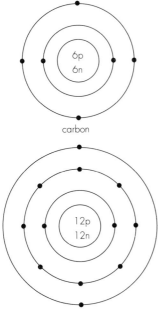

Figure 2.16   carbon

magnesium

2.3 See Figure 2.17.

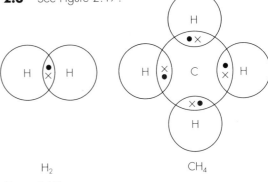

H_2 CH_4

Figure 2.17

2.4 Na^+ 2.8 (one electron less than Na 2.8.1).
Cl^- 2.8.8. (one electron more than Cl 2.8.7).

2.5 See Figure 2.18.

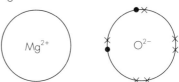

Figure 2.18

Note that in magnesium oxide two electrons are given to the oxygen atom by the magnesium atom.

2.6 See Figure 2.19.

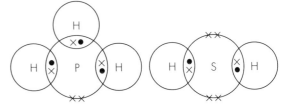

phosphine   hydrogen sulphide

Figure 2.19

2.7 See Figure 2.20.

Figure 2.20

In lithium fluoride, the lithium atom gives one electron to the fluorine atom.

2.8

Carbon	6 protons	6 electrons	2.4
Oxygen	8	8	2.6
Chlorine	17	17	2.8.7

Carbon 6 protons 6 electrons 2.4
Oxygen 8 8 2.6
Chlorine 17 17 2.8.7

2.9 See Figure 2.21.

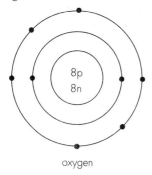

oxygen

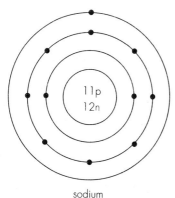

sodium

Figure 2.21

2.10 (a) Hydrogen 1; fluorine 2.7. (b) See Figure 2.22.

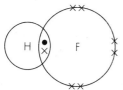

Figure 2.22   hydrogen fluoride, HF

2.11 (a) Carbon 2.4; oxygen 2.6. (b) See Figure 2.23.

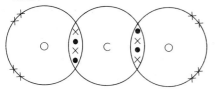

carbon dioxide, CO_2

Figure 2.23

2.12

	Mg	$2 \times Cl$	Mg^{2+}	$2 \times Cl^-$
Protons	12	2×17	12	2×17
Electrons	12	2×17	10	2×18
Structure	2.8.2	$2 \times (2.8.7)$	2.8	$2 \times (2.8.8)$
Charge	0	0	2^+	$2 \times 1^- = 2^-$

2.13 See Figure 2.24

sodium oxide, Na_2O

Figure 2.24

Chapter 3

3.1 In a solid, the particles are tightly packed, held in fixed positions and move only by vibration about a fixed point. In a liquid, the particles move freely but remain tightly packed and attract one another. The particles in a gas are widely separated, they move quickly, collide frequently and have no attraction between them. A gas occupies a large volume by comparison with a solid or liquid.

3.2 In diffusion, particles of different substances in a gas or liquid move randomly until they are evenly mixed. In evaporation, particles in a solid or liquid with higher than average energy escape from surface of the substance into the gas phase.

3.3 Any four factors from: (i) concentration; (ii) temperature; (iii) light; (iv) pH or acidity; (v) a catalyst; (vi) particle size.

3.4 (a) A catalyst is a substance that increases the rate of a reaction but is unchanged at the end of the reaction. (b) An enzyme is a complex protein produced by living things. It acts as a catalyst in biological reactions.

3.5 An enzyme is usually most active in a narrow pH range. If the pH moves away from the optimum pH value, the activity falls to zero.

3.6 (i) Reactions (b) and (c) are reversible. (ii) The equilibrium is dynamic because although the reactants continually combine to give the products and the products continually break down to the starting materials, the concentrations of each do not change.

3.7 Any three of the following comparisons are suitable: A solid has a fixed shape; a gas has no fixed shape. A solid has a fixed volume; a gas has no fixed volume. A solid has particles fixed in one position; a gas has freely moving particles. A solid has close-packed particles; a gas has widely separated particles. The attraction between particles in a solid is very strong; there is almost no attraction between particles in a gas.

3.8 A liquid has close-packed particles which attract one another but which can move freely. This gives the liquid a fixed volume but no fixed shape.

3.9 When solid salt is added to water, the particles in the salt are struck frequently by the moving water particles. Salt ions are broken away and mix with the water particles to give a solution.

3.10 Diffusion; particles; rapidly; randomly.

3.11 (a) Increase; (b) decrease; (c) increase; (d) decrease.

3.12 (a) Initial high rate at pH 7 falls rapidly to very low level for a small pH rise and remains at a low level at pH 12. (b) Very low rate at pH 1, stays low until near to pH 7 then rises to high rate. (c) Low rate at pH 3, rises to a high rate at about pH 7, then falls to low rate again at pH 9.

3.13 Carry out the reaction in a closed flask. Use a manometer or gas syringe connected to the flask to measure the rate of decrease in volume (look up Warburg flask, Warburg respirometer or Warburg manometer in your biology textbook).

3.14 See answers to Q3.6 for dynamic equilibrium and Q3.20 for reversible reactions.

3.15 Vibrations; fixed point; liquid; move freely; quickly; attraction; volume.

3.16 (a) Diffusion. Particles of pheromone mix with the air until they are evenly spread. The particles reach the male moth and are detected by it. (b) Evaporation. Heat from the skin gives some water particles higher energy and movement so they escape from the droplets of perspiration. This continues until all the water has evaporated. (c) Dissolving. Water particles in the saliva collide with sugar particles, gradually dislodging them until all the sugar has dissolved. The fly takes up the sugar solution.

3.17 As Q3.3.

3.18 (a) Catalase is a catalyst. (b) An enzyme catalyst brings hydrogen peroxide particles on to a special site on its surface where they decompose to water and oxygen particles. These then diffuse away.

3.19 A higher concentration of urea particles leads to more collisions between urea and urease particles and thus more reactions occur to give a greater reaction rate.

3.20 Glucose and fructose combine to give sucrose, but the reaction may be reversed with sucrose breaking down to glucose and fructose. Thus this is a reversible reaction.
For the meaning of a dynamic equilibrium, see the answer to Q3.6.

Chapter 4

4.1 Any three properties from (a), (c), (d), (e). Properties (b), (f) and (g) are typical of an alkali.

4.2 (i) (d) HCl and (f) HNO_3. Sulphuric acid, hydrochloric acid, nitric acid and phosphoric acid are typical strong acids. (ii) (a) H_2CO_3 and (b) CH_3COOH. Citric acid, tartaric acid, carbonic acid, lactic acid and ethanoic acid are typical weak acids.

4.3 (a) pH 3 to 6; (b) pH 12 to 14; (c) pH 8 to 11; (d) pH 0 to 2.
Any value within the ranges given is acceptable.

4.4 Hydrogen ion, H^+, reacts with hydroxide ion, OH^-, to give water, H_2O.

4.5 Dip a piece of litmus or universal indicator paper into the solution. The paper becomes red (strong acid) or orange–yellow (weak acid).

4.6 They contain the hydrogen ion H^+.

4.7 (a) Orange–yellow; (b) violet; (c) red; (d) orange–yellow; (e) yellow.

4.8 A base is a substance that neutralises an acid to give a salt and water. It may be soluble or insoluble. An alkali is a soluble base.

4.9

hydrochloric + ammonia $\longrightarrow$ ammonium + water
acid   solution   chloride
HCl   + NH_4OH $\longrightarrow$ NH_4Cl + H_2O

4.10 Citric acid, tartaric acid, ethanoic acid or any acid in Table 10.1.

4.11 $$H \xrightarrow{\text{water}} H^+(aq) + e^-$$
The electron is part of an anion.

4.12 Any four from: (i) sour taste; (ii) water soluble; (iii) pH less than 7; (iv) turn universal indicator red or yellow; (v) give hydrogen ions in water; (vi) are corrosive; (viii) react with a base to give salt and water.

4.13 (a) pH 0 to 2; (b) pH 7.4; (c) pH 6; (d) pH 2.5; (e) pH 12 to 14; (f) pH 6.5.

4.14 (a) A base is a substance that will react with an acid to give a salt and water only. It may be soluble or insoluble. An alkali is a soluble base. (b) Hydrogen ion H^+ and hydroxide ion OH^-.

(c) hydrogen ion + hydroxide ion $\longrightarrow$ water
$$H^+ \quad + \quad OH^- \quad \longrightarrow H_2O$$

4.15 phosphoric + calcium $\longrightarrow$ calcium + water
    acid   hydroxide   phosphate

Chapter 5

5.1 The solid melts to a liquid and then boils to give a gas.

5.2 The rate will increase to about twice the initial value.

5.3

$(4 \times 412) + 612$ 436 kJ $(6 \times 412) + 348$
$= 2260\,kJ$ $= 2820\,kJ$
Reactants: $2260 + 436 = 2696\,kJ$
                   Products: $2820\,kJ$
Heat of reaction = $2820 - 2696 = 124\,kJ$
One mole of ethene is involved in the equation and the bond energies of products are greater than reactants; therefore the heat of reaction is $-124\,kJ\,mol^{-1}$.

5.4 Place the solution in a beaker and set up the circuit shown in Figure 5.3. If the solution is a conductor the bulb will light.

5.5 Aqueous solutions of (a), (c) and (d) are conductors.

5.6 Sodium ethanoate solution consists wholly of ions (Na^+ and CH_3COO^-), and ions conduct the current. Ethanoic acid solution contains mainly molecules (CH_3COOH) with only very few ions (H^+ and CH_3COO^-). Only the ions conduct electricity and so conductivity is poor.

5.7 (a) The clear solution deposits a white solid as the albumen is denatured; (b) the solid melts to a liquid and then boils to a gas.

5.8 $CH_4 \quad + \quad 2O_2 \quad \longrightarrow \quad CO_2 \quad + \quad 2H_2O$
     4×412 2×496 2×743 4×463
     $= 1648\,kJ$ $= 992\,kJ$ $= 1486\,kJ$ $= 1852\,kJ$
Reactants: $1648 + 992 = 2640\,kJ$
           Products: $1468 + 1852 = 3338\,kJ$
Heat of reaction is $3338 - 2640 = 698\,kJ$.
The equation has one mole of methane and the products have greater bond energies than reactants. The heat of reaction is $-698\,kJ\,mol^{-1}$

5.9 Sulphuric acid gives hydrogen ions (H^+), hydrogensulphate ions (HSO_4^-) and sulphate ions (SO_4^{2-}) in water. The hydrogen cations move to the cathode; the hydrogensulphate or sulphate anions move to the anode.

5.10 Sodium hydroxide gives sodium ions (Na^+) and hydroxide ions (OH^-) in water. The sodium cations move to the cathode; the hydroxide anions move to the anode.

5.11 Lactic acid solution contains mainly molecules with only a few ions to carry the current. The ions are formed in a reversible reaction:
lactic $\rightleftharpoons$ hydrogen +   lactate
acid   ions   ions

$$CH_3CHCOOH \quad \rightleftharpoons \quad H^+ \quad + \quad CH_3CHOO^-$$
$$\quad\;\; OH \qquad\qquad\qquad\qquad\qquad\qquad\;\; OH$$

5.12 (a) The solid sodium chloride melts to give a liquid, this boils to form a gas; (b) The solid glucose melts and then the clear liquid darkens to a brown liquid. This liquid burns or chars to leave a black solid.

5.13 In a solution of magnesium chloride the ions are free to move and carry an electric current. The solid has the ions held rigidly in place: they cannot move to carry the current.

5.14 Hydrochloric acid in water gives hydrogen ions (H^+) and chloride ions (Cl^-). The cations (H^+) move to the cathode carrying the current. At the cathode each gains an electron, $H^+ + e^- \rightarrow H$. The anions (Cl^-) go to the anode and carry the current. They react at the anode by giving up an electron, $Cl^- \rightarrow Cl + e^-$. The electrons pass through the anode, the wires, battery and go to the cathode (see Section 5.3, page 37, and Figure 5.2, page 36).

5.15 'Electrolysis' is the chemical reaction that takes place when ions in a solution reach an electrode (cathode or anode). 'Electrolyte' is a substance, usually a solution such as phosphoric acid solution, that conducts electricity and undergoes electrolysis.

5.16 Ammonia in water forms ammonium ions (NH_4^+) and hydroxide ions (OH^-) in a reversible reaction:

ammonia + water $\rightleftharpoons$ ammonium ions + hydroxide ions

$$NH_3 + H_2O \rightleftharpoons NH_4^+ + OH^-$$

Most of the ammonia stays as molecules and few ions are available to carry the current. Ammonia is a weak electrolyte.

5.17 The uptake of nutrients such as potassium, nitrate or ammonium ions by plant roots, or the migration of sodium ions across the membrane of an axon in nerve impulses.

Chapter 6

6.1 (a) Sucrose (O), oxygen (R); (b) sodium (O), chlorine (R); (c) hydrochloric acid (N), sodium hydroxide (N); (d) ethanol (O), oxygen (R); (e) carbon dioxide (N), water (N).

6.2 Oxidation is the loss of electrons.

6.3 (a) A reductant is a substance that provides hydrogen, takes away oxygen or provides electrons in a chemical reaction.
(b) Substances (i), (iii) and (iv) are reductants.

6.4 (a) 'Redox' describes a process that involves oxidation and reduction.
(b) calcium + chlorine $\longrightarrow$ calcium chloride

$$Ca + Cl_2 \longrightarrow CaCl_2$$

(c)

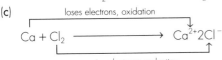

6.5 (a) Reduction; (b) neither; (c) oxidation; (d) neither.

6.6 methanol + oxygen $\longrightarrow$ carbon + water
dioxide

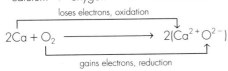

6.7 calcium + oxygen $\longrightarrow$ calcium oxide

loses electrons, oxidation

$$2Ca + O_2 \longrightarrow 2(Ca^{2+}O^{2-})$$

gains electrons, reduction

6.8 sodium + chlorine $\longrightarrow$ sodium chloride

loses electrons, oxidation

$$2Na + Cl_2 \longrightarrow 2(Na^+Cl^-)$$

gains electrons, reduction

6.9 (a) Hydrogen, oxidised; oxygen, reduced;
(b) calcium, oxidised; chlorine, reduced.

6.10 In the reaction:

glucose + oxygen $\longrightarrow$ carbon dioxide + water

glucose is OXidised while oxygen is REDuced. Redox means a process in which these two parts occur together.

6.11 (a), (d) and (f) are reductants; (c) is an oxidant.

6.12 magnesium + chlorine $\longrightarrow$ magnesium chloride

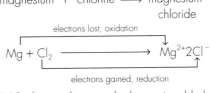

6.13 (a) Reduction, because hydrogen is added;
(b) reduction, because oxygen is taken away;
(c) oxidation, because hydrogen is taken away;
(d) oxidation, because oxygen is added and hydrogen taken away.

Chapter 7

7.1 CH_4, formed by anaerobic decay; H_2O, major constituent of all cells or transport media; HCl, stomach acid; H_2S, energy source for sulphur bacteria.

7.2 Hydrogen loses an electron to form the hydrogen ion. It has a sour taste and turns universal indicator red (or other properties given in Section 4.2, page 29).

7.3 Hydrogen has relative atomic mass 1; deuterium relative atomic mass 2. Deuterium is used to trace the path of hydrogen in biological reaction mechanisms.

7.4 Water is a solvent, a transport medium, and an environment for aquatic organisms (or other ways given in Section 7.1, page 46).

7.5 Nitrogen gas is taken in by nitrogen-fixing soil bacteria, or bacteria in root nodules of leguminous plants. Nitrogen is reduced to ammonia, which is taken up by the plant and synthesised into protein. Nitrogen combines with oxygen in thunderstorms to form nitrogen oxides. In the presence of air, these oxides dissolve in water to form nitric acid. This forms nitrates in the soil, which are taken up by plants.

7.6 NO_3^-, NO_2^- and NH_4^+. Sodium nitrate, $NaNO_3$; calcium nitrate, $Ca(NO_3)_2$; sodium nitrite, $NaNO_2$; ammonium chloride, NH_4Cl; ammonium sulphate, $(NH_4)_2SO_4$.

7.7 Harvesting crops reduces soil fertility. This problem can be corrected by adding manure, compost or fertilisers to the soil.

7.8 Any three of: nitrate ion, nitrite ion, ammonia, ammonium ion, nitrogen.

7.9 H_3PO_4, $-PO_3H_2$. Adenosine di- or triphosphate.

7.10 phosphoric $\longrightarrow$ hydrogen + dihydrogen-
acid   ions   phosphate
                                        ions

$$H_3PO_4 \longrightarrow H^+(aq) + H_2PO_4^-$$

Further ionisation steps also occur:

$$H_2PO_4^- \longrightarrow H^+(aq) + HPO_4^{2-}$$
$$HPO_4^{2-} \longrightarrow H^+(aq) + PO_4^{3-}$$

7.11 (a) A beech tree gains water by root uptake and loses it by transpiration and respiration through leaves.
(b) A pigeon gains water by drinking and eating and loses it by respiration and excretion.
(c) The ocean gains water by rain and run-off as rivers and loses it by evaporation.

7.12 (a) Sodium nitrate, $NaNO_3$; (b) ammonium nitrate, NH_4NO_3; (c) sodium nitrite, $NaNO_2$.

7.13 Strong bonds exist between the atoms in nitrogen gas, and considerable energy is needed to break the bonds and form nitrogen compounds. Only a limited number of organisms can carry out this process.

7.14 Animals eat plants containing plant proteins.

7.15 Urea, uric acid or ammonia.

7.16 Nitrogen gas combines with oxygen in thunderstorms to give nitrogen oxides. In the presence of air, these oxides dissolve in water to give nitric acid, which then forms nitrates in the soil.

7.17 Denitrification is the breakdown of nitrogen compounds in a series of stages to nitrogen. Nitrate ions are reduced by denitrifying bacteria to nitrite ions and then to ammonia or nitrogen.

7.18 Ammonia is an excretion product of some animals. It is formed by the decay of dead animals and plants and by denitrification of nitrate and nitrite ions. Ammonia may be nitrified by bacteria to nitrite and nitrate ions, or denitrified to nitrogen gas.

7.19 The following conversions in the cycle are oxidation reactions: nitrogen to nitrate ion; nitrite to nitrate ion; ammonia to nitrite ion.

7.20 Any suitable example such as unsaturated oils being reduced to saturated fats:

unsaturated oil + hydrogen $\longrightarrow$ saturated fat

7.21 Any five stages from the following: evaporation from oceans; condensation of water vapour to clouds; rain; run-off of water to streams; uptake by plant roots; transpiration from plants; drinking by animals; excretion by animals.

7.22 Ethanoic acid gives hydrogen ion and ethanoate ions in water:

$$CH_3COOH \longrightarrow H^+(aq) + CH_3COO^-$$

7.23 Nitrification is the process by which nitrogen gas is converted into ammonia by nitrifying bacteria or blue–green algae/cyanobacteria. Bacteria in soil or root nodules convert nitrogen into ammonia.

7.24 Reduction occurs in the conversion of: nitrate ion into plant protein; nitrate into nitrite ion; nitrite ion into ammonia.

7.25 Denitrifying bacteria can use nitrate ions as an alternative to oxygen in respiration.

7.26 Ammonium sulphate, $(NH_4)_2SO_4$; ammonium nitrate, NH_4NO_3; sodium nitrate, $NaNO_3$.

7.27 Nitrite ion is formed by denitrification of nitrate ion. Nitrite ion is denitrified to nitrous oxide and oxidised to nitrate ion by various bacteria in the cycle.

7.28 Nitrogen is essential for proteins and nucleotides.

7.29 Nitrogen compounds are required as fertilisers to ensure satisfactory crop yields.

7.30 Phosphorus is required for membrane phospholipids and energy-transfer compounds.

7.31 Adenosine di- and triphosphates.

7.32 Calcium phosphate, $Ca_3(PO_4)_2$.

Chapter 8

8.1 Any three from: coal, peat, oil, natural gas and calcium carbonate minerals (chalk, limestone, marble).

8.2 Carbon dioxide, CO_2, is taken up by plants in photosynthesis and given out by plants and animals in respiration. The bicarbonate ion, HCO_3^-, is the form in which carbon dioxide is carried in the blood. It is taken in by plants linked with cations such as Ca^{2+} and Mg^{2+}

Calcium carbonate, $CaCO_3$, forms parts of bones, teeth and shells of animals.

8.3 Calcium bicarbonate. This is formed by rain water containing carbonic acid dissolving calcium carbonate from rocks like limestone.

8.4 Any four from: respiration or combustion; photosynthesis; decay of dead organisms; formation of calcium carbonate minerals; rain; dissolving of calcium carbonate minerals; formation of carboniferous deposits.

8.5 An organic compound contains mainly carbon and hydrogen and has carbon atoms joined to one another.

8.6 C_3H_8

8.7 Compounds with the same molecular formula but different structures.

8.8 ethene + water ⟶ ethanol

8.9 The —OH group.

8.10 Carbon has four electrons in the outer shell. Each of the four hydrogens has one electron, giving a total of eight, or four pairs. Each pair is linked with a hydrogen, giving four electron pair bonds. If these are arranged as far apart as possible, a tetrahedral structure is given (see page 63).

8.11 Oxygen has six electrons in the outer shell. The two hydrogens each have one electron. This gives a total of eight electrons or four pairs: two pairs are linked with hydrogens to give two electron pair bonds; the two pairs left over are unshared pairs. This gives a tetrahedral structure of electron pairs, but a bent molecule because there are only two electron pair bonds. The unshared pairs repel each other strongly so the bond angle is reduced from 109° to 104° (see page 64).

8.12 Oxygen has six electrons in the outer shell, O^+

has one less, five. Three hydrogens each have one electron, giving a total of eight or four pairs: three pairs join with hydrogen forming three electron pair bonds; one pair is left over as an unshared pair. Four electron pairs give a tetrahedral structure and three electron pair bonds give a pyramidal ion. The unshared pair repels the shared pairs, so the bond angle falls from 109° to about 106°.

8.13 The carbon atom has four outer-shell electrons, plus three from the three hydrogens (each has one electron) and one from nitrogen. This gives a total of eight electrons or four pairs. This gives a tetrahedral shape about carbon. Nitrogen has five electrons, the two hydrogens each have one electron and one of the four on carbon, giving a total eight electrons or four pairs. Thus there is a pyramidal shape about nitrogen of three atoms, with an unshared pair making up the fourth corner of the tetrahedron.

8.14 carbonic + magnesium ⇌ magnesium
acid   carbonate   bicarbonate
H_2CO_3 + $MgCO_3$ ⇌ $Mg(HCO_3)_2$
Yes, magnesium bicarbonate is a soluble form of magnesium. It is an important trace element for plants.

8.15 It undergoes dissociation (ionisation) to form hydrogen ions. These have acidic properties.

8.16 These organisms take up carbon as bicarbonate ion and use it to form their shells (made of calcium carbonate). Shells of the dead zooplankton sink to form sediments and eventually calcium carbonate minerals.

8.17 (a)   (b) butane, C_4H_{10}.

8.18 (b) and (d). Alkanes have the general formula C_nH_{2n+2}; only these two fit that formula.

8.19 C_nH_{2n}. Ethene:

8.20 propene + hydrogen → propane

$$
\begin{array}{c}
\text{H} \\
| \\
\text{H}-\text{C} \\
\| \\
\text{H}-\text{C} \quad + \quad \begin{array}{c}\text{H}\\|\\\text{H}\end{array} \quad \rightarrow \\
| \\
\text{H}-\text{C}-\text{H} \\
| \\
\text{H}
\end{array}
\qquad
\begin{array}{c}
\text{H} \\
| \\
\text{H}-\text{C}-\text{H} \\
| \\
\text{H}-\text{C}-\text{H} \\
| \\
\text{H}-\text{C}-\text{H} \\
| \\
\text{H}
\end{array}
$$

8.21 See the first part of answer to Q8.34.

8.22 (a) Limestone is composed of shells of dead marine plankton that have collected as sediments and then been heated and crushed in the Earth. (b) Dead vegetation has collected over a long period and then been heated and crushed by natural processes deep in the Earth's crust.

8.23 (a) carbon dioxide + water $\rightleftharpoons$ carbonic acid
$$CO_2 + H_2O \rightleftharpoons H_2CO_3$$

(b) carbonic acid $\rightleftharpoons$ hydrogen ion + bicarbonate ion
$$H_2CO_3 \rightleftharpoons H^+(\text{hydrated}) + HCO_3^-$$

bicarbonate ion $\rightleftharpoons$ hydrogen ion + carbonate ion
$$HCO_3^- \rightleftharpoons H^+(\text{hydrated}) + CO_3^{2-}$$

8.24 (a) Carbon as plant material collects in large quantities when plants die. The material is subjected to heat and pressure below the Earth's surface, where it may remain for long periods as coal or oil. (b) The shells of dead plankton form sediments of calcium carbonate. The sediments are subjected to heat and pressure and may be immobilised as minerals in the Earth.

8.25 C_nH_{2n+2}.

8.26 carbon dioxide and water.

methane + oxygen $\longrightarrow$ carbon dioxide + water
$$CH_4 + 2O_2 \longrightarrow CO_2 + 2H_2O$$

8.27 $CH_3CH_2CH{=}CH_2$; $CH_3C{=}CH_2$;
$$\quad\quad\quad\quad\quad\quad\quad | $$
$$\quad\quad\quad\quad\quad\quad\quad CH_3$$
$$CH_3CH{=}CHCH_3$$

8.28

$$
\begin{array}{c}
\text{H} \\
| \\
\text{H}-\text{C} \\
\| \\
\text{H}-\text{C} \quad + \quad \begin{array}{c}\text{O}-\text{H}\\|\\\text{H}\end{array} \quad \longrightarrow \\
| \\
\text{H}
\end{array}
\qquad
\begin{array}{c}
\text{H} \\
| \\
\text{H}-\text{C}-\text{O}-\text{H} \\
| \\
\text{H}-\text{C}-\text{H} \\
| \\
\text{H}
\end{array}
$$

8.29 (i) Alcohols; (ii) methanol, ethanol, propanol;
(iii)
$$
\begin{array}{c}
\text{H} \quad \text{H} \quad \text{O} \\
| \quad\;\; | \quad\;\; \| \\
\text{H}-\text{C}-\text{C}-\text{C}-\text{O}-\text{H} \\
| \quad\;\; | \\
\text{H} \quad \text{H}
\end{array}
$$
(iv)
$$
\begin{array}{c}
\text{H} \\
| \\
\text{H}-\text{C}-\text{O}-\text{H} \\
| \\
\text{H}-\text{C}-\text{H} \\
| \\
\text{H}
\end{array}
\quad \longrightarrow \quad
\begin{array}{c}
\text{H} \\
| \\
\text{H}-\text{C} \quad\quad \text{O}-\text{H} \\
\| \quad + \quad | \\
\text{H}-\text{C} \quad\quad \text{H} \\
| \\
\text{H}
\end{array}
$$

8.30 (i) Two; (ii) (a) or (c) or (d) or (f), and (b) or (e);
(iii) yes; (iv) (a), (c), (d) and (f) are one isomer; (b) and (e) are the second isomer. (Note that (a) and (c) are the same; the molecule in (a) is simply (c) turned over end on end. (d) and (a) are the same because the molecules can bend about any carbon atom. It helps to trace the chain of carbon atoms from one end to the other, count the number of carbon atoms in the chain, and then imagine the bent chain straightened out. (d) Straightened out is (a); (f) becomes (c) in the same way and we have already seen that (c) is the same as (a).)

8.31 The silicon atom has four outer-shell electrons (like carbon), add four from four hydrogens, total eight electrons or four pairs. This gives a tetrahedral shape from four electron pairs each bound to a hydrogen. It has the same structure as methane (see page 63).

8.32 The carbon atom has four outer electrons, plus three from three hydrogen atoms and one from the nitrogen atom, total eight electrons or four pairs. Therefore a tetrahedral shape about carbon, four electron pairs with an atom on each. The nitrogen atom with a positive charge has $5 - 1 = 4$ electrons; add three from the three hydrogen atoms and one from the carbon atom, overall eight electrons giving four pairs. Thus there is a tetrahedral shape about nitrogen as well.

8.33 The methyl, CH_3, carbon has four outer electrons, plus three from the three hydrogen atoms and one from the second carbon to give a total of eight or four pairs of electrons. Each electron pair is linked with an atom thus the shape is tetrahedral about the carbon. The carbon atom bound to oxygen has four outer electrons, plus two from two hydrogen atoms, one from the first carbon atom and one from the oxygen atom; a sum of eight or four pairs. Again there is a tetrahedral shape around the carbon. The oxygen has six outer electrons, add one from carbon and one from hydrogen to give a total of eight or four pairs. Two pairs are bond pairs, to carbon and hydrogen, and two pairs are unshared pairs so the tetrahedral arrangement of electron pairs gives a bent shape of bond pairs around oxygen.

8.34 Phosphorus has five outer shell electrons, add three from three hydrogens to give eight or four pairs of electrons in phosphine, PH_3. There are three bond pairs to the three hydrogen atoms and one unshared pair left over. The molecule is pyramidal in terms of bond pairs, with the unshared pair making up the fourth position of a tetrahedron. It is the same as ammonia (see page 64). The phosphonium ion, PH_4^+, differs in that phosphorus with a positive charge has four outer electrons while the four hydrogen atoms each supply one electron to give a total of eight or four pairs. There are four bond pairs and so the shape is tetrahedral: it is like the ammonium ion (see page 65).

Chapter 9

9.1 (a) (iii); (b) (iv); (c) (ii); (d) (v); (e) (i); (f) (vi).

9.2 (ii) Propan-2-ol; (iii) pentanal; (iv) pentan-2-one; (v) 2,3-dihydroxypropanal (D-glyceraldehyde).

9.3

hemiacetal   hemiketal

They are identical except for the **R** and **H** indicated in bold.

9.4 If the compound you have chosen has:
- the prefix hydroxy- or suffix -ol then it is an alcohol;
- the prefix aldo- or suffix -al then it is an aldehyde;
- the prefix keto- or suffix -one then it is a ketone.

9.5

D-fructose-   aldolase   D-glyceraldehyde- + dihydroxy-
1,6-diphosphate   ⇌   3-phosphate   acetone-3-
                                                         phosphate

9.6

9.7 (a) Butane-1,3-diol; (b) butanone (numbering is not needed as the ketone must be in the 2 position); (c) 1-hydroxypropanone [with more than one functional group preference in naming is (1) aldehyde, (2) ketone, (3) alcohols but 2-ketopropan-1-ol would also be clear]; (d) butanal.

9.8 (i) (c); (ii) (c); (iii) (a); (iv) (a) and/or (b); (v) (a); (vi) (b); (vii) (a).

Chapter 10

10.1 (a) butanoic acid; (b) butanedioic acid; (c) ethanoic acid; (d) octanoic acid.

10.2 The abbreviated structure for decanoic acid is:

$\bigwedge\!\!\bigwedge\!\!\bigwedge$COOH

10.3 Ion (COOH part of molecule) is COO⁻.

10.4

$-C\overset{\displaystyle O}{\underset{\displaystyle OH\cdots O=C}{}}$

10.5 A carboxyl group and a hydroxyl group.

10.6

(a) $\underset{\displaystyle RS\overset{O}{C}R}{}$ (b) $\underset{\displaystyle RO\,\overset{O}{\underset{OH}{P}}OH}{}$

10.7 (a) but-2-enedioic acid; (b) ethanoic acid.

10.8 Abbreviated structures are:

(a) $\bigwedge\!\!\bigwedge\!\!\bigwedge\!\!\bigwedge$COOH

(b) HOOC$\bigwedge\!\!\bigwedge$COOH

10.9

$-C\overset{\displaystyle O\cdots HOR}{\underset{\displaystyle OH}{}}$

10.10 Major form is the ion —COO⁻.

10.11 (a) 2-hydroxybutanoic acid; (b) hexanedioic acid; (c) 2-methylpropanoic acid; (d) benzoic acid.

10.12 Palmitic acid.

10.13 Major form is the ion —COO⁻. The ion is called nonanoate.

10.14 (a) $CH_3OH + HCOOH \rightarrow H_2O + CH_3OCH$ (with O double bond); (b) product is an organic ester, methyl methanoate.

10.15 (a) The conditions required are too harsh for the cell; (b) thioesters.

10.16 Nucleic acids and ATP.

Chapter 11

11.1 (i) primary; (ii) secondary; (iii) secondary; (iv) tertiary.

11.2 1,1-dimethylethanamine or 1,1-dimethylethylamine.

11.3 (a) proline or hydroxyproline; (b) histidine; (c) tryptophan.

11.4 (a)

(b) nicotinamide-containing molecules; (c) redox reactions.

11.5 The amine is deprotonated and uncharged.

11.6 The ability to form hydrogen bonds.

11.7 (i) secondary; (ii) primary; (iii) tertiary; (iv) primary.

11.8 (i) propan-2-amine or propyl-2-amine; (ii) propan-1-amine or propyl-1-amine; (iii) 3-aminobutan-2-one; (iv) 3-aminopropanal.

11.9 (i) charged and protonated (—NH₃⁺); (ii) mainly uncharged and deprotonated; (iii) uncharged and deprotonated (—NH₂); (iv) charged and protonated.

11.10 (i) primary; (ii) tertiary; (iii) secondary; (iv) primary.

11.11 (a) 1-aminopropanone; (b) butyl-1-amine or butan-1-amine; (c) ethan-1,2-diamine or ethyl-1,2-diamine; (d) 2-aminoethanol; (e) 3-aminopropanoic acid.

11.12 (i) purine; (ii) pyrrolidine; (iii) indole; (iv) imidazole; (v) pyridine; (vi) pyrimidine.

11.13 Redox transfer or electron carrier.

11.14 (a) >C=O⸱⸱⸱⸱H—N—; (b) —OH⸱⸱⸱⸱:N—.

11.15 Partial double bonding.

11.16 —NH₂, deprotonated and uncharged.

Chapter 12

12.1 Two features from: α-carbon; side-chain; α-amino group; α-carboxyl group.

12.2 (a) alanine or valine; (b) aspartic acid; (c) histidine or lysine; (d) (i) aspartic acid; (ii) valine; (iii) alanine; (iv) serine.

12.3 α-helix, β-pleated sheet.

12.4 (i) Hydrogen bonding: α-helix – parallel to axis; β-sheet – right angles to axis. (ii) Number of strands: α-helix – 1; β-sheet – at least 2.

12.5 Hydrogen bonding.

12.6 (a) alanine–phenylalanine; (b) aspartate–arginine, (c) cysteine–cysteine; (d) any two from arginine, aspartate, glutamine and cysteine.

12.7 α-amino group.

12.8 (a) D; (b) Ile-Tyr-Pro-Val-Ala-Asp-Asp-Arg-Leu-Cys; (c) isoleucine, proline, valine, alanine, leucine.

12.9

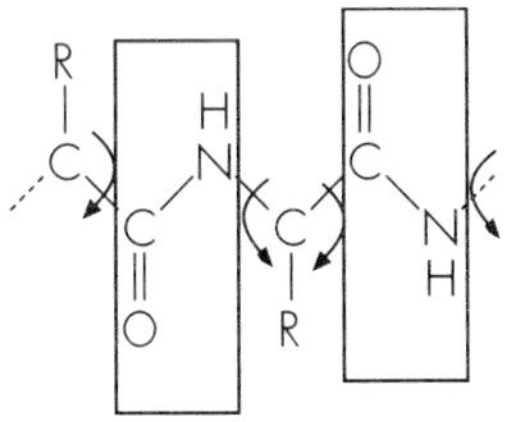

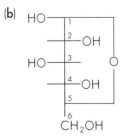

(c)

12.10 3.6.

12.11 Proline.

12.12 (a) Hydrogen bonds between amide hydrogen and carbonyl oxygen; (b) direction of hydrogen bonds, number of strands involved, destabilising amino acids.

12.13 Cysteine.

12.14 Arginine, lysine, histidine.

12.15 (a) 1 = amino acid at N-terminus, 12 = amino acid 12 away from N-terminus; (b) TCDYGAVPLKCS; (c) 8, proline; (d) cysteine (2 and 11); (e) 1, 2, 4, 5, 11, 12; (f) Yes; Asp (3) with Lys (10).

12.16 Ionic bonds (salt links), hydrophobic interaction, hydrogen bonds, covalent bonds.

12.17 Answers as Q12.16.

Chapter 13

13.1 (a) (i) aldotetrose; (ii) ketopentose; (iii) aldopentose; (iv) ketohexose; (v) aldotetrose. (b) (i) D; (ii) L; (iii) L; (iv) D; (v) D.

13.2 (a) (i) and (iii); (b) (iv) mirror image; (c) (i) or (ii).

13.3 (a)

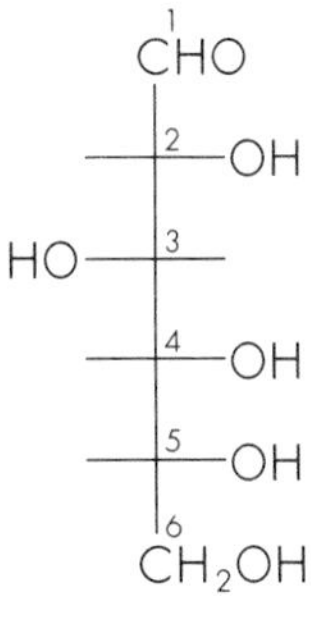

(b)

Fischer

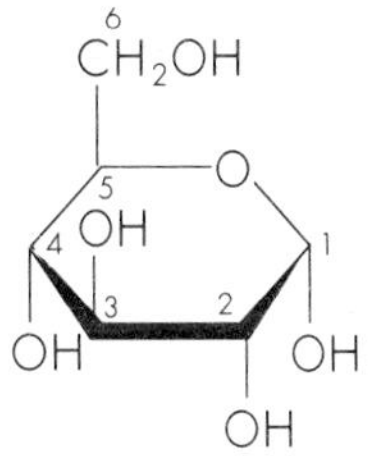

13.4 A homopolysaccharide is a polysaccharide that consists entirely of one type of sugar monomer.

13.5

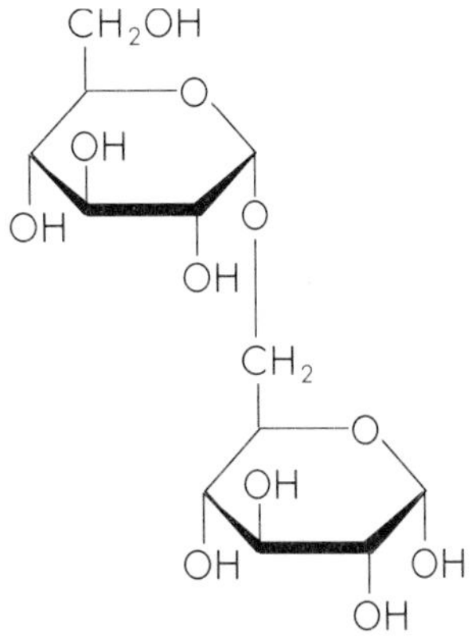

13.6 The ability to form intra- and interchain hydrogen bonds.

13.7 The sugars are: (i) aldopentose; (ii) ketohexose.

13.8 (a) (i), (ii), (iv); (b) (i) and (iii); (c) (ii); (d) (ii) and (iv).

13.9 (a)

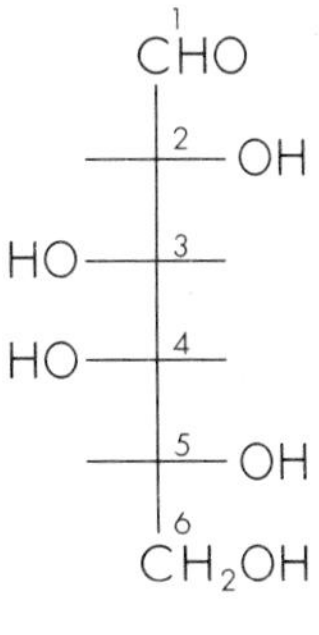

(b) carbonyl on carbon-1 with hydroxyl on carbon-4.

(c)

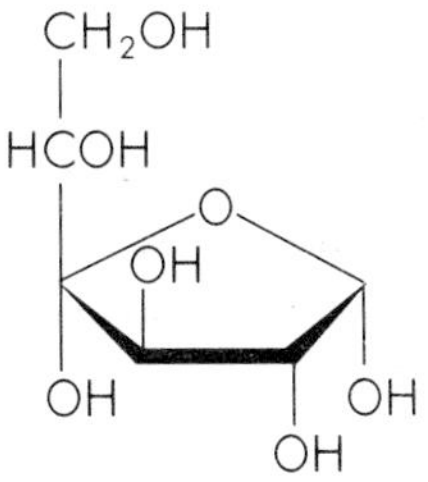

13.10

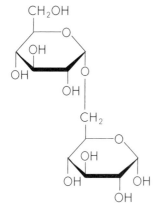

13.11 (a) Aldoses are (i) and (v); ketoses are (ii), (iii) and (iv); (b) (iii), (iv) and (v) are D-sugars; (c) (ii) and (iii) or (i) and (v) are enantiomers; (d) (iii) and (iv) are epimers.

13.12

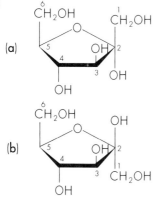

13.13 A polymer of three sugars linked together by glycosidic bonds in which one of the sugars must be different.

13.14

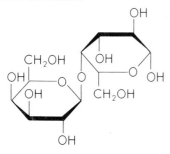

13.15 Any two of: compact, stable and easily digested.

Chapter 14

14.1 Monoacylglycerol.

14.2 A fatty acid in which the carbon chain contains one double bond.

14.3 Fats are solids at room temperature, oils are liquids.

14.4

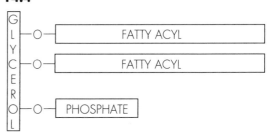

14.5 An amphiphilic molecule is one that both likes and dislikes water.

14.6

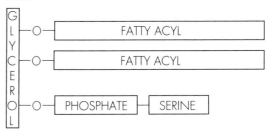

14.7 Phospholipids are amphiphilic molecules. A bilayer has the hydrophilic part of phospholipid in contact with water, while the hydrophobic parts are shielded.

14.8 First, draw a phosphatidic acid (diacylglycerol phosphate), then draw the structure of ethanolamine: $HOCH_2CH_2NH_2$. Join up ethanolamine by removing an OH group from ethanolamine to the phosphate (from which a hydrogen should be removed to make a P—O—C bond).

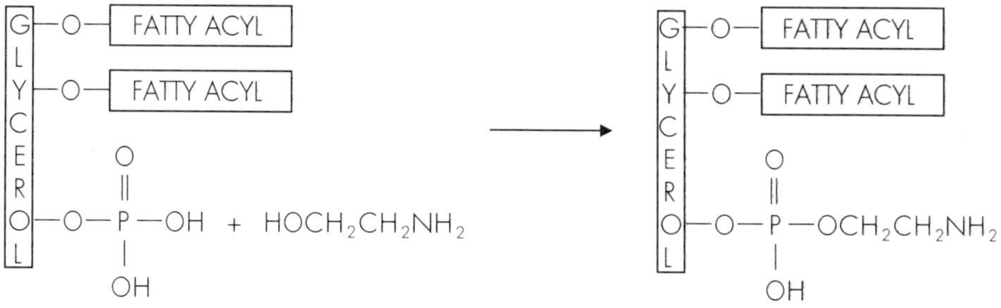

phosphatidic acid + ethanolamine $\longrightarrow$ phosphatidylethanolamine

14.9 An ester bond.

14.10 Oils have a higher percentage of unsaturated fatty acids than fats.

14.11 Hydrogenation is the artificial reduction of the carbon–carbon double bonds in polyunsaturated fats to reduce the degree of unsaturation.

14.12 The phosphate group is hydrophilic; the fatty acyl groups are hydrophobic.

14.13

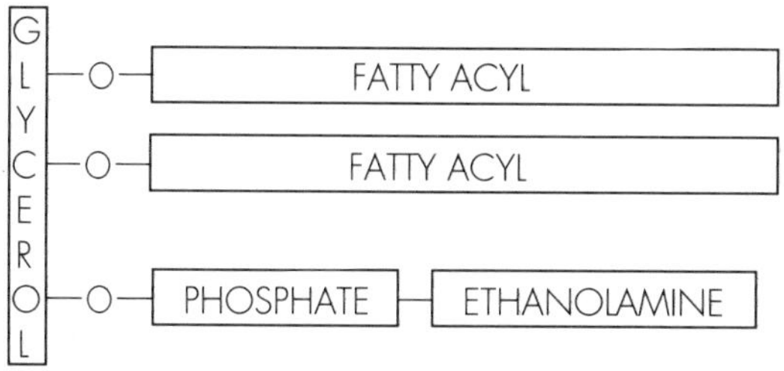

14.14 Gases and small hydrophobic molecules.

Chapter 15

15.1 Polypeptides or proteins.

15.2 Base and sugar (nucleosides have no phosphate).

15.3 (a) dCDP;

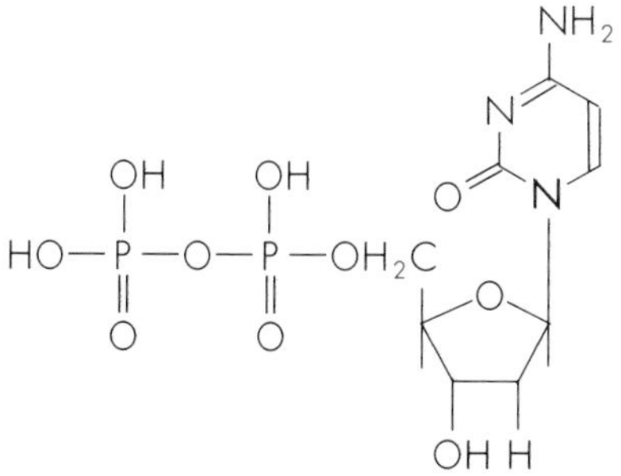

15.4 Phosphate group.

15.5 (a) Ribose sugar; (b) phosphate.

15.6 T G G G C A T C

15.7 Three.

15.8 Messenger RNA.

15.9 Adenosine-5'-triphosphate.

15.10 (a) (i) TMP; (ii) dCTP; (iii) dATP; (iv) ATP.

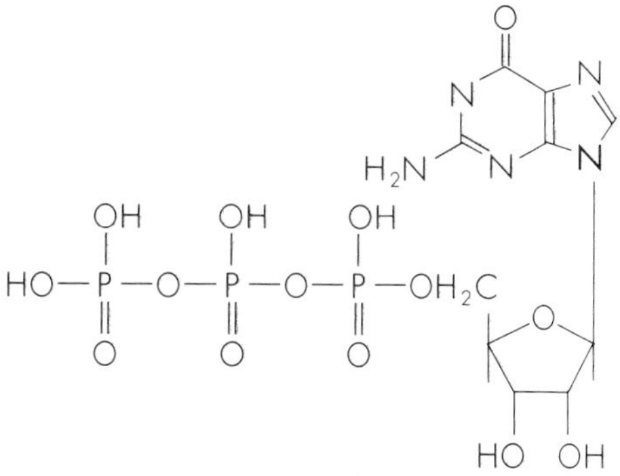

15.11 (a) T C G G C T C C C A T A T; (b) There are two daughter strands, each complementary to one of the parent strands, A G C C G A G G G T A T A and T C G G C T C C C A T A T; (c) The 5' and 3' refer to the attachment of the phosphate to sugars on neighbouring nucleotides.

15.12 In the genes, which are DNA.

15.13 Base, sugar, phosphate (or diphosphate or triphosphate).

15.14

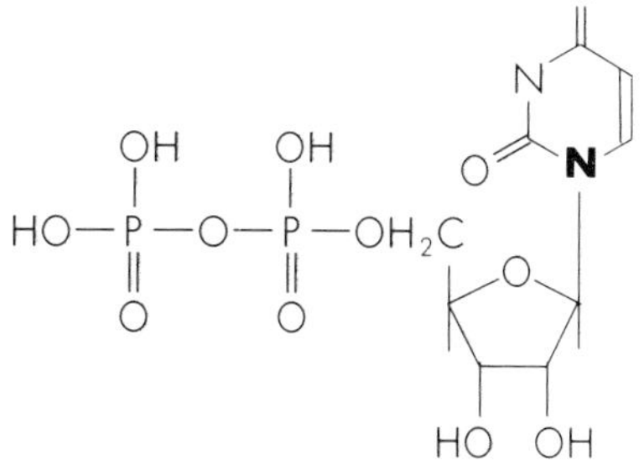

(b) UDP

15.15 The 5' hydroxyl of one nucleotide to the 3' hydroxyl of the next in the sequence.

15.16 (a) The base cytosine; (b) the vertical line represents the sugar ribose, with C^1 at top and C^5 at bottom. The diagonal line goes from C^5 of one sugar (at bottom) to C^3 of the next (in the middle).

15.17 They give the best fit for hydrogen bonding. The ratio of A : T and C : G is always 1 no matter what the source of DNA.

15.18 Transcription.

15.19 Any two from: carriers of genetic information; cellular messenger; cellular energy carrier; coenzyme.

Chapter 16

16.1 (a) rate = k[fumarate][water]. (b) 'rate' is the speed with which fumarate concentration is reduced with time; 'k' is a constant for this reaction; '[fumarate]' and '[water]' are the concentrations of the two reactants.

16.2 Any three from: specific to a reaction; very efficient; most effective at a specific pH; rendered inactive on heating; proteins.

16.3 (a) An enzyme-catalysed reaction is saturated when an increase in the initial concentration of substrate does not increase the rate of reaction. (b) The order is zero.

16.4 An enzyme is inhibited when a substance binds to the enzyme and slows down the reaction of the substrate.

16.5 A reaction that gives out energy.

16.6 See Figure 16.7 (page 159).

16.7 A coupled reaction links an exergonic reaction to an endergonic reaction. The former reaction drives the latter.

16.8 (a) rate = k[dihydroxyacetone phosphate]; (b) rate = k.

16.9 (a) Activation energy is the energy barrier that has to be overcome before a reaction can take place. (b) An enzyme reduces the activation energy.

16.10 The substrate reacts reversibly with the enzyme to form an enzyme–substrate complex. The complex then decomposes reversibly to give the product and regenerate the enzyme.

16.11 An inhibitor links reversibly to the enzyme. The substrate has less enzyme with which to react, and so the reaction slows down.

16.12 Photosynthesis, that is the combination of carbon dioxide and water to form sugars and oxygen, uses energy. This energy is supplied by sunlight.

16.13 See Figure 16.11.

16.14 (a) glucose + fructose $\longrightarrow$ sucrose; (b) rate = k[glucose][fructose]

16.15 The order of reaction is the power to which the substrate concentration is raised in the rate equation. (It is usually 1 or zero).

16.16 The specific nature of an enzyme means that it only mediates one (or a very few) reactions, so unwanted reactions do not occur alongside the desired process. The enzyme needs to be efficient so that reactions take place rapidly under mild conditions and the cell (and the organism) functions efficiently.

16.17 See Figure 16.1 (page 154).

16.18 (a) and (b), see Figure 16.2 (page 155).

16.19 (a) Inhibited means that the phosphorylation of glucose is slowed down by glucose-6-phosphate. (b) Feedback control refers to

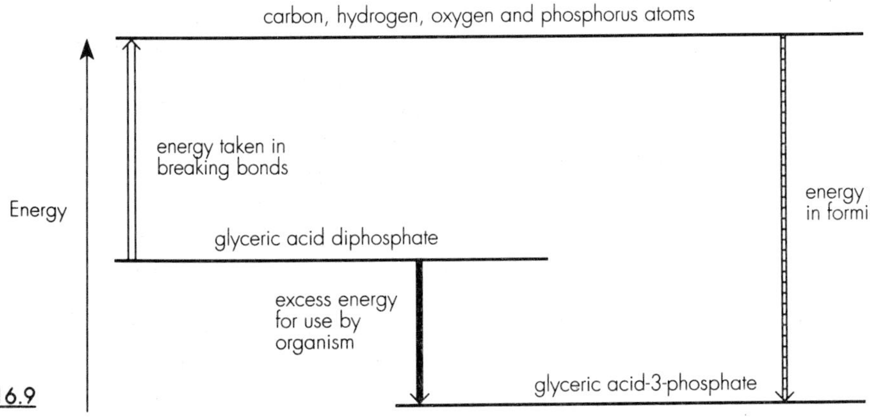

carbon, hydrogen, oxygen and phosphorus atoms

Figure 16.9

the slowing down of a reaction by a reaction product, which acts as an inhibitor to the process.

16.20 Exergonic reactions give out energy, while endergonic reactions take in energy.

16.21 $ATP + H_2O \rightarrow ADP + P_i + energy$

16.22 See Figure 16.10 (page 161).

Chapter 17

17.1 (a) Oxidation; (b) oxidation; (c) reduction.

17.2 (a) acetaldehyde; (b) NADH; (c) NADH; (d) acetaldehyde; (e)
acetaldehyde $+ 2H^+ + 2e^- \rightleftharpoons$ ethanol
$NADH + H^+ \rightleftharpoons NAD^+ + 2e^- + 2H^+$

17.3 Electrons flow from more negative E'_0 to more positive E'_0. (a) Acetaldehyde/ethanol $E'_0 = -0.2$ V, NADH/NAD$^+$ = -0.32 V; electrons flow from NADH to ethanol. Reaction will therefore run forward.
(b) ubiquinone$_{(ox)}$/ubiquinone$_{(red)}$ $E'_0 = 0.1$ V, cytochrome $c = 0.22$ V; electrons flow from ubiquinol to cytochrome c. Reaction will therefore run backwards.

17.4 ATP (or water).

17.5 Ubiquinone found in mitochondria; plastoquinone in chloroplasts.

17.6 (a) Fe^{2+} is the reductant, Cu^{2+} is the oxidant. (b) Pyruvate is the oxidant, NADH is the reductant. (c) Oxygen is the oxidant, glucose is the reductant.

17.7 (a)
cytochrome $b(Fe^{2+}) \longrightarrow$ cytochrome $b(Fe^{3+}) + e^-$
cytochrome $c(Fe^{3+}) + e^- \longrightarrow$ cytochrome $c(Fe^{2+})$

(b)
pyruvate $+ 2e^- + 2H^+ \longrightarrow$ lactate
$NADH + H^+ \longrightarrow NAD^+ + 2e^- + 2H^+$

17.8 (a) Electrons flow from ferredoxin(+2) to cytochrome $c(+3)$. (b) Electrons flow from cytochrome b_1 (+2) to cytochrome $c(+3)$.

17.9 Reduced.

17.10 (a) cytochrome a; (b) cytochrome c;
(c) cytochrome a is the oxidant, cytochrome c is the reductant;
(d)
cytochrome $a(Fe^{3+}) + e^- \longrightarrow$ cytochrome $a(Fe^{2+})$
cytochrome $c(Fe^{2+}) \longrightarrow$ cytochrome $c(Fe^{3+}) + e^-$

(e) cytochrome a is the electron acceptor, cytochrome c is the electron donor.

17.11 (a) Electrons flow from acetate/acetaldehyde to NAD^+/NADH. NADH/NAD$^+$ gets reduced, i.e. the reaction runs backwards.
(b) Electrons flow from NADPH/NADP$^+$ to fumarate/succinate. Succinate gets reduced and reaction proceeds in the forward direction.

17.12 NADPH and ATP.

17.13 Choose any two from: NAD^+, NADP$^+$, NMN, FAD and FMN.

Chapter 18

18.1 Lambda (symbol λ).

18.2 10×10^{-16} s^{-1} (because it has the higher frequency).

18.3 There are two, one at 340 nm and the other at 260 nm.

18.4 This is the most sensitive (largest change in absorbance for a given change in concentration).

18.5 2×10^{-5} M or 2×10^{-5} mol dm^{-3}.

18.6 Any two from: resonance energy transfer, heat, light emission, chemical reaction.

18.7 ATP and NADPH.

18.8 1 nm = 10^{-9} metres;
$3.8 \times 10^{-7} \times 10^9 = 380$ nm. The other limit is 780 nm.

18.9 Solutions of chlorophyll absorb red and blue light but let green light pass through. It is this green light the eye detects.

18.10 $A = 2.5 \times 10^{-4} \times 6220 \times 1 = 1.56$ absorbance units.

18.11 Figure 18.13 shows the wavelength. The distance between any two points in successive waves is λ. Two different places where wavelengths can be measured have been shown (see page 200).

18.12 Metres (nm is normally used for visible wavelengths).

18.13 The arrangement of electrons in the molecular structure.

18.14 $A = \epsilon cl$;
$c = A/\epsilon l = 1 \div 8630$
$= 1.16 \times 10^{-4}$ mol dm^{-3}.

18.15 Resonance energy transfer.

18.16 Light absorption causes a change in E'_0 in PSI which is capable of leading (by electron transfer) to $NADP^+$ reduction.

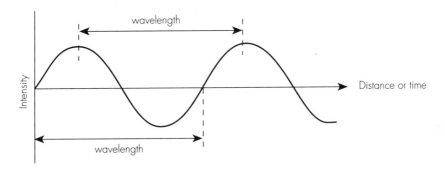

Figure 18.13 The wavelength of a sine wave

Chapter 19

19.1 $^M_NA = ^{18}_8O$; $^MA = ^{18}O$.

19.2 ^3_2He.

19.3 Disintegrations per minute.

19.4 Separation of different compounds dissolved in a solvent, based upon their affinity (stickiness) towards beads.

19.5 $^M_NA = ^{22}_{11}Na$, and $^{23}_{11}Na$, $^MA = ^{22}Na$ and ^{23}Na.

19.6 $^{35}_{16}S \rightarrow \beta$-particle $+ ^{35}_{17}Cl$.

19.7 Any two from: (auto)radiography, electric current and light emission.

19.8 The experiment in Example 19.4 could be stopped at many time points, the presence of newly formed intermediates detected and a sequence of appearance worked out.

19.9 $^M_NA = ^{35}_{16}S$, $^MA = ^{35}S$.

19.10 $^{40}_{19}K \rightarrow \beta$-particle $+ ^{40}_{20}Ca$.

19.11 Development of X-ray film by radiation emission.

19.12 Rate of respiration can be measured by either $^{14}CO_2$ production after trapping gas or $^{14}C_6H_{12}O_6$ disappearance.

INDEX

1																1	2
H																H	He
1.0079																1.0079	4.0026
3	4											5	6	7	8	9	10
Li	Be											B	C	N	O	F	Ne
6.941	9.0122											10.811	12.011	14.007	15.994	18.898	20.180
11	12											13	14	15	16	17	18
Na	Mg											Al	Si	P	S	Cl	Ar
22.990	24.305											26.982	28.086	30.974	32.066	35.473	39.948
19	20	21	22	23	24	25	26	27	28	29	30	31	32	33	34	35	36
K	Ca	Sc	Ti	V	Cr	Mn	Fe	Co	Ni	Cu	Zn	Ga	Ge	As	Se	Br	Kr
39.098	40.078	44.956	47.88	50.942	51.996	54.938	55.847	58.933	58.69	63.546	65.39	69.732	72.61	72.922	78.96	79.904	83.80
37	38	39	40	41	42	43	44	45	46	47	48	49	50	51	52	53	54
Rb	Sr	Y	Zr	Nb	Mo	Tc	Ru	Rh	Pd	Ag	Cd	In	Sn	Sb	Te	I	Xe
85.468	87.62	88.906	91.224	92.906	95.94	98	101.07	102.91	106.42	107.87	112.41	114.82	118.71	121.75	127.60	126.90	131.29

7	⇦ Atomic number
N	⇦ Symbol for nitrogen
14.007	⇦ Relative atomic mass

Partial periodic table of the elements